HOUSE CARPENTRY SIMPLIFIED

NELSON L. BURBANK

Formerly Instructor, Building Vocational High School, Cincinnati, Ohio

Author of *House Construction Details; Practical Job Pointers; Shopcrafter's Manual*

Co-Author of *Handbook of Building Terms and Definitions*

Sixth Edition
of the book formerly titled
HOUSE CARPENTRY and JOINERY

as revised by

CHARLES PHELPS

SIMMONS-BOARDMAN PUBLISHING CORPORATION

CONTENTS

Library of Congress Catalog Card No. 58-8548

Printed in the U.S.A.

SIXTH EDITION COPYRIGHT 1958 BY SIMMONS-BOARDMAN PUBLISHING CORP.

PREVIOUS EDITIONS COPYRIGHT 1936, 1937, 1940, 1942, 1952
BY SIMMONS-BOARDMAN PUBLISHING CORP.

PREFACE

House Carpentry Simplified fully describes each step or operation of dwelling construction, from the selection of tools to the completion of the structure, neglecting only certain subsidiary functions such as those of the plumber, the electrician, the painter. Good, up-to-date working information on current practices and techniques are here made available in graphic step-by-step delineation, equally invaluable to the journeyman, the homeowner, or the apprentice. Through successive revisions up to the present one over one hundred thousand copies have been sold, including many adoptions for apprentice training in schools throughout the country. The homeowner will find the proper descriptions that will enable him to build additions to existing property or make alterations or repairs, without expensive mistakes.

The sixth edition has been retitled because the word "joinery" in the former title *House Carpentry and Joinery,* while valid, has gradually declined in usage over the years.

The book has been printed by letterpress from all new type and engravings. All previous photographs have been replaced by more modern ones and many up-to-date drawings have been either added or substituted for others.

The number of pages has been increased from 232 to 256. The chapter on *Tools* has been expanded from 6 to 15 pages to show a most complete and modern assortment. The *Glossary of Building Terms* has been totally revised and carefully screened by research and comparison to be most representative of the terms applicable to the subject at hand. Two newly added chapters are *Structural Parts of a House,* delineated on a drawing of a modern structure, and *Heating Installations and Air Conditioning.* Two new appendixes are *Prefabrication* and *Safety for the Carpenter.*

Mr. Phelps' revision of the book was done with the cooperation of the publishers of *American Builder* magazine, who made available their sources of material and authenticating factors.

NELSON L. BURBANK

ACKNOWLEDGMENTS

Grateful acknowledgments are accorded the following business concerns, organizations, and persons for their generous cooperation in the way of illustrations and information drawn upon:

Abbey Photography, Inc., St. Petersburg, Fla.
American Brass Co., Waterbury, Conn.
American Builder magazine, New York, N. Y.
American Forest Products Industries, Inc., Washington, D. C.
American Institute of Architects, Washington, D. C.
Amerock Corp., Rockford, Ill.
Amore Builders, Pittsburgh, Pa.
Andersen Corp., Bayport, Minn.
Armstrong Cork Co., Inc., Lancaster, Pa.
S. C. Atkins Co.
Atlas Press Co., Kalamazoo, Mich.
Aviore Co., Pittsburgh, Pa.
Badgely Corp., Rockville Center, N. Y.
Beacon Photograph Co.
Berger Furnace Mfg. Co., Pittsburgh, Pa.
Ernest Bihler, Omaha, Neb.
Bilco Corp., New Haven, Conn.
H. Brace, Inc.
Kenneth S. Brown, Seattle, Wash.
Buckingham Studio, Washington, D. C.
Zema Bumgardner, Seattle, Wash.
Samuel Cabot, Boston, Mass.
CECO Steel Products Corp., Chicago, Ill.
Clark Houses, Lima, Ohio
Concrete Engineering Corp., Omaha, Neb.
Crex Patent Column Co., Chicago, Ill.
Leonard Delano, Portland, Ore.
Detroit Steel Products Co., Detroit, Mich.
DeWalt Products Co., Lancaster, Pa.
F. W. Dodge Corp., New York, N. Y.
Douglas Fir Plywood Assn., Tacoma, Wash.
Eberhard Faber Pencil Co., New York, N. Y.
Ernest Homes, New Orleans, La.
Etling Co., Barberton, Ohio
Fairgate Rule Co., Inc., Cold Spring, N. Y.
Federal Housing Administration, Washington, D. C.
Fenestra, Inc., Detroit, Mich.
Fitch, Schiller & Frank
Flury & Crouch, West Palm Beach, Fla.
Forest Products Laboratory, Madison, Wis.
Frankel Co., Detroit, Mich.
F. & S. Construction Co.
General Bronze Corp., Long Island City, N. Y.
General Electric Co., Bridgeport, Conn.
General Timber Service, Inc., St. Paul, Minn.
Gerholz Community Homes

Goldblatt Tool Co., Kansas City, Mo.
B. F. Goodrich Co., New York, N. Y.
Great Lakes Steel Corp., Stran-Steel Div., Detroit, Mich.
Great Neck Saw Mfrs., Inc., Mineola, N. Y.
Hardwood Plywood Institute
J. Harr
Harwood Products Co., Neenah, Wis.
Hawthorne Roofing Tile Co., Cicero, Ill.
Hess Bros.
Infra Insulation, Inc., New York, N. Y.
Ingersoll-Rand, Phillipsburg, N. J.
International Harvester Co., Chicago, Ill.
Johns-Manville, New York, N. Y.
Jones & Laughlin Steel Corp., Pittsburgh, Pa.
Kipton Industries, Royersford, Pa.
Herman Kroll, Great Neck, L. I., N. Y.
Lakeshore Products, Woodinville, Wash.
Lawrence & Hagen Studio
Len-Art Photographers
E. M. Long Co., Cadiz, Ill.
Lumber Research Council
Macober Steel Co., Canton, Ohio
The Majestic Co., Inc., Huntington, Ind.
Masonite Corp., Chicago, Ill.
Rudolph A. Matern, Architect, & Associates, Jamaica, N. Y.
Frank Lotz Miller, New Orleans, La.
Millers Falls Co., Greenfield, Mass.
Minnesota & Ontario Paper Co., Insulite Div.
Modern Homes, Inc., Dearborn, Mich.
Dorothy M. Moore
National Lumber Mfrs. Assn., Washington, D. C.
National Mfg. Co., Sterling, Ill.
National Mineral Wool Assn., New York, N. Y.
O'Neill Lumber Co., San Carlos, Calif.
Ozark Industries, Portland, Ore.
Pancho's Photography, Manhattan Beach, N. Y.
Charles Parker Co., Meriden, Conn.
Rondal Partridge
Dorothy Paul
Pease Woodwork Co., Cincinnati, Ohio
Pencil Points, New York, N. Y.
James H. Perrell
Portable Electric Tools, Chicago, Ill.
H. K. Porter, Inc., Somerville, Mass.
Porter-Cable Machine Co., Syracuse, N. Y.
RCS Sales Corp., Joliet, Ill.
Floyd Ray, Long Beach, Calif.

Tom Reilly, Portland, Ore.
Frederick L. Richards, Pasadena, Calif.
W. M. Ritter Co., Columbus, Ohio
Rockwell Mfg. Co., New York, N. Y.
George J. Rossi, San Mateo, Calif.
George Miles Ryan, Minneapolis, Minn.
Sargent & Co., New York, N. Y.
Sears-Roebuck, Chicago, Ill.
Sholz Homes, Inc., Toledo, Ohio
Julius Shulman, Los Angeles, Calif.
Sigman-Ward, New York, N. Y.
Simplex Forms Systems, Inc., Rockford, Ill.
Skil Corp., Chicago, Ill.
Sonotube
Southern California Gas Co.
Richard O. Spencer, Hollywood, Calif.
Stanley Works, New Britain, Conn.
Steel Corner Tape Co.
Steel Joist Institute
Harold Steinkamp, Batesville, Ind.
Stern & Price, Cupertina, Calif.
Storm Lumber Co., New York, N. Y.
Strand Products Co.
Alfred L. Tank, Los Angeles, Calif.
Howard Teas, Malverne, N. Y.
Techbuilt, Inc., Lexington, Mass.
Thor Power Tool Co., Long Island City, N. Y.
Thyer Mfg. Co., Toledo, Ohio
Timber Engineering Co., Washington, D. C.
Charles W. Totten
Trane Co., LaCrosse, Wis.
Leon Trice, New Orleans, La.
Truscon Steel Co., Youngstown, Ohio
Underwood Corp., New York, N. Y.
United Shoe Machinery Corp., Boston, Mass.
U. S. Mineral Wool Co., Stanhope, N. J.
Dean Vannice
The Village, Inc., Memphis, Tenn.
Webster Electric Co., Racine, Wis.
Wen Products, Inc., Chicago, Ill.
West Coast Lumbermen's Assn., Portland, Ore.
Weyerhauser Sales Co., St. Paul, Minn.
L. S. Whaley, Long Beach, Calif.
R. Marvin Wilson, Cleveland Heights, Ohio
Wood Conversion Co., New York, N. Y.
Wood-Fibre Board Co., New York, N. Y.
Wright Power Saw Co.
Zibell Industries, Atlanta, Ga.

1

Tools

In this chapter are illustrations of fundamental tools used by the carpenter. They are grouped in the categories of *measuring tools, hand tools, powered hand tools, powered stationary bench or pedestal tools*. Additional tools and many variations of a type exist of course, but effort has been made here to illustrate the basic tools of the carpenter.

There is adequate reference material available for the study of the techniques of tool uses, both from many books on the subject and from the printed matter of various manufacturers, so such study has not been included in this book, with the exception that as an essential to the basic study of roof framing the use of the steel square is described in graphic detail in Chapter 13—Roof Framing.

MEASURING TOOLS

6B 5B 4B 3B 2B B HB F H 2H 3H 4H 5H 6H 7H 8H 9H

The Grading of Lead Pencils.

The grades in which drawing pencils are made: A description of each grade is as follows: 6B, softest and blackest; 5B, very, very soft and very black; 4B, very soft and very black; 3B, very soft and black; 2B, soft and black; B, soft; HB, medium soft; F, firm; H, medium; 2H, hard; 3H, very hard; 4H, extra hard; 5H, very, very hard; 6H, very, very hard and firm; 7H, extra hard and firm; 8H, extra hard and extra firm; 9H, hardest and firmest.

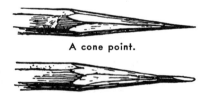

A cone point.

A chisel point.

Two types of points to use in making drawings.

Pencil clasp.

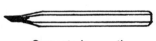

Carpenter's pencil.

The carpenter's pencil differs from the drawing pencil in that it has a flat shape and a chisel-shaped lead rather than either a round shape or a six-sided shape.

Flat scale.

Triangular scale.

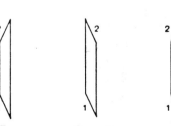

Two-bevel.

Opposite bevel.

Four-bevel.

Triangular.

Numbering of bevels looking at left end of scales.

1

MEASURING TOOLS—(Contd.)

Folding rule.

Push-pull steel tape.

Wooden marking gauge.

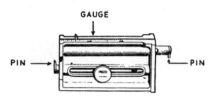

Hinge gauge.

Mortise gauge.   Trammel points.

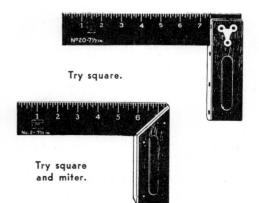

Try square.

Try square and miter.

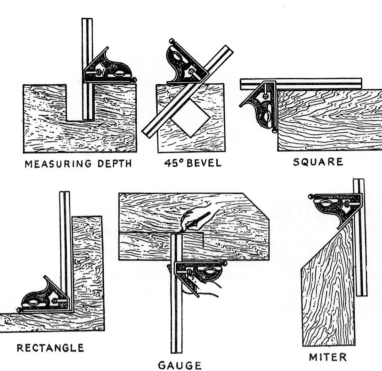

MEASURING DEPTH   45° BEVEL   SQUARE

RECTANGLE   GAUGE   MITER
                  Combination square.

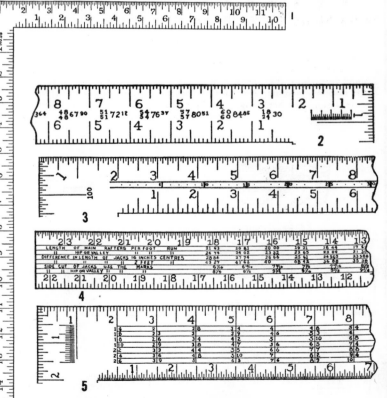

Steel square: 1, front face; 2, brace measure; 3, octagon square; 4, rafter table; 5, board measure.

MEASURING TOOLS—(Contd.)

Studder's square.

Hermaphrodite calipers.

Inside calipers.

Outside calipers.

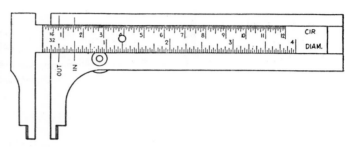

Slide caliper for inside and outside measurement.

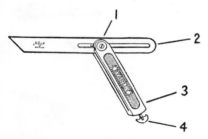

Sliding bevel: 1, adjusting screw; 2, blade; 3, butt; 4, locking screw.

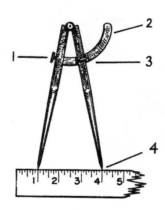

Wing compass details; 1, adjusting screw; 2, angle indicator; 3, set-screw; 4, points.

Nail set.

Center punch.

Drift punch.

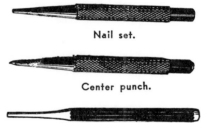

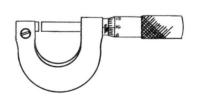

Micrometer.

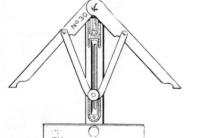

Angle dividers.

Plumb bob.

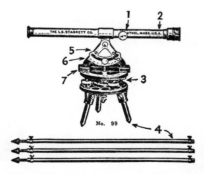

Transit level: 1, telescope adjusting screw; 2, telescope; 3, level adjusting screws; 4, tripod legs; 5, quadrant; 6, degree of angles; 7, level.

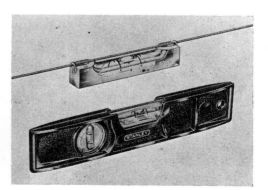

Top, line level; bottom, plumb level.

MEASURING TOOLS—(Contd.)

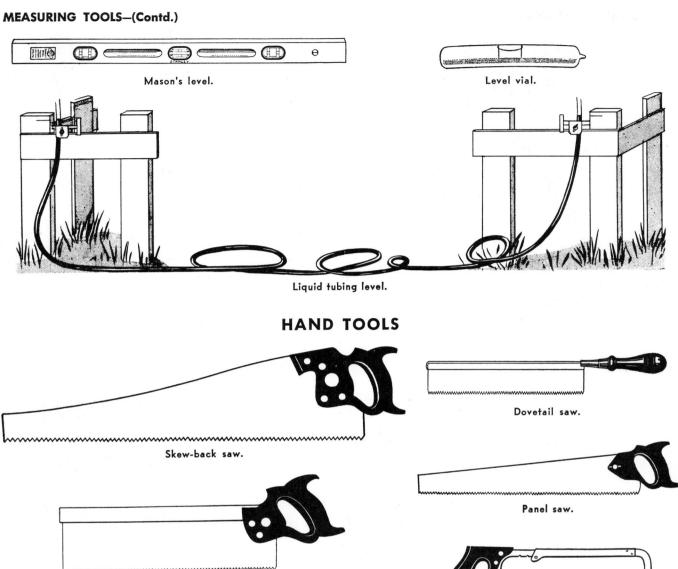

Mason's level.

Level vial.

Liquid tubing level.

HAND TOOLS

Skew-back saw.

Dovetail saw.

Panel saw.

Back saw or tenon saw.

Hack saw.

Straight-back saw.

Compass saw.

Coping saw.

Cabinet saw.

HAND TOOLS—(Contd.)

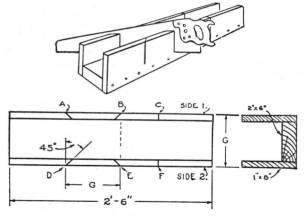

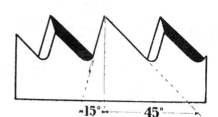

Wooden miter box.

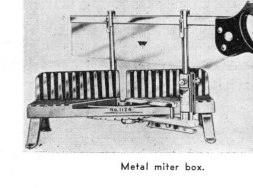

Metal miter box.

Crosscut saw teeth.

Rip saw teeth.

Stud driver.

CROSS PEEN HAMMER   STRAIGHT PEEN HAMMER

BALL-PEEN HAMMER   SOFT METAL OR PLASTIC HAMMER

PLAIN FACED CLAW HAMMER   RIVETING HAMMER

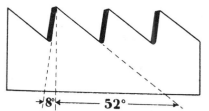

DOUBLE FACE SLEDGE   CROSS PEEN SLEDGE   STRAIGHT PEEN SLEDGE

RAWHIDE MALLET   RAWHIDE-FACED MALLET

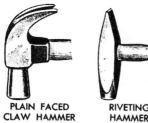

RUBBER MALLET   WOODEN MALLET

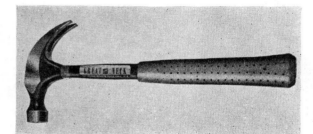

Curved-claw hammer with tubular air cushion.

Half hatchet.

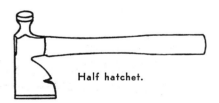

HAND TOOLS—(Contd.)

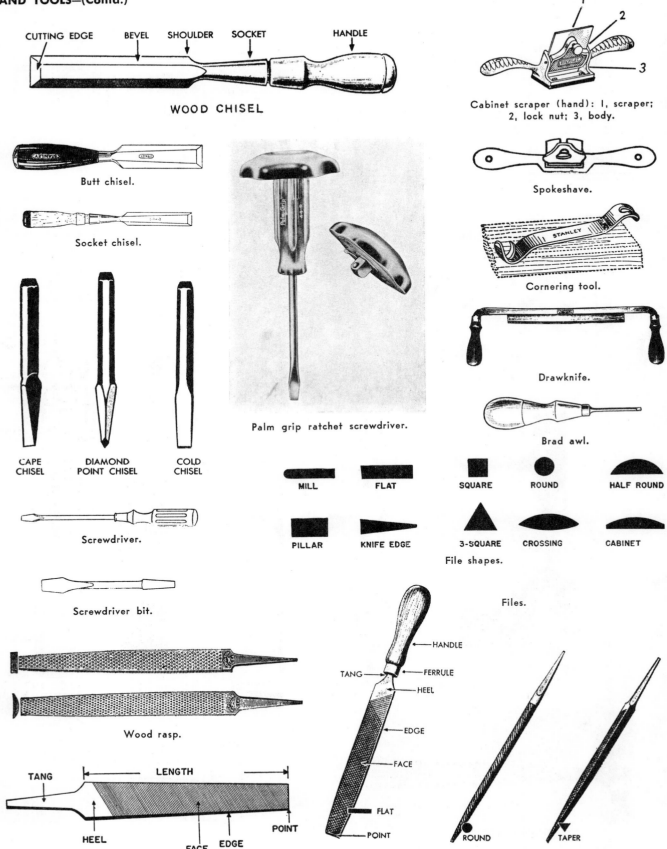

CUTTING EDGE   BEVEL   SHOULDER   SOCKET   HANDLE

WOOD CHISEL

Cabinet scraper (hand): 1, scraper;
2, lock nut; 3, body.

Butt chisel.

Socket chisel.

Spokeshave.

Cornering tool.

CAPE
CHISEL   DIAMOND
POINT CHISEL   COLD
CHISEL

Drawknife.

Palm grip ratchet screwdriver.

Brad awl.

Screwdriver.

MILL   FLAT   SQUARE   ROUND   HALF ROUND

PILLAR   KNIFE EDGE   3-SQUARE   CROSSING   CABINET

File shapes.

Screwdriver bit.

Files.

Wood rasp.

HANDLE

TANG   FERRULE

HEEL

EDGE

FACE

TANG   LENGTH

FLAT

HEEL   FACE   EDGE   POINT   POINT

ROUND   TAPER

HAND TOOLS—(Contd.)

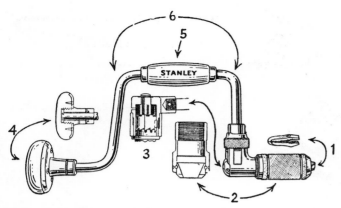

Bit brace details: 1, interlocking jaws; 2, sleeve; 3, box ratchet; 4, ball-bearing head; 5, threaded handle; 6, sweep.

Hand drill.　Breast drill.

Augur bit details.

CUTTER

SCREW　SPUR　TWIST

SHANK

Bench stop.

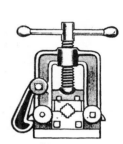

C clamp or carriage clamp.

Pipe vise.

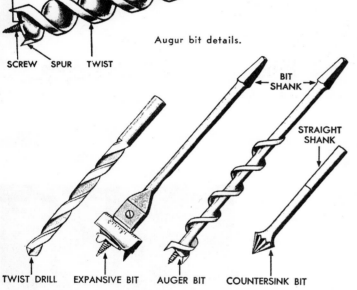

BIT SHANK

STRAIGHT SHANK

TWIST DRILL　EXPANSIVE BIT　AUGER BIT　COUNTERSINK BIT

Types of bits.

Bench vise.

Ripping bar.

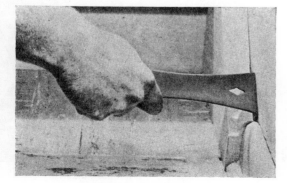

Molding pry bar.

Tacker.

HAND TOOLS—(Contd.)

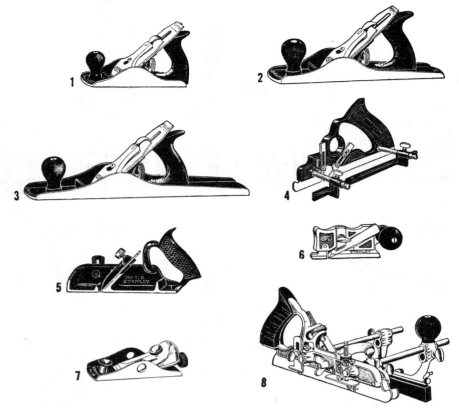

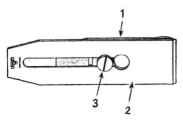

Plane iron: 1, cap iron; 2, cutting iron; 3, lock screw.

Oil stone.

Brick tongs.

Planes: 1, smoothing plane; 2, jack plane; 3, fore plane; 4, dado plane; 5, rabbet plane; 6, side rabbet plane; 7, block plane; 8, Stanley 45 plane.

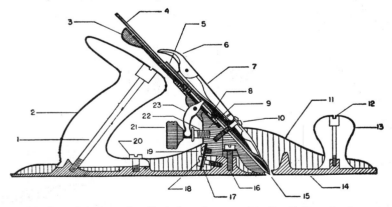

Smoothing plane details: 1, handle bolt and nut; 2, handle; 3, lateral adjusting lever; 4, blade; 5, cap-iron or blade; 6, cam lever; 7, cap; 8, cap-iron screw; 9, frog; 10, cap screw; 11, plane bottom; 12, knob bolt and nut; 13, knob; 14, face; 15, throat; 16, frog screw; 17, frog clip; 18, frog adjusting screw; 19, frog clip screw; 20, handle toe bolt; 21, adjusting nut; 22, cutter adjusting screw; 23, Y-adjusting level.

Circular (or compass) plane: 1, flexible bottom; 2, adjusting lever; 3, adjusting screw; 4, lever cap; 5, plane iron adjust-set; 6, plane handle; 7, plane iron; 8, cam; 9, bottom adjusting nut.

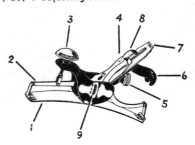

Sash-door holder.

HAND TOOLS—(Contd.)

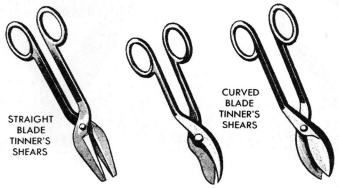

STRAIGHT BLADE TINNER'S SHEARS

CURVED BLADE TINNER'S SHEARS

CURVED BLADE TINNER'S SHEARS

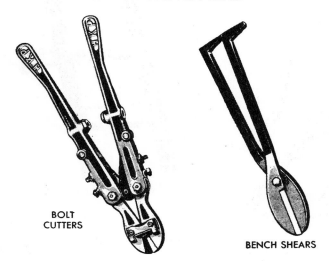

BOLT CUTTERS

BENCH SHEARS

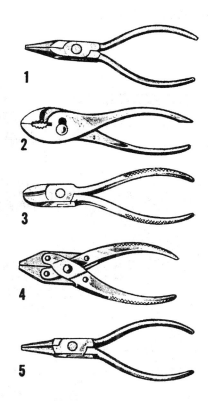

1
2
3
4
5

Pliers: 1, adjustable combination; 2, half-round-nose; 3, diagonal cutting nippers; 4, flat-nosed; 5, round-nosed.

Nippers.

Metal-lath cutter.

Plywood carrying device.

Using plywood carrying device.

HAND TOOLS—(Contd.)

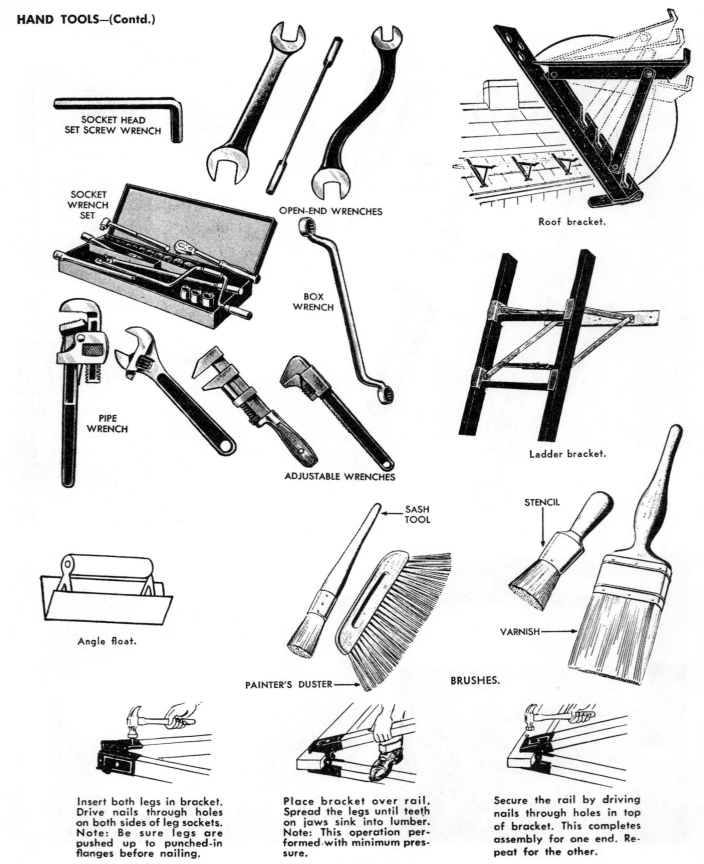

SOCKET HEAD
SET SCREW WRENCH

SOCKET
WRENCH
SET

OPEN-END WRENCHES

BOX
WRENCH

PIPE
WRENCH

ADJUSTABLE WRENCHES

Roof bracket.

Ladder bracket.

Angle float.

SASH
TOOL

STENCIL

VARNISH

PAINTER'S DUSTER

BRUSHES.

Insert both legs in bracket. Drive nails through holes on both sides of leg sockets. Note: Be sure legs are pushed up to punched-in flanges before nailing.

Place bracket over rail. Spread the legs until teeth on jaws sink into lumber. Note: This operation performed with minimum pressure.

Secure the rail by driving nails through holes in top of bracket. This completes assembly for one end. Repeat for the other.

SAW HORSE BRACKETS.

POWERED HAND TOOLS

Trimming saw.

Power saw with reciprocating blade.

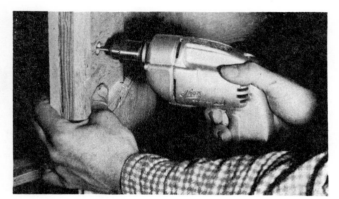

Electric hand drill.

Bayonet saw.

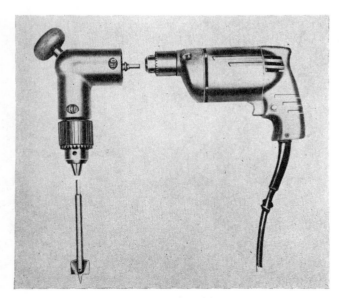

Easy access drill attachment.

POWERED HAND TOOLS—(Contd.)

Powered star drill.

Orbital sander.

Automatically fed nail driver.

Pony trowel.

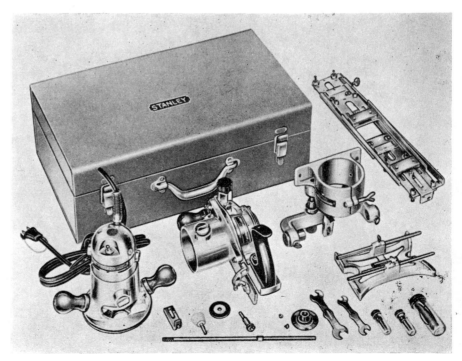

Door hanging equipment kit: planer, mortiser, leveling device.

POWERED HAND TOOLS—(Contd.)

Electronic soldering gun and
plastic-tile cutter

Sander and polisher.

Cord reel for power tools.

POWERED STATIONARY TOOLS

Circular saw.

Lathe (without table).

Drill press.

Jointer.

Band saw.

Radial cutoff saw.

Shaper.

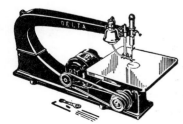

Jig saw (without table).

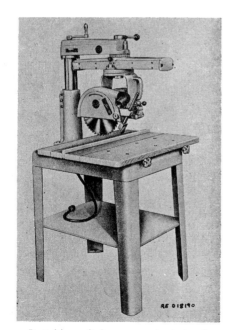

Portable radial saw on steel stand.

TOOL BOX

The following drawings and stock bill show how to make an excellent tool chest from one panel of ½" x 4'0" x 5'0" exterior plywood where but one side of the plywood is seen from the exterior.

To withstand the stress of being moved frequently with the weight carried, dadoed or rabbeted joints fastened with glue are specified throughout. After parts are cut to sizes indicated, rabbet the edges, dado and bandsaw the end panels **G** as required. Assemble the fixed and hinged sections of the chest, nail **M** and **N** to divider **U** before installing in slots, and attach supporting blocks **S** for sliding saw rack. Nail through front, bottom, and back into edges of **S** for extra strength.

Glue and nail drawer shelf **J** to divider **T** before installing and nailing through top and back into edges of **T**. Assemble the saw rack to fit the sizes of hand saws and assemble drawers as shown. Attach handles, casters and hinges after applying finish.

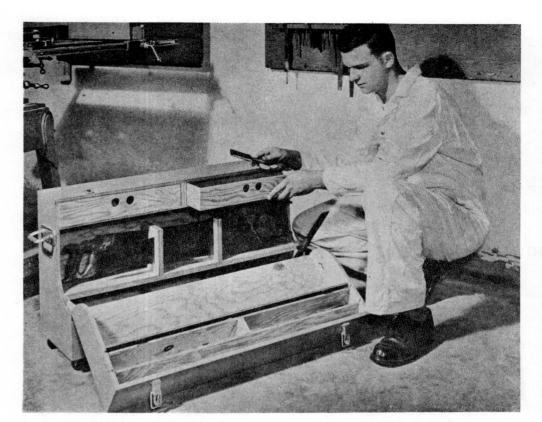

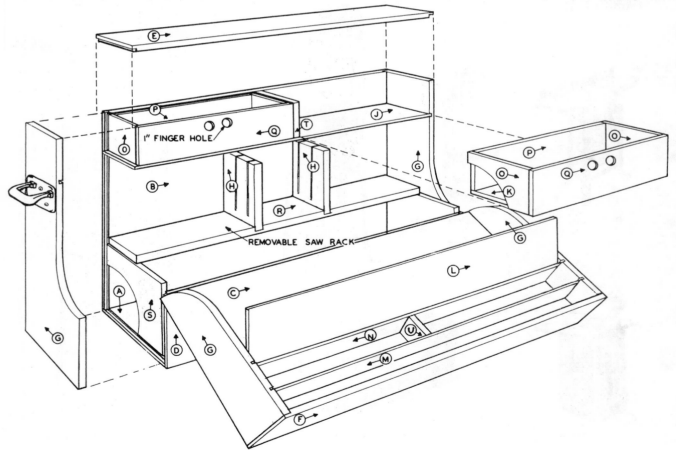

1" FINGER HOLE

REMOVABLE SAW RACK

Right: Front assembly of members.

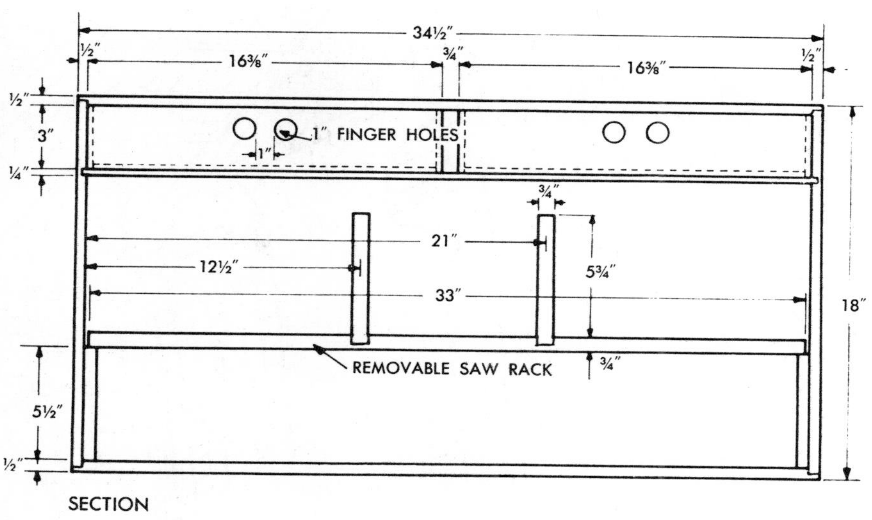
34½"
½"
16⅜"
¾"
16⅜"
½"
3"
¼"
1" FINGER HOLES
1"
21"
12½"
33"
5¾"
18"
REMOVABLE SAW RACK
5½"
SECTION

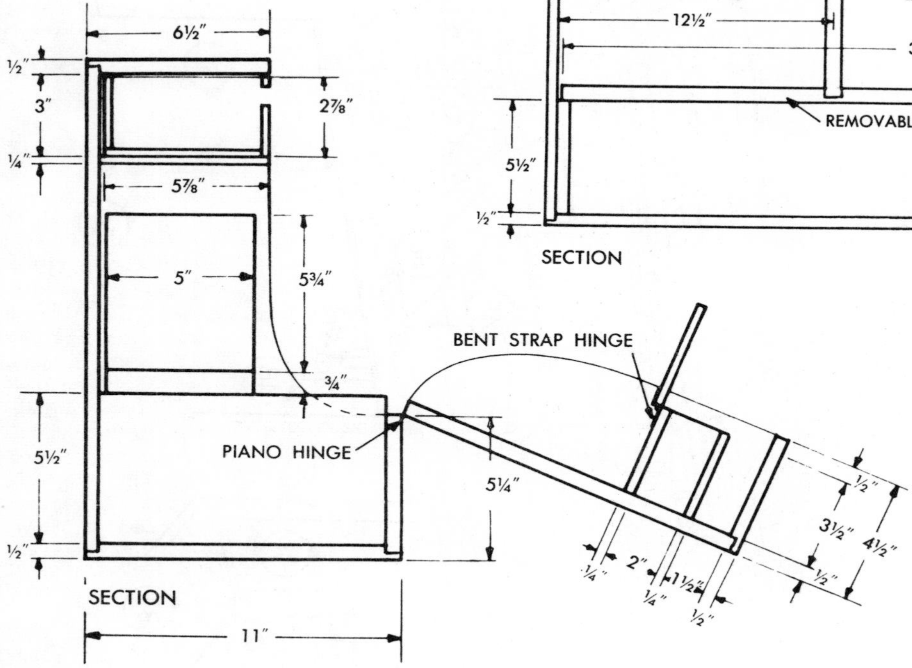
6½"
½"
3"
2⅞"
¼"
5⅞"
5"
5¾"
BENT STRAP HINGE
¾"
PIANO HINGE
5½"
5¼"
3½"
4½"
2"
1½"
SECTION
11"

Left: End assembly of members.

PARTS SCHEDULE

CODE	NO. REQ'D	SIZE	PART IDENTIFICATION
A	1	11"x34½"	Bottom
B	1	17½"x34½"	Back
C	1	12½"x34½"	Front
D	1	5"x34½"	Front
E	1	6½"x34½"	Top
F	1	4½"x34½"	Top
G	2	10½"x17½"	Ends
H	2	5"x6⅛"	Saw Rack Support
J	1	6"x34"	Drawer Shelf
K	2	5⅝"x15⅞"	Drawer Bottom
L	1	4"x33½"	Level Box Lid
M	1	3½"x34"	Level Box Divider
N	1	3½"x34"	Level Box Back
O	4	2⅞"x5½"	Drawer Sides
P	2	2⅝"x15⅞"	Drawer Backs
Q	2	2⅞"x16⅜"	Drawer Fronts
R	1	5"x33"	Saw Rack Bottom
S	2	5½"x10"	Saw Rack
T	1	3"x6"	Drawer Divider
U	1	2"x3¾"	Level Box Divider
	1 Ea.	34½"	Piano Hinge
	2 Ea.	—	Strap Fasteners
	4 Ea.	—	Casters (Optional)
	2 Ea.	—	Metal Handles

Miscellaneous—4d and 6d Finish Nails
Waterproof Glue

The parts schedule lists the sizes of each part to be laid out and cut from the single sheet of plywood as shown on the cutting diagram.

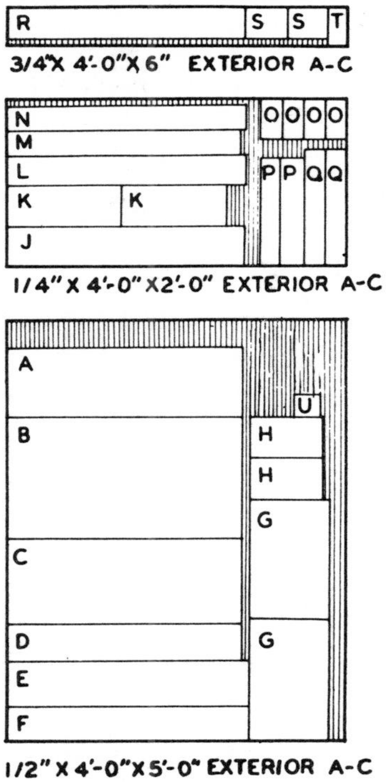
R S S T
3/4"X 4'-0"X 6" EXTERIOR A-C
N
M
L
K K
J
O O O O
P P Q Q
1/4" X 4'-0" X 2'-0" EXTERIOR A-C
A
B
C
D
E
F
U
H
H
G
G
1/2" X 4'-0" X 5'-0" EXTERIOR A-C

CUTTING DIAGRAM

2

Structural Parts of a House

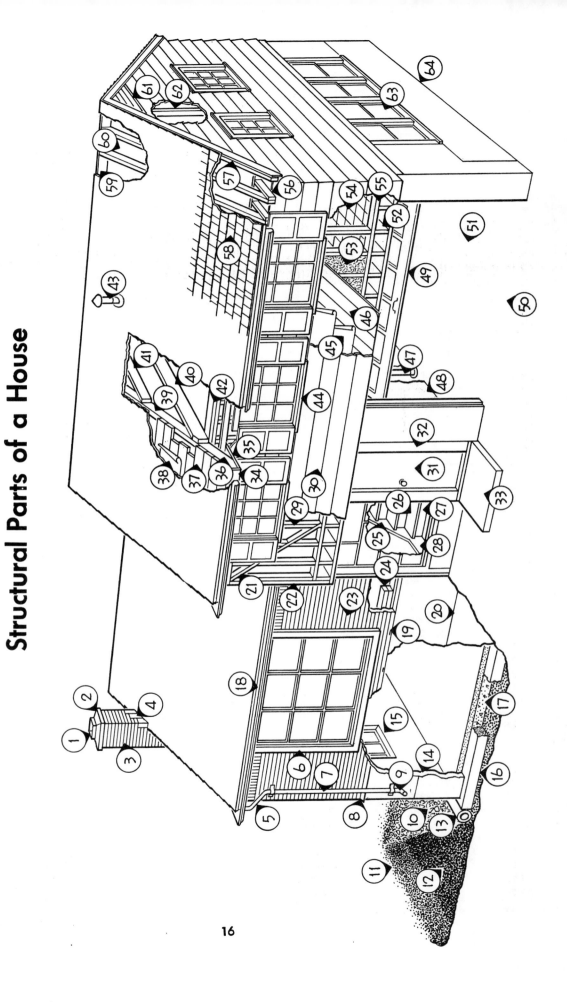

1. Flue
2. Chimney cap
3. Brickwork of chimney
4. Chimney flashing
5. Downspout gooseneck
6. Window trim
7. Leader, downspout
8. Termite shield
9. Downspout elbow
10. Porous fill
11. Topsoil
12. Subsoil
13. Drain tile
14. Foundation wall
15. Basement window
16. Foundation wall footing
17. Cinder fill
18. Gutter
19. Weep hole
20. Waterproofing
21. Corner bracing
22. Double studding
23. Brick veneer
24. Sill
25. Stringer
26. Stair tread
27. Stair riser
28. Baseboard
29. Studding
30. Beveled siding
31. Front door
32. Door trim
33. Entrance platform
34. Fascia

35. Soffit
36. Rafter overhang
37. Roof boards
38. Vapor barrier
39. Rafter
40. Ceiling joist
41. Collar beam
42. Double plate
43. Roof ventilator
44. Window sill
45. Building paper
46. Diagonal sheathing
47. Basement post (lally column)
48. Interior wall
49. Upward-acting garage door
50. Garage
51. Concrete floor or slab
52. Floor joist
53. Rockwool insulation
54. Asphalt tile floor
55. Sole plate
56. Lookout
57. End rafter
58. Roofing shingles
59. Ridge
60. Attic space
61. Louver
62. Gable stud
63. Double-hung window
64. Grade
65. Cross-bridging
66. Girder
67. Plywood subflooring
68. Finish flooring

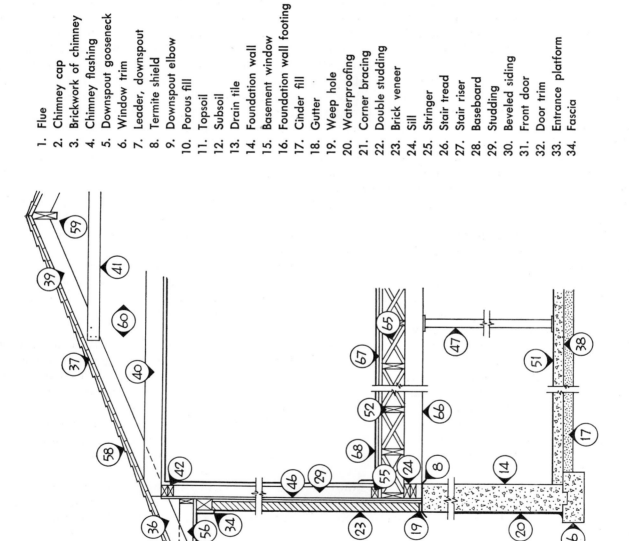

3

House Plans and Specifications

The plans or directions for the actual construction work on a house consists of a set of house plans and specifications. The specifications are written instructions and regulations about the many detailed phases of the work. The set of house plans consists of a series of drawings.

Plans and specifications may be obtained in one of three ways. One is to purchase a set of stock plans and specifications from a stock plan company. Another is to have them drawn up by an experienced contractor or builder. The third way is to hire an architect. The latter will also supervise the construction of the building. The services of an architect are usually called for when a house is to cost a considerable amount, otherwise money can be saved by buying a good set of stock plans and having a contractor make such minor changes in them as may be desired by the owner.

An architect is one who consults any party contemplating the erection of a building, draws the necessary set of plans and supervises the construction until completion. An architect must have professional as well as practical training. He usually specializes in some particular phase of construction, such as small houses, public buildings, office buildings, churches, bridges, roads, etc.

The architect consults the prospective owner or builder, renders several free-hand sketches, learns the desires and requirements, and draws a set of plans which are approved by the owner.

One may classify the work on a drawing as line work, lettering, and figures. Line work and lettering may be slightly inaccurate but the figures must never be so on a worthwhile drawing. Dimensions must be checked for accuracy. The smaller dimensions must be checked to harmonize with the over-all totals. One must learn to check over-all dimensions against fractional or smaller ones. Refer to a floor plan drawing in the set of house plans. Locate the over-all length and width of the house. Mark it down. Locate the room dimensions and the wall thickness. Add the room dimensions and the wall thicknesses along the length of the house. Does it equal the total length given? What is the area of each room?

The arrangement of rooms within the outside walls is a challenging and interesting study. The room arrangement suitable to one family may not suit another. An approach to the arrangement of rooms often is made by analyzing the activities of the occupants. This analysis is made up of three important factors. The first is based upon the activities of each occupant, the second upon the sizes of furniture to be used, and the third upon the placement of the furniture.

Carry out the list of furniture for the typical activities of the father. Next begin on the list for the mother. Complete the list by listing activities of a girl and a boy of about high school age. These lists need not be too extensive but should be typical activities. After completing the list for the father avoid duplicating items of furniture in the other lists.

Obtain catalogs of furniture from local sources or from mail order concerns. Make a list of the typical sizes of furniture called for in the previous lists. Typical sizes of some furniture are as follows:

davenport, 32″ x 80″	dresser, 24″ x 42″
buffet, 36″ x 60″	straight chair, 18″ x 18″
double bed, 54″ x 80″	morris chair, 26″ x 26″
single bed, 36″ x 80″	dining table, 48″ x 48″
kitchen table, 24″ x 36″	library table, 30″ x 48″
refrigerator, 26″ x 36″	upright piano, 38″ x 78″
kitchen cabinet, 26″ x 48″	bookcases, 16″ x 42″, etc.
kitchen range, 28″ x 36″	

Now make a choice of furniture for the above listings and lay off the sizes on paper to scale, such as ⅛″ equals 2″ of furniture size. Cut out these rectangles and arrange them on a large sheet of kraft in the proper rooms.

After all rectangles have been cut out, properly labeled for father, mother, boy, girl, guest, listing all occupants of one item if such is used by all, begin to arrange in room placement. It is surprising how this method of shaping room arrangements works out. Keep in mind that rooms are not outlined and then the rectangles placed on, but the reverse. After a suitable arrangement is made of the furniture, draw single lines through the groupings of furniture to see how the rooms will arrange themselves by this method. Keep in mind that proper distances must be kept between the furniture rectangles, due allowance being made for windows and doors, passageways, etc.

Move the rectangles around until a satisfactory arrangement is made. Then draw single lines for the rooms, symbols for window, door, and stair openings. One then has an outline of a floor plan built up from the activities approach.

If two floors are needed, arrange the rectangles for the first and second floors. After this is tried for a few times attempt to arrange for all possible activities, such as carried on in the laundry, study, garage, hobby room, etc. Many serviceable floor plans can be made in this manner and it will prove very interesting and fascinating.

The drawing of an object or objects often must be made larger or smaller than actual size. This process is called drawing to scale or making the drawing in a relative proportion. The most commonly used standard proportions or scales are:

Full size: 12″ on drawing is equal to 12″ on the object.
Half size: 6″ on drawing is equal to 12″ on the object.
Quarter size: 3″ on drawing is equal to 12″ on the object.
Eighth size: 1½″ on drawing is equal to 12″ on the object.

Obtain a scale and a rule. Place the rule in the left hand and the scale on the right hand. Turn the scale to any one of the different faces or scales and see that the zero on the scale is at the first mark on the rule. If the quarter scale is used, see how the quarter scale divisions match up with every quarter inch on the rule.

All drawings must have on them the scale used. They are designated as follows: ¼″ = 1′-0″; or ¼″ = 1′3″; or 1″ = 3″; or ½″ = 1′, and so on.

The following shows the relation of the rule to the scale, the scale being turned to the ¼″ scale:

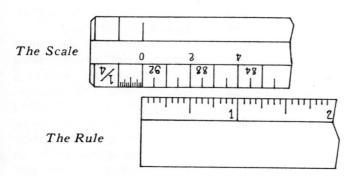

Study the flat scale, the triangular scale, and the rule. Obtain catalogs of several drafting room supply dealers and inspect the illustrations of the scales. Read the important descriptive matter given in the catalogs.

A set of house plans contains floor plans, elevations, plot plan, roof layout, and elevations in section, together with some details of important parts of the dwelling. It would be quite impossible to show all details on the plans, elevations, or sections. Hence the need for two or three sheets of the set of plans to detail the smaller parts of the dwelling. A *detail* is a drawing expressed in one of the standard methods of shape representation, generally orthographic projection, showing all the necessary views for the proper construction of a part or parts of a house. Many details are shown in full size while others are shown with a scale of ¼″ equaling 1″ or ½″ equaling 1″.

The following parts of a dwelling are given as suggested assignments for detailing. Locate the parts in details in this book and other books, obtaining as much information about a particular item as possible before starting instrument drawing. Make preliminary sketches of a particular study, for example, porch joists, getting together details from a few good sources. Then draw a detail of a porch joist assembly.

Parts of a dwelling which might be detailed are: flat sill, box sill, pier footing, girder post, joist-balloon frame, joist-box frame, pier anchors, braced frame sill, box-frame sill, lapped joist at top of girder, girder-balloon frame, girder-western frame, studding, rough flooring, partition framing, common rafter, ridge piece, and braced framing girt.

The following drawing is a detail of a cornice

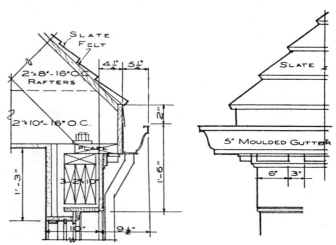

Example of a detail drawing: Cornice section at window head.

section. Observe the end view of each part of each member is shown in relation one to another. Observe the side view of the assembly at the right.

Study with great care the list of materials that go to make up a framed dwelling. Obtain prices from a local supply house and figure out the cost based upon a plan of your own choosing or upon the plans that accompany this text. Prices of material vary in different localities as do prices of labor or wage rates. An apprentice or journeyman carpenter does not usually estimate the cost of work but he should become acquainted with these costs nevertheless. *Simplified Carpentry Estimating*, by Wilson and Rogers, is a recommended book on the subject.

Board measure is the term used to indicate that a board foot is the unit of measurement of lumber. A board foot is the quantity of lumber contained in, or derived from, by drying, planing, or working, or any combination of these means, a piece of rough green lumber 1″ thick, 12″ wide and 1′ long or its equivalent in thicker, wider, narrower, or longer lumber.

Grading of Lumber

Ordinary construction lumber is graded on the basis of quality in two main classes—select lumber and common lumber. Select lumber has but very few minor objectionable characteristics, is smoothly finished and can be used as a whole for finishing purposes or where large, clear pieces are required. The selects are divided into two main groups: A and B grades, suitable for natural finishing, and C and D grades, which have blemishes somewhat greater than those in the first class, but blemishes which can be covered with paint.

Common lumber may contain numerous characteristics which do not permit its use for finishing purposes but which still permit its use for general utility and construction purposes. The two principle classifications here are boards and dimensions. Boards are graded as No. 1, No. 2, No. 3, No. 4 or No. 5. These grades are not equivalent in all species. Dimension is graded as No. 1, No. 2 or No. 3.

Size Standard

Lumber sizes are based on its rough, green dimensions. For example, although described as 4 inch by 4 inch, which is the "nominal" size, a piece which has been dried and dressed on four sides is actually $3\frac{5}{8}$ inch by $3\frac{5}{8}$ inch. The first figure quoted in lumber dimensions indicates nominal thickness; the second, width; and the third, if there is one, is the length. Lengths on common lumber normally are in multiples of two feet.

Common boards, or boards, or a general purpose item available at all lumber yards in one or more of the kinds of wood most frequently used in building. The standard nominal widths are 4, 6, 8, 10, 12 inches or wider. Although the grades shown are from No. 1 through No. 5, the very lowest grades of any species are almost never available in retail yards. Their use is mainly for special industrial purposes. Boards are produced with square edge, dressed and matched (tongue-and-groove), or with a shiplap joint. The largest uses for common boards are subfloors, sheathing, roof boards, barn boards, rough siding and concrete forms.

Dimension Lumber

Dimension is primarily framing lumber, used for joists, rafters and studding. Strength, stiffness, and uniformity of size are essential requirements. Dimension is nominally two inches in thickness dressed to $1\frac{5}{8}$ inches. Widths are usually nominal 4, 6, 8, 10 or 12 inches and lengths normally run from 6 to 20 feet in multiples of 2 feet. Dimension lumber thicker than 2 inches and longer than 20 feet is made but such is used in comparatively small quantities. Basically dimension lumber is graded to fill the requirements of framing for buildings.

STUDY OF A MODEL HOUSE

On the following pages are complete plans and details of an interesting house around which effective study can be made.

In the plan of this house the entrance level is the big feature. A partition separates this level into two sections, front to back. The front section is a generous-sized entrance foyer which gives access to the living-dining and kitchen level, up five steps. The rear part—referred to as a balcony—has a direct approach to the recreation area, down seven steps. A door off this balcony opens to the garage, down one step. Powder room and laundry are also off the entrance level.

The bedroom level, above foyer and balcony, is approached from the living room level.

In this case, juggling the levels of the house has been the means of establishing an interesting plan pattern, which in turn has made possible a change of pace in the design pattern of the exterior. The various levels are all cleverly contained within two basic design units, one for the living-dining-kitchen, the other for the foyer-garage and bedrooms. Both are direct in their design approach and depend upon good fenestration and the proportional relation of walls to the roof surfaces.

There are two other aspects of this plan that also rate special notice—the recreation room and the garage. Because of the position of the basement room, the balcony, rail and steps and the large window wall actually become a part of the

Four levels for living are hidden behind a well-balanced front.

room and can be treated accordingly. The garage with a battery of four large windows on the side wall can double for playroom.

The structural elements of the walls are masonry veneer and frame placed on 10-inch thick concrete foundations. One half of the house contains a basement, the balance is a slab on grade. Exterior materials are face brick and asbestos shingles on the side walls, with asphalt shingles covering the roof.

House from rear, showing back door to entrance level and large window which lights basement room.

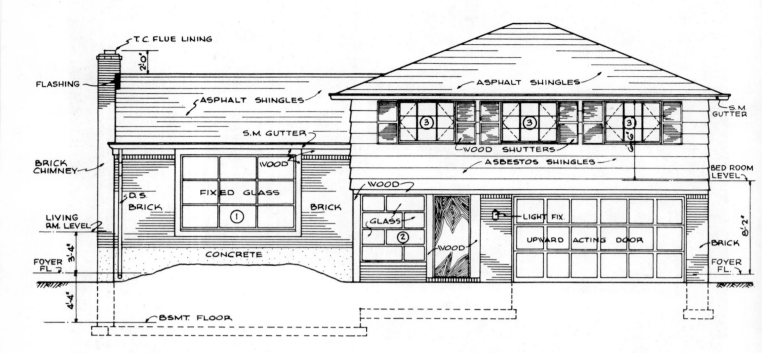

FRONT ELEVATION
SCALE: 1/8" = 1'0"

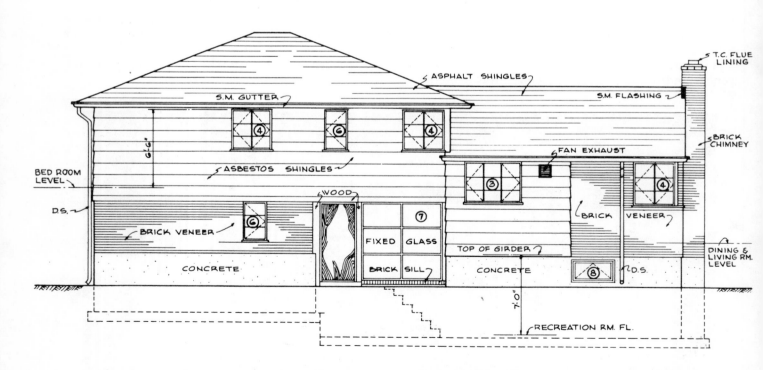

REAR ELEVATION
SCALE: 1/8" = 1'0"

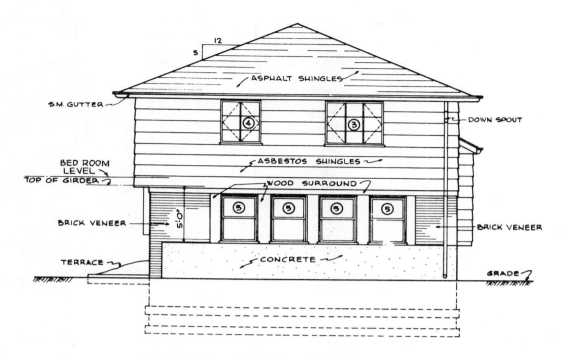

12
5

ASPHALT SHINGLES

S.M. GUTTER

DOWN SPOUT

④

③

BED ROOM
LEVEL
TOP OF GIRDER

ASBESTOS SHINGLES

WOOD SURROUND

BRICK VENEER

5'-0"

⑤ ⑤ ⑤ ⑤

BRICK VENEER

TERRACE

CONCRETE

GRADE

RIGHT SIDE ELEVATION
SCALE: 1/8"=1'-0"

DESIGN NO. A.B 219

AMERICAN BUILDER BLUE PRINT SERIES
DESIGNED BY
RUDOLPH A. MATERN ARCHITECT & ASSOC.
JAMAICA 32, NEW YORK

Simmons-Boardman Publ. Corp., 30 Church St., New York 7, N.Y.

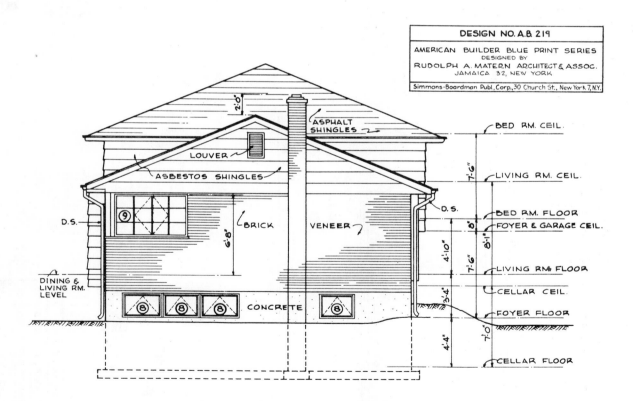

2'-0"

ASPHALT
SHINGLES

LOUVER

ASBESTOS SHINGLES

BED RM. CEIL.

7'-6"

LIVING RM. CEIL.

D.S.

⑨

BRICK

VENEER

D.S.

BED RM. FLOOR
FOYER & GARAGE CEIL.

6'-8"

6'

8'-1"

4'-10"

7'-6"

LIVING RM. FLOOR

DINING &
LIVING RM.
LEVEL

⑧ ⑧ ⑧

CONCRETE

⑧

3'-4"

CELLAR CEIL.

FOYER FLOOR

7'-0"

4'-4"

CELLAR FLOOR

LEFT SIDE ELEVATION
SCALE: 1/8"=1'-0"

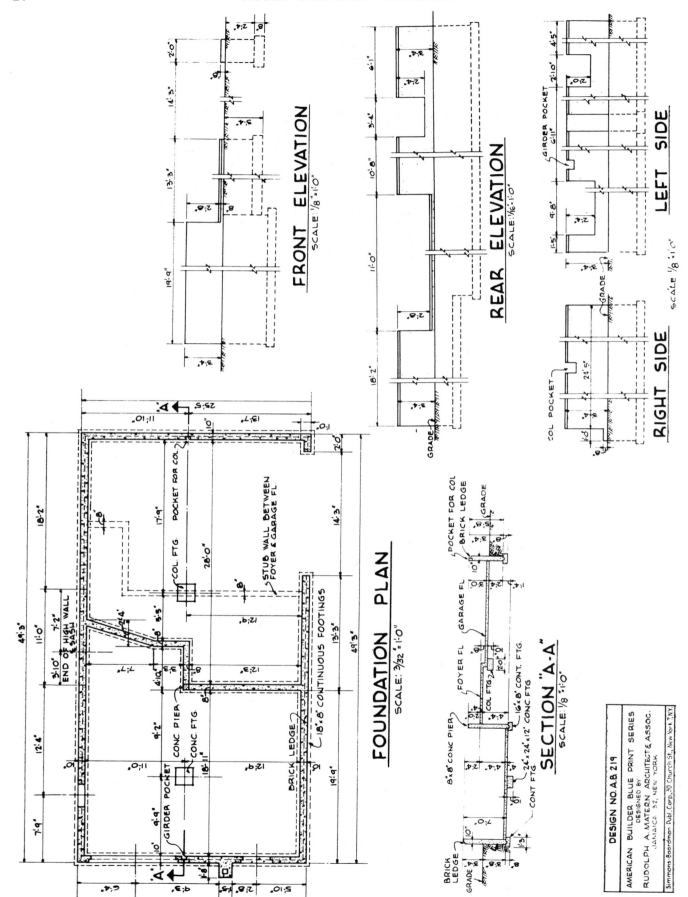

FRONT ELEVATION
SCALE: 1/8"=1'-0"

REAR ELEVATION
SCALE: 1/16"=1'-0"

LEFT SIDE

RIGHT SIDE

SCALE: 1/8"=1'-0"

FOUNDATION PLAN
SCALE: 3/32"=1'-0"

SECTION "A-A"
SCALE: 1/8"=1'-0"

DESIGN NO. A.B. 219
AMERICAN BUILDER BLUE PRINT SERIES
DESIGNED BY
RUDOLPH A. MATERN ARCHITECT & ASSOC.
JAMAICA 32, NEW YORK

Simmons-Boardman Publ. Corp., 30 Church St., New York 7, N.Y.

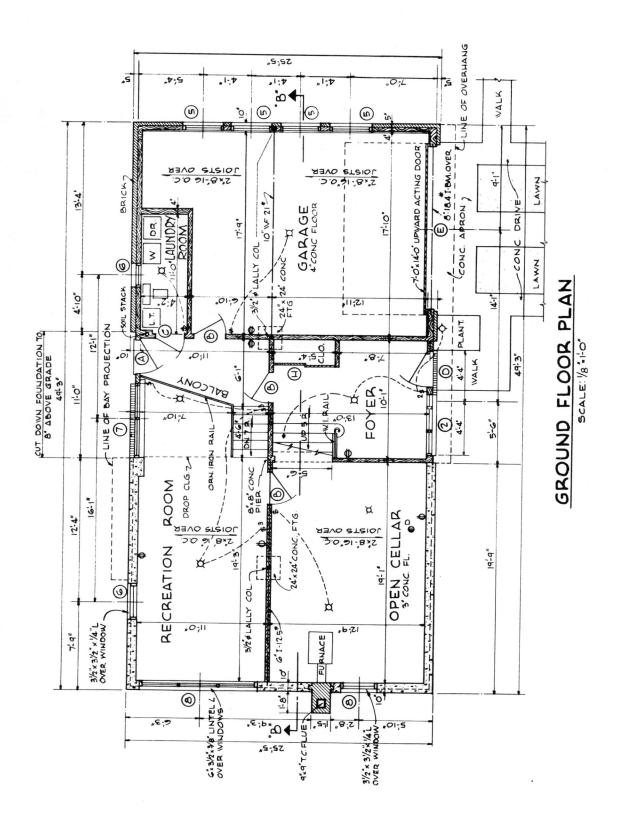

GROUND FLOOR PLAN

SCALE: 1/8"=1'-0"

DESIGN NO. A.B 219

AMERICAN BUILDER BLUE PRINT SERIES
DESIGNED BY
RUDOLPH A. MATERN ARCHITECT & ASSOC.
JAMAICA 32, NEW YORK

Simmons-Boardman Publ. Corp., 30 Church St., New York 7, N.Y.

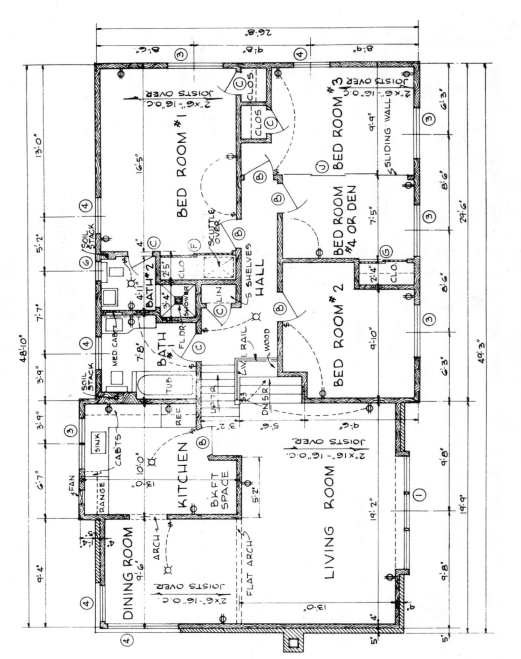

LIVING & BED ROOM LEVEL

SCALE: 1/8"=1'-0"

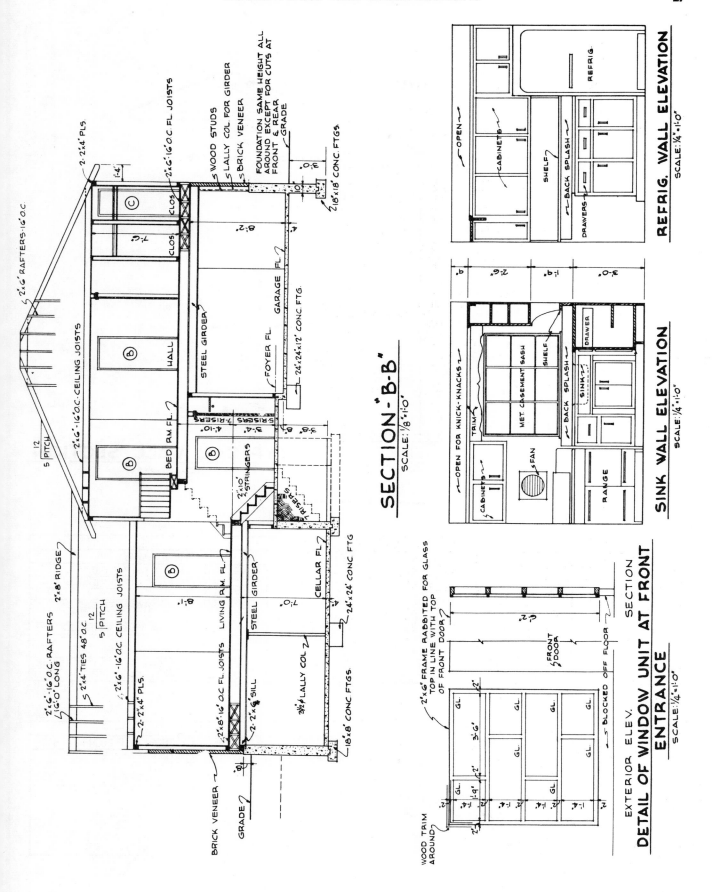

SECTION-"B-B"
SCALE: 1/8"=1'-0"

REFRIG. WALL ELEVATION
SCALE: 1/4"=1'-0"

SINK WALL ELEVATION
SCALE: 1/4"=1'-0"

EXTERIOR ELEV.   SECTION
DETAIL OF WINDOW UNIT AT FRONT
ENTRANCE
SCALE: 1/4"=1'-0"

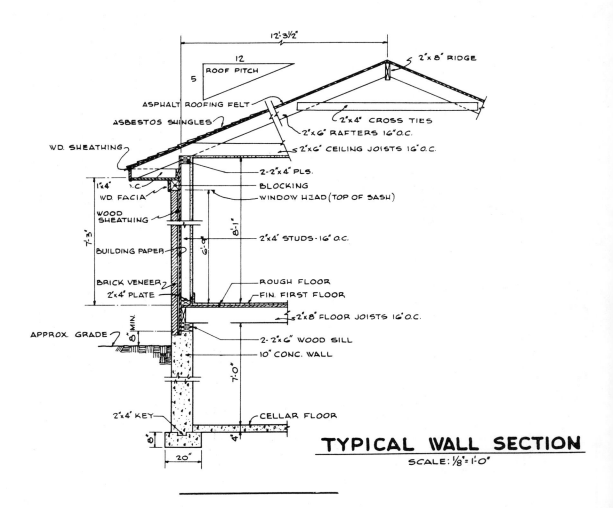

TYPICAL WALL SECTION
SCALE: 1/8" = 1'-0"

~ ROOM FINISH SCHEDULE ~

LOCATION	FLOOR	WALLS	CEILING	REMARKS
RECREATION RM.	ASPHALT TILE	PLASTER	PLASTER	PINE TRIM-OAK STAIR TREADS
FOYER	ASPHALT TILE	PLASTER	PLASTER	PINE TRIM-OAK STAIR TREADS
LAVATORY	ASPHALT TILE	PLASTER	PLASTER	PINE TRIM
LIVING ROOM	OAK FLOOR	PLASTER	PLASTER	PINE TRIM-OAK STAIR TREADS
DINING ROOM	OAK FLOOR	PLASTER	PLASTER	PINE TRIM
BATH ROOMS	CERAMIC TILE	PLASTER	PLASTER	PINE TRIM-4'0" HIGH TILE WAINSCOT
BED ROOMS	OAK FLOOR	PLASTER	PLASTER	PINE TRIM
HALL	OAK FLOOR	PLASTER	PLASTER	PINE TRIM
CLOSETS	OAK FLOOR	PLASTER	PLASTER	PINE TRIM-ONE SHELF & CLOTHES POLE
KITCHEN	ASPHALT TILE	PLASTER	PLASTER	PINE TRIM-BIRCH CABINETS

~ WINDOW SCHEDULE ~

MARK	GLASS SIZE	REMARKS
1	9-LTS-36"x24"	FIXED GLASS- WD. FRAME & MUNTINS
2	8-LTS-36x14, 20x14"	FIXED GL. WD. FRAME & MUN. SEE ELEV.
3	9-LTS-12"x18"	METAL CASEMENT SASH & FRAME
4	6-LTS-12"x18"	METAL CASEMENT SASH & FRAME
5	30"x18"	DOUBLE HUNG WOOD SASH & FRAME
6	3-LTS-12"x18"	METAL CASEMENT SASH & FRAME
7	6-LTS-36"x24"	FIXED GLASS- WD. FRAME & MUNTINS
8	1-LT-32"x18"	METAL BASEMENT SASH & FRAME
9	12-LTS-12"x18"	METAL FRAME & SASH

~ DOOR SCHEDULE ~

MARK	SIZE	DESCRIPTION
A	2'-8"x 6'-6"x 1 3/4"	FLUSH PANEL
B	2'-8"x 6'-6"x 1 3/8"	FLUSH PANEL
C	2'-6"x 6'-6"x 1 3/8"	FLUSH PANEL
D	3'-0"x 6'-6"x 1 3/4"	FLUSH PANEL
E	7'-0"x 14'-0"	UPWARD ACTING DOOR
F	2- 3'-0"x 6'-6"	SLIDING DOORS
G	2- 2'-0"x 6'-6"	SLIDING DOORS
H	2- 2'-6" x 6'-6"	SLIDING DOORS
J	4- 2'-6" x 6'-6"	SLIDING DOORS

QUANTITY LIST OF MATERIALS
For American Builder Blueprint House No. 219

General Information

House — Type	frame and masonry
Area	1,250 sq. ft.
Cube	25,000 cu. ft.
	exclusive of bay and overhang
	Height taken for cube was 20 feet
Garage — Area	included above

Excavating

Trench for foundation	160 lin. ft.
Chimney and column footings	3 footings required
Excavation for basement	115 yds.

Cement Work

Foundations	790 cu. ft.
Concrete work	247 sq. ft. 3 in. thick
	410 sq. ft. 4 in. thick
Anchor bolts	44 — ½"x10"
Waterproofing	325 sq. ft.

Masonry

Type	brick
Walls	516 sq. ft. — 4" walls
Window sills	14 lin. ft. stone sills
Chimney	66 cu. ft.
Flue lining	24 lin. ft. 9"x9"
Cap	brick and cement

Iron Work

Structural	930 lbs.
Lally columns	1 — 3½" dia. — 4' long
	1 — 3½" dia. — 7' long
	1 — 3½" dia. — 8' long
Metal railings	3 sets approx. 25 lin. ft.
Miscellaneous	1 — 6"x3½" x⅜"x10'8" angle iron lintel
	2 — 3½"x3½"x¼"x 4'0" angle iron lintel

Millwork

Windows — Type .... casement, hinged, double hung and fixed
Material .... wood and steel
Windows glazed including trim:
Full data on sizes given on complete set of working drawings

Exterior doors:
One marked "A"* .... 2'8"x6'6"x1¾"
One marked "D" .... 3'0"x6'6"x1¾"
Garage door .... 14'0"x7'0"
Exterior millwork .... shutters — 3 pr. synthetic louvers
Entrance fascias — 2 sets (plain type)
louvers — one
Interior doors including jamb and trim
Type: Flush .... 7 marked B* — 2'8"x6'6"x1⅜"
6 marked C — 2'6"x6'6"x1⅜"
Sliding .... 2 marked F — 3'0"x6'6"
2 marked G — 2'0"x6'6"
2 marked H — 2'6"x6'6"
4 marked J — 2'6"x6'6"
*As indicated on working drawings

Special interior millwork:
Stairs .... 1 set 5 risers, 66" wide
1 set 7 risers, 38" wide
Cabinets .... 2 sets of upper and lower kitchen cabinets
Special .... 1 special 2"x6" sash frame at front entrance with stops

Carpentry

Foundation plates	double 2"x6" — 300 lin. ft.
Joists	37 — 2"x8"x14'0"
	37 — 2"x8"x12'0"
Bridging	400 lin. ft. 1"x3"
Studding and plates	1,800 lin. ft. 2"x4" plate
	450 pcs. — 2"x4"x8'0"
Ceiling joist	5 — 2"x6" — 18'0"
	12 — 2"x6" — 14'0"
	23 — 2"x6" — 16'0"
	32 — 2"x6" — 12'0"
Roof rafters	4 hip rafters — 2"x8" — 18'0"
	92 — 2"x6" — 16'0"
	Ridge 1 pc. — 2"x8" — 24'0"
	1 pc. — 2"x8" — 6'0"
	8 — 2"x4" cross ties 16'0" long
Subfloor	1,600 bd. ft. of 1" D&M sheathing
Roof sheathing	2,200 bd. ft.
Side wall sheathing	1,100 bd. ft. D&M
Side wall materials	950 sq. ft. asbestos shingles
Furring	350 lin. ft. 1"x2"

Carpenter stairs
1 set of 7 risers — 2 — 2"x10" stringers 8' long
7 pcs. stepping stock 3' long
7 — 1"x8" risers
1 set of 5 risers — 3 — 2"x10"x6' stringers
5 pcs. stepping stock 5'6" long
5 — 1"x8" risers

Flooring — hardwood	830 sq. ft.
softwood	300 sq. ft.
asphalt tile	425 sq. ft.
ceramic floor tile	100 sq. ft.
	plus 4'0" high wainscot in bathrooms
Exterior material soffits	800 b.f. 1" D&M
eaves	350 lin. ft. 1" fascia board

Sheet Metal

Gutters	170 lin. ft.
Downspouts	53 lin. ft.
Flashing	at chimney and valleys

Roofing

Type	asphalt shingles
Area	18 squares

Interior Walls and Ceiling

Area to be covered	6,000 sq. ft.

● *This quantity list will be subject to variation depending on the common practices in various sections and municipalities of the country, the techniques of individual builders, the types of materials available locally and cost factors. The list published here is a suggested one, complete enough so that it can be used in arriving at a reasonably accurate estimate of the quantities and cost of materials that will be required to complete the structure. It was prepared by experts at the Edward Hines Lumber Co., Chicago.*

TYPICAL SET OF OPEN SPECIFICATIONS

GENERAL—The construction shall equal or exceed the applicable FHA Minimum Construction Requirements and shall comply with all applicable codes and regulations, zoning ordinances, etc. The highest of all the foregoing shall govern. Each item of material or equipment shall equal or exceed that described or indicated. All parts shall be sound and all construction free of faults. All work shall be performed in a workmanlike manner, and in accordance with the best practice. For final acceptance, all buildings shall be complete and ready for occupancy, with all equipment installed, connected, and in operating condition and all utility connections completed.

1. GENERAL CONDITIONS: The following conditions are intended to apply to all subcontractors and workmen who are in any way connected with the execution of the work, and to remain in force until the completion of the entire work.

Each subcontractor shall clean up and remove all debris resulting from his work and leave the premises in a neat condition satisfactory to the supervisor.

NOTE: Each contractor is to conform to plans and specifications, but in no way should the workmanship or material used in the construction be below the minimum requirements of the Federal Housing Administration. On completion of his contract and before final payment is made, each contractor will furnish the owner with a waiver of lien stating that he has paid all bills for labor and material.

2. COMPLIANCE WITH CITY ORDINANCES: The contractor will comply with all City Building and Health Ordinances in every respect and state laws pertaining to construction and safety of buildings and public, even if every item involved to do this is not especially mentioned in these specifications, or shown on the plans.

3. INSURANCE: Contractor agrees to carry all necessary compensation and liability insurance to protect the owners from any and all claims for damages or injury to the public, workmen, or property during the course of the construction.

4. PERMITS: Contractor shall obtain and pay for all permits required by the Building, Health, and Electrical Departments for the performance of the work specified herein.

5. EXCAVATING: Contractor agrees to furnish labor and equipment necessary to excavate to depth as shown on plan. All excavated black dirt is to be set aside, so that on completion of house it will be used for grading. Contractor agrees to backfill and rough-grade around house. No backfilling is to be done until outside foundation walls are damp-proofed. Contractor agrees to do all necessary excavating for septic tank and tile for drainage field if called for on plans and in accordance with local ordinances. He will remove from premises any and all trees that will interfere with the construction of this building, but only by permission of owner.

CONCRETE

GENERAL: Applicable provisions of "General Conditions" govern work under this section.

This contractor is to provide all articles, materials, and labor necessary and required for the completion of work.

WORK INCLUDED: Furnish labor and materials necessary to complete all concrete work indicated on plans and pay for all water permits.

Cooperate with other trades regarding installation of imbedded items.

CONCRETE MIX: Concrete mix shall be 1 part portland cement, 3 parts clean sand, and 5 parts coarse aggregates. All aggregates shall pass through a 4-mesh screen except coarse aggregates which shall pass through a screen having openings ¾" in diameter.

FORMS: Forms shall be tight and rigid to sustain the concrete without leakage and shall be clean inside when the concrete is poured. Forms shall be left in place until the concrete is self-supporting.

ANCHORS: Anchors shall be looped, crumped for anchorage.

REINFORCING: Two ½" round rods shall be placed in the bottom of all footings. All reinforcing bars shall be of intermediate grade.

Provide 6/6 x 10/10 wire mesh reinforcing in basement floor slab and garage floor slab before slab is poured.

ANCHORS, ETC.: Anchors, bolts, sleeves, dowels, inserts, etc. as required shall be properly located and built in as the work progresses.

FLOOR SLAB: Where concrete slabs are indicated on plans the thickness indicated shall be maintained throughout. Floor shall be furnished without a separate topping and shall be sloped to drain where drains are indicated. Topping shall be laid integral with base concrete.

SPLATTER BLOCKS: Provide concrete splatter blocks where shown on plans.

MASONRY

This contractor will be governed by preceding general conditions and will pay for any and all permits to complete his branch of the work.

Where brick or stone veneer are called for on plans, this is to be laid up in a 10 percent cement mortar, colored as may be decided by owner.

Brick or stone veneer is to be anchored to frame structure with corrugated 18-gauge galvanized iron anchors spaced not more than 32" apart in either direction. Face brick is to cost —— per M and will be selected by owner. Stone veneer will be as shown on plans.

This contractor will furnish and install all the necessary steel lintels, columns and steel beams as shown on plans, and all metal areas which will be bolted to walls.

Where necessary or shown on plans, it will be the duty of this contractor to construct for the plumber a catch basin of proper size as may be required by local ordinance.

This is to be built of brick with waterproof cement mortar and a 3″ concrete floor, allowing necessary openings for sewer tile at proper heights.

Common brick walls where shown on plans are to be of thickness as marked, laid up in mortar as for veneer, straight and true, and bonded every fifth course. Contractor will also furnish and set in place any flagstone for terraces or porches that may be shown on plans.

Where pipe railing or wrought-iron railings are shown on plans, these are to be furnished and installed by this contractor. He will furnish and install the necessary fireplace damper and lintel over fireplace opening when fireplace is indicated on plans. Facing for fireplace is to be as shown on plans with hearth as shown and cast-iron ash door as may be required.

Contractor will furnish the necessary tile flue lining as shown on plans for chimney, also the cast-iron cleanout doors for ash dump and flue.

Where cast-iron vents are shown in walls for crawl space, these are to have controlled louvres with screened back and are to be set where indicated on plans.

On completion, this contractor will remove all debris caused by his work, and clean down brick or stone veneer, leaving same in a neat and workmanlike condition.

CARPENTRY

GENERAL: Applicable provisions of "General Conditions" govern work under this section.

FRAMING LUMBER: All framing lumber, including joists, rafters, headers, stringers, shall be #1 Douglas fir or hemlock.

All studs, plates, caps, bucks, sleepers shall be #2 Douglas fir. Ribbon boards, collar beams, ridge boards, bracing, furring and grounds shall be 1″ Douglas fir.

All subflooring and roof sheathing shall be 1″ Douglas fir or ½″ fir plywood.

Wall sheathing shall be 1″ Douglas fir, or ¾″ composition sheathing.

All exterior trim shall be ponderosa pine of thickness indicated.

Beveled siding shall be 10″ face ponderosa pine.

Porch ceiling shall be ⅝″ x 4″ M. & B. Douglas fir, or 5-ply white pine plywood.

FRAMING: General: Frame, fit closely, set framing accurately to required lines and levels; secure rigidly in place.

Set rafters, joists, rough stair stringers with crown edge up, maintain bottom edges free from pronounced defects.

Frame members for passage of pipes and ducts. Avoid cutting structural members. Keep framing 2″ away from chimneys.

Provide any special framing not indicated or specified to complete work in best workmanlike manner.

Do nailing, spiking in thorough manner; use nails of ample size; use spikes larger than 20d where practicable.

PARTITION WALLS: Frame partitions with 2″ x 4″ studs 16″ on center unless otherwise indicated.

Anchor plates of exterior walls to concrete foundation with ½″ bolts. Double studs at openings. Make headers for opening up to 48″ wide of 2 pieces of stud material set on edge. For wider openings, see details. Spike corners thoroughly; make solid. Provide bearing partitions with double top plates. Provide partitions with one row of horizontal blocking, full width of studding; cut in, nail securely.

Provide exterior walls to be sheathed with fiberboard with 1″ x 4″ diagonal braces let into studs, one of each face at each corner; extend braces full stud height. Cut in nailing strips as required for support of fixtures of all kinds.

FLOOR FRAMING: Provide joists with 4″ bearings; where built in, provide fire cut with 3½″ bevel. Carry joists framing into headers, girders, on joist hangers, where possible, lap joists; spike together at bearings; spike to studs where same occur.

Frame floor openings with headers, and trimmers. Frame pieces of 2″ x 4″ material between joist ends for nailing diagonal rough floor.

ROOF FRAMING: Assemble, fit, set members to exact slopes indicated. Make rafter tops from true plane. Make valley, ridge, hip members of equal depth to cut on rafters. Erect valley, hips, ridges straight, true intersections of roof planes. Provide blocking between rafters where necessary to form nailings for roof sheathing. Spike rafters to wall plates or bolt with clip angles.

BRIDGING: Floor and roof joists are to have one run of cross bridging for spans over 6′0″ but less than 16′0″. Bridging to be wood of 1″ x 3″ stock. Ends are to be bevel cut to afford firm contact with joist sides.

Wall sheathing: 1″ stock; apply horizontally, or ¾″ compo board.

Roof sheathing: 1″ stock; lay in level courses.

Subflooring 1″ x 6″ dressed, square-edge material, or 5-ply plywood. Stagger butt joints.

Where tile floor occurs, construct subfloor of dressed and matched materials set at proper height of 2″ x 4″ strips; nail to floor joist sides. Chamfer joist tops.

Lay 1″ x 2″ wood sleepers over rough floor to provide channels for electric conduit.

SHEATHING PAPER: Install sheathing paper or asphalt saturated felt over sheathing and subfloor. On floors turn up material under baseboard 3″.

INSULATION: Install batt insulation as per manufacturer's instructions, 2″ thick in side walls, 4″ thick in ceiling.

Insulation shall be installed between studs and joists.

DOOR FRAMES, EXTERIOR: Unless otherwise indicated, wood door frames for exterior doors are to be 1⅝″ thick, double rabbeted from solid stock for doors and screens of thickness specified.

WINDOW FRAMES: Completely assembled windows with sash fitted in place will be acceptable. All sash is to be 1⅜″ thick, except where noted on plans.

WOOD LOUVER VENTILATORS: Construct ventilators as per details. Plank frame 1⅝″ thick to be routed out to receive ½″ louver slats. Secure insect screen to the back face of louver. Provide ¾″ batten shutters, secured to inside of frame with screws.

FLOORS: New floors shall be clean and in good condition before finish is applied. Paste filler shall be applied to all open-grain wood floors. Shellac finish shall be the number of coats of shellac specified.

WALLBOARD SURFACES: The contractor shall be responsible for the condition of walls and ceilings made ready for finish. All new work shall receive two coats of oil paint as specified, finish and color called for.

WALL PAPER: Surfaces shall be prepared for papering similarly to the method required for paint.

PLUMBING

WORK INCLUDED: The work to be done under this heading is subject to the general conditions and includes the furnishing of all labor and materials, equipment, and services necessary for the proper completion of all plumbing.

REGULATIONS: All work shall be done in accordance with the rules and regulations of the local authority having jurisdiction.

MATERIALS: All materials shall be the best of their respective kinds, suitable for the conditions and duties imposed on them at the building.

WORKMANSHIP: All materials and equipment shall be installed and completed in a first-class, workmanlike manner in accordance with the best modern methods and practices. All fixtures to be properly vented and revented and in accordance with the sanitary code of city, county, or state in which this building is being built.

Where necessary it will be the duty of this contractor to drill a well of sufficient depth for approved usable water, with necessary casings and pipes, and connected to an automatic pump and pressure tank, which in turn will be connected to various fixtures in the building.

GUARANTEE: The contractor shall further guarantee to make good all defects in workmanship and material and equipment installed by him which may develop during a period of one year from date of acceptance.

FIXTURES: Contractor shall install all new fixtures where shown on plans. They shall be complete with all necessary brass valves and fittings.

Provide floor drains where indicated on plans.

It is optional whether copper or brass tubing is used instead of galvanized iron pipe for all water supply work. Install cast-iron sewer pipe under house, tile pipe outside, of proper size.

ELECTRIC WORK

WORK INCLUDED: The work to be done under this heading is subject to the general conditions and includes the furnishing of all labor, materials, equipment, and services necessary for the proper completion of all the electrical work involved.

REGULATIONS: All work shall be done in accordance with the rules and regulations of the local authority.

MATERIALS: All material shall be approved standard products, and shall be labeled under the re-examination service of the Underwriters Laboratories, Inc., and shall conform to the requirements of the National Electric Code.

Unless otherwise specified the following minimum standards shall govern:

(a) Conductors shall not be smaller than No. 14 B and S for voltages of 110 or greater.

(b) Service switch shall be 60-ampere, fused or circuit breaker protected safety type, mounted on approved panel.

(c) Branch circuits shall be protected by fuses or circuit breakers having a maximum capacity of 15 amperes.

(d) Outlet boxes shall be black-japanned or zinc-coated steel.

(e) Switches shall be flush, toggle or tumble type, 10-ampere, 125-volt, single-pole, double-pole, or three-way as specified.

(f) Receptacles shall be duplex type set flush with the wall.

WORKMANSHIP: All workmanship shall be in accordance with the National Electric Code of the National Board of Fire Underwriters. The contractor shall lay out all work so as to require a minimum amount of cutting and patching to finish surfaces. Wiring shall run concealed through walls and ceilings.

GUARANTEE: The contractor shall guarantee all labor and material installed, as well as the proper operation of the installation, for a period of one year from date of completion and final acceptance of the work.

HEATING

WORK INCLUDED: The work to be done under this heading is subject to the general conditions and includes the furnishing of all labor, materials, equipment, and services necessary for the proper completion of all heating.

REGULATIONS: All work shall be installed in accordance with the requirements of controlling building, fire, and safety codes.

MATERIALS: All materials and devices shall be new and of such quality, quantity, capacity, and size to assure the plant fulfilling the requirements of the guarantee.

WORKMANSHIP: All materials and equipment shall be installed and completed in a first-class workmanlike manner.

TYPE OF HEATING: The owner reserves the right to specify the type of heating he prefers, and it will be the duty of this contractor to furnish and install this system in accordance with local or state ordinances. This contractor will install a heating plant of sufficient capacity to maintain a temperature of 72 deg. F. inside when the outside temperature is at a maximum low for that certain locality.

This contractor will furnish and supply all necessary new materials and labor to complete this part of the contract in a workmanlike manner, and on completion furnish the owner with a guarantee stating that this heating plant will comply with the above, and will replace all defective parts which may develop for a period of one year from date of acceptance. He will pay for any and all permits and acceptance fees and leave the plant in a working condition.

DOOR FRAMES, INTERIOR: Frames shall be ¾" thick with ½" thick stop nailed to frame.

INTERIOR TRIM: All trim for doors and windows shall be ¾" x 3⅝". Base ¾" x 3⅝". Threshold (oak) at bathroom door. Hook strips in closets ¾" x 3⅝". Picture molding in all rooms except kitchen, bath and rear entry, ¾" x 1¾" molded. Install at ceiling as directed.

FINISH FLOORS: All oak floors indicated in room finish schedule shall be selected 2¼" face material.

Repair damaged portions of wood subfloor, replace defective boards, renail any subflooring which does not present firm bearing. Clean surface free of all foreign matter. Surface is to be dry before finish flooring is laid.

Lay flooring with close joints; drive up tightly; blind-nail with 8d (cut steel) nails into each floor joist. Alternate joists so there will be at least two boards between them.

Machine sand flooring; hand-scrape around edges not accessible by machine. Leave in condition for finishing.

SHELVES: Make shelves of ¾" thick material. Provide clothes closets with 2 shelves and a 1¼" hanging rod. Support upper shelf on shelf cleats ¾" x 1⅝".

Make shelves in linen and towel closets of indicated width.

WALL SURFACES

APPLICATION: Furnish labor and material necessary to apply a single ply of ½" gypsum wallboard to the face of all partition and wall studs and to the ceiling joist of basement and first floor. Care shall be exercised to see that all studs and rafters are true to line and present an even surface for the application of wallboard.

All joints are to be carefully taped and all nails depressed for the reception of joint filler.

SHEET METAL WORK

GUTTERS: All gutters shall be box type and shall extend around eave of house, and garage where noted on drawings. The average depth of gutters shall be 5 inches, constructed of 26-gauge galvanized iron.

DOWNSPOUTS: Furnish and install rectangular corrugated 2" x 3" downspouts of 26-gauge galvanized iron on walls of house, and garage as noted on drawings.

FLASHING: Flash and counter flash on roof and sidewalls as required. Base flashing shall extend at least 6 inches up vertical surfaces and at least 6 inches out on roofs. Provide flashing at head and sills of windows and head of doors. All metal shall be 28-gauge.

ROOFING

MATERIAL: All shingles shall be thick-butt three-tab strip asphalt shingles, size 12" x 36", weight 210 pounds per square. Before applying shingles contractor shall cover the roof with 15-pound saturated asphalt felt, lapping all joints not less than 2 inches and nailed to roof boards with galvanized barbed nails. All shingles shall be of an approved standard manufacture and shall be applied in accordance with directions on the package.

GLASS AND GLAZING

WORK INCLUDED: Work done includes furnishing of labor and materials, equipment necessary for the proper completion of all glass and glazing work.

Unless otherwise specified all glass shall be new process double-strength clear window sheets and shall be first quality, free from bubbles, and shall not distort the vision.

Mirrors of approved grade shall be manufactured on plate glass and installed where shown on plans.

GLAZING: Contractor shall set all glass and mirrors in the best possible manner and in such a way that there will be an equal bearing the entire width of pane. All glass in exterior wood frames shall be bedded in putty, tacked in place and face-puttied. All putty work shall be left smooth and free from marks and other defects. The contractor shall thoroughly clean all glass, both inside and out, before he leaves the job.

TILE WORK

KINDS OF TILE: Floors in bathroom shall be of ceramic mosaic tiles, either hexagon, square, round, or oblong, and of the size specified. All tile shall be of standard grade.

Wall tile in bathroom shall be gazed 4 x 4 inch tie, 4'6" high, with cap, interior coved corners, exterior coved corners and base.

TILE INSTALLATION: All tiles shall be firmly secured in place. Joints shall be well filled and lines kept straight and true and all finished surfaces shall be brought to true and level planes. Upon completion, all tile work shall be left clean.

PAINTING AND DECORATING

WORK INCLUDED: Work to be done includes furnishing all labor, materials, equipment, and services necessary to the proper completion of all painting and decoration work.

PREPARATION OF SURFACES: All surfaces to be painted shall be thoroughly cleaned and properly prepared, leaving a smooth finish to receive paint, either by sanding, the application of steel wool, or scraping.

All new work, exterior, shall be primed after same has been installed. Nail holes, cracks, and similar blemishes shall be neatly puttied after priming.

EXTERIOR WOODWORK: All exterior woodwork shall receive three coats of lead and oil paint or prepared paint, one prime coat and two finish coats.

EXTERIOR METAL WORK: After cleaning all metal with a coarse brush, the surface shall be covered with a coat of iron oxide or asphalt paint. Inside of all gutters shall be given one coat of red lead or asphalt paint. All metal shall be given two coats of lead and oil paint.

STRUCTURAL IRON: All structural iron shall be given one coat of red lead and two coats of lead and oil paint.

INTERIOR DECORATING: All prime coats shall be lead and oil or other approved prime coat material. All wood surfaces to receive paint shall be smoothed before application of primary coat by sandpapering or the use of steel wool. Shellac finish shall receive two coats; varnish finish shall receive one coat unless otherwise specified.

4

Laying Out the Building Site and Excavating

A plot plan is made of the building lot, showing outline of house dimensions, and in case of sloping lot a supplement showing contour dimensions is made.

The excavation is the cavity in the building site in which the foundation footings and foundation walls of a dwelling are placed. A surveyor establishes the corners of the building lot and of the house for the staking and laying out of the excavation.

Actual work in the erection of a house begins with the excavation for the foundation. This work should not be started until the plans, specifications, contracts, and in cities, building permits, are in hand. With the start of excavation the work of the journeymen craftsmen begins.

Newer types of houses, particularly in warmer climates, have no basements or cellars. Space is provided for the heating plant, laundry, or automobile in rooms on the first-floor level.

In locating the place for the foundation on the building lot, first find the property line stakes or other surveyor's marks. If these stakes have not been placed, the local community will authorize a surveyor to locate the property line, the street line, and the sidewalk line.

Obtain the distance the foundation is to be set over from one of the side property lines. Measure in with the steel tape and locate the outside lines of the foundation wall. Nail together the batter boards and place in position. Stretch a chalk line and measure and drive stakes as shown. Tie the chalk line to the stakes. Obtain the width and length of the foundation of the house from the plot plan or from the basement plan and lay off these lines.

Check each corner for squareness by using the six-eight-ten method (see illustration). Mark off with a spade the line of excavation so that the excavating contractor will have a mark on the ground to use as a guide. Remove the chalk line but not the stakes to allow the workmen to remove the earth.

Observe the grading and hauling contractor as he removes the earth from the marked-off area where the house is to be built. See that enough earth is removed to allow the worker to build up forms for the foundations if forms are to be used. See that the floor of the excavation is fairly level and that proper excavation is made for wall and post footings. See that the side walls of the excavation are trimmed and that proper ditches are made for drainage.

Visit or envision a building lot on which is found grass, brush, trees, and water. Building lots are not always level. Some slope from front to rear, others from rear to front, or to one side. They may have exposed rock formation. A house must be placed to the best advantage on a building lot. It should harmonize with houses in its immediate vicinity.

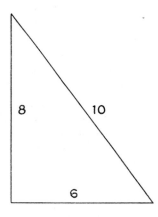

The 6-8-10 method: The square of the hypotenuse of a right triangle is equal to the sum of the squares of the other two sides. [Sometimes called also the 3-4-5 method, or Pythagorean Theorum.]

Since the volume of any solid is found by multiplying the thickness by the width by the length, the amount of earth removed in excavating is obtained by multiplying these three dimensions in order to estimate the cost.

What is the depth, width, and length of the excavation? What is the content in cubic feet? In cubic yards? (27 cu. feet. = 1 cu. yard.) What is the cost of removing the earth for the foundation of the accompanying set of plans at the prevailing price per cubic yard?

Skid shovel (International-Drott).

Back-hoe and loader (International).

HOW TO USE A TRANSIT

How to Lay Out a Building (Fig. 1): Using the plumb bob, suspended from the hook under the spindle, locate the station mark on corner of the lot or building to be laid out. Center the instrument directly over this point by shifting the legs of the tripod so that the plumb bob hangs directly over the station point. To bring plumb bob to this position, loosen leveling screws and shift instrument until the plumb bob points to center. Level up the instrument by tightening the leveling screws.

Street line in the illustration is X. The corner of the proposed building is L, distance from the street line PL. Then a distance RT should be measured from the street, equal to PL, at a point determining the length of the proposed building. Now the line LT is parallel with the street. And LT represents the two front corners of the building.

To get the line at right angles to LT, leave the sights on the stake at T and turn the eyepiece end of the telescope to the left until the vernier has turned a right angle, or 90°. A sight along this new position will give the line LM, on which the necessary distance is measured off to determine the corner M. Now move level to T, and go through same operation to determine corner N.

To prove the correctness of the survey, check the distance MN, to see that it is the same as the distance LT.

When a Building Is Not a Rectangle (Fig. 2): In such a case, proceeed as previously explained. However, additional points must be arranged for, and in that respect small errors are likely to creep in. In all cases, first lay out a large rectangle, along the outside extremities of the proposed building. This is represented by ABCD. These points established, the remaining portion of the layout will consist of small rectangles. Each of these can be laid out and proved separately. In the illustration (Fig. 2) these other rectangles are represented by EFGD, HIJC, KLMA and NOPQ.

Establishing Levels with a Transit: Set up the instrument where points may be seen through the telescope. Level up the transit and take a reading where cross-hair cuts on the measuring rod. The rod is then moved to the second point to be established. Then rod is raised or lowered until the original reading is located. The bottom of the

rod is then on the same level with the original point.

Measuring Differences in Elevation (Figs. 3 and 4): If the instrument has been properly leveled and is not out of adjustment, the line of sight set up by the telescope when locked in the level position is horizontal in any direction. To obtain the difference in elevation between two points, such as points A and B, Fig. 3, set up and level the instrument at an intermediate point, adjusting the tripod to any convenient height. Sight on a rod held over point A, note the reading where the horizontal cross-hair of the telescope cuts the graduation on the rod. Then, with the rod held on point B, rotate the telescope in a horizontal plane, again sight on the rod and note where the horizontal cross-hair cuts the graduation on the rod. The difference between the reading at A (6 ft.) and the reading at B (6½ ft.) will give the difference in elevation between the two points. Point B is ½ ft. lower than point A. In making these readings, the telescope must be carefully focused on the rod or other object on which it is sighted.

When for any reason such an irregularity of the ground or a large difference in elevation, the two points whose difference in elevation is to be determined cannot be sighted from a single point, "intermediate points" must be used, as shown in Fig. 4.

Establishing Points on a Line (Fig. 5): The transit may be used to establish points on a line as when a number of stakes in line—but at different heights—are to be located. Swing the two locking levers out of the way and loosen the vertical-motion clamp screw so that the telescope is free to rotate in the vertical plane. Level the instrument and center it accurately by means of the plumb bob and shifting center over the first point. Then release the two locking levers and the vertical circle clamp screw and sight the telescope on the most distant visible known point of the line. Lock the horizontal-motion clamp screw to prevent the telescope from moving out of the vertical plane in which the stakes are to be set, and place the vertical cross-hair exactly on the point with the tangent screw. Then, by rotating the telescope in the vertical plane, the exact location of any number of stakes on that line may be instantly determined, Fig. 5.

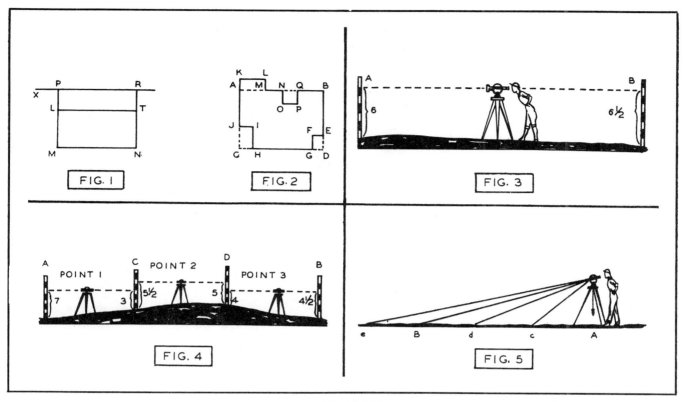

FIG. 1 FIG. 2 FIG. 3

FIG. 4 FIG. 5

PLOT PLAN

TYPICAL GRADING & PLANTING PLAN
All Grades Shown are Minimum

Planting Notes
T– One High Tree 3" to 6" Diameter – Bare Rooted
E– Two Evergreens 3' to 4' High, Balled & Burlapped
D– Six Deciduous Shrubs 2' to 3' High – Bare Rooted

No High-Growing Shrub or Bush Shall be Placed
in Front of a Window

Plot plan.

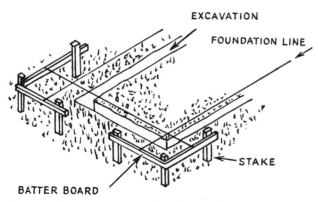

EXCAVATION
FOUNDATION LINE
STAKE
BATTER BOARD

Temporary boards leveled and nailed to stakes at the corners
of an excavation to mark the lines of the foundation and to
aid the mason in keeping the wall plumb.

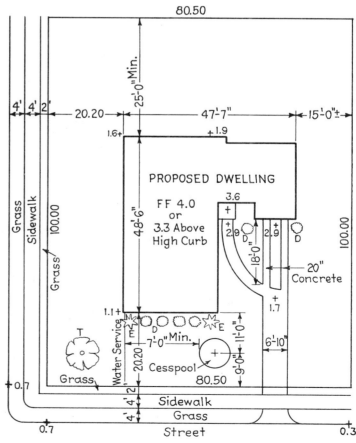

PROPOSED DWELLING

FF 4.0
or
3.3 Above
High Curb

Cesspool

20" Concrete

Grass

Sidewalk

Water Service

Grass

Sidewalk
Grass
Street

80.50
100.00
100.00

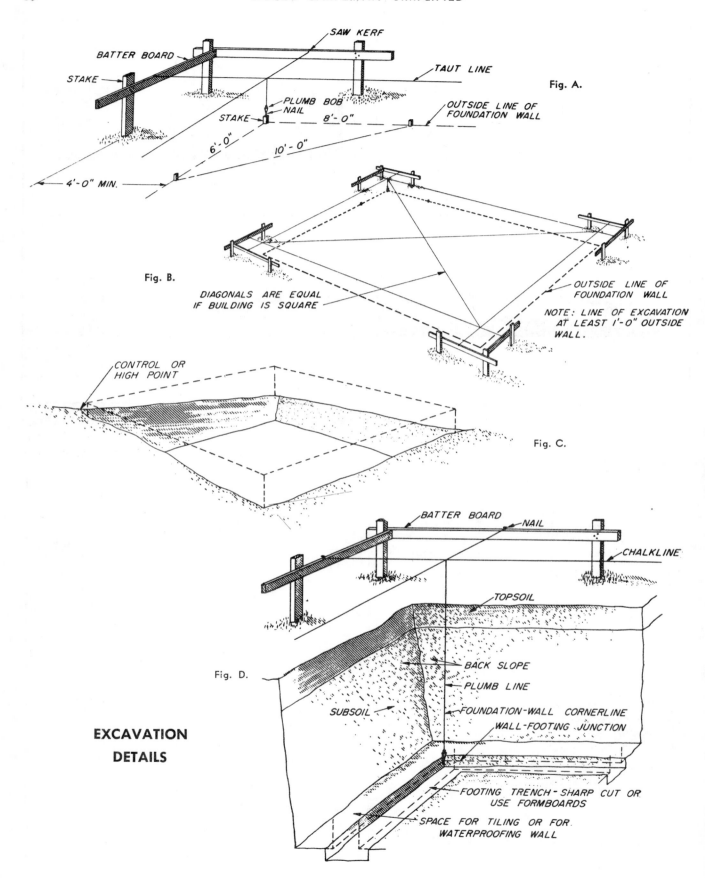

BATTER BOARD

SAW KERF

STAKE

TAUT LINE

Fig. A.

PLUMB BOB
NAIL

STAKE   8'- 0"

OUTSIDE LINE OF
FOUNDATION WALL

6'- 0"

10'- 0"

4'- 0" MIN.

Fig. B.

DIAGONALS ARE EQUAL
IF BUILDING IS SQUARE

OUTSIDE LINE OF
FOUNDATION WALL

NOTE: LINE OF EXCAVATION
AT LEAST 1'-0" OUTSIDE
WALL.

CONTROL OR
HIGH POINT

Fig. C.

BATTER BOARD

NAIL

CHALKLINE

TOPSOIL

Fig. D.

BACK SLOPE

PLUMB LINE

SUBSOIL

FOUNDATION-WALL CORNERLINE

WALL-FOOTING JUNCTION

**EXCAVATION
DETAILS**

FOOTING TRENCH - SHARP CUT OR
USE FORMBOARDS

SPACE FOR TILING OR FOR
WATERPROOFING WALL

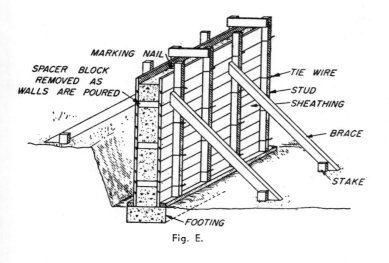

SPACER BLOCK REMOVED AS WALLS ARE POURED

MARKING NAIL

TIE WIRE
STUD
SHEATHING

BRACE

STAKE

FOOTING

Fig. E.

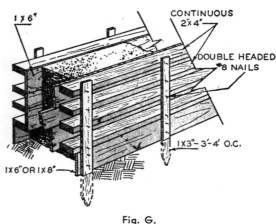

1 x 6"

CONTINUOUS 2"x 4"

DOUBLE HEADED #8 NAILS

1 X 3"- 3'- 4' O.C.

1X6" OR 1X8"

Fig. G.

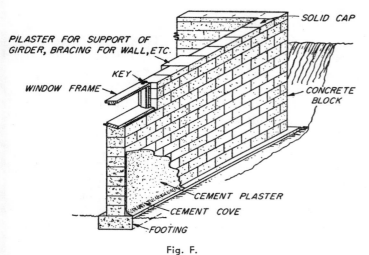

PILASTER FOR SUPPORT OF GIRDER, BRACING FOR WALL, ETC.

SOLID CAP

KEY

WINDOW FRAME

CONCRETE BLOCK

CEMENT PLASTER
CEMENT COVE
FOOTING

Fig. F.

Small stakes are driven into the earth at the exact corners of the structure and small nails or tacks are driven into the top of the stakes for exact measurements. After locating the corners of the building,

batter boards are erected about 4' beyond the foundation lines. The illustration *A* shows a corner stake and a batter board at one corner of the proposed excavation while illustration *B* shows the placing of four sets of batter boards at the four corners. Chalk line is put in place to designate the outside line of excavation.

If the building site or lot is not level, a control or high point is established at the highest point or highest batter board to establish the depth of the excavation and the height of the foundation wall. This method is shown in diagram *C*.

After the earth is removed by the tractor excavator or back digger the footing trench is accurately measured as shown in detail *D*.

Foundation walls may be of poured concrete, as shown in the drawing *E* or of concrete block construction as shown in detail *F*.

If a basementless dwelling is erected, a trench is dug and forms are built up as shown in the sketch *G*. The detail *H* shows a combined concrete slab and foundation for a basementless structure.

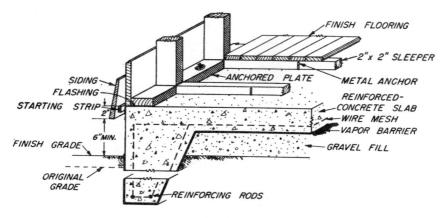

FINISH FLOORING

2"x 2" SLEEPER

ANCHORED PLATE

METAL ANCHOR

SIDING
FLASHING
STARTING STRIP

REINFORCED-CONCRETE SLAB
WIRE MESH
VAPOR BARRIER
GRAVEL FILL

2"

6" MIN.

FINISH GRADE

ORIGINAL GRADE

REINFORCING RODS

Fig. H.

5

Foundation Forms and Foundations

In some sections of the country a basement is provided for storage, laundry, home workshop, or recreation room. Some modern homes utilize the latest developments in household conveniences, but as most of the latter do not occupy much space they do not always require the construction of an additional room.

Regardless of the particular circumstances, a strong foundation is necessary. Even though a basement is not needed, footings and foundation walls must be properly constructed, and the local building code will have to be consulted to find out what kinds of foundations are allowed.

Obtain the sizes and locations of all footings, both for the foundation wall and girder posts, from the details in the house plans. If the footings are to be formed by the shapes of the trenches in the earth, no wood or other types of forms will be necessary. The side walls of the earth should be carefully measured and trimmed. The concrete is then poured into these trenches and allowed to set for at least three days in dry weather and six days in damp weather. Concrete is most generally purchased by the cubic yard and sent to the job from a common mixing point by companies which specialize in supplying ready-mixed concrete.

If footings require forms, erect these according to the details in the plans, or study the illustrations. Obtain the height of the foundation walls from the details. Mark off the height on a pole and erect it in one of the corners of the excavation near the batter boards. If this height does not exceed that of the batter boards, a chalk line can be restrung on the batter boards and the height of the outside wall line of the forms can be lined up by means of the original chalk-line layout. If the height of the foundation cannot be measured on the batter boards, then longer stakes must be erected and the chalk line must be strung on the stakes at the proper height.

The type of forms will be indicated in the specifications and on the drawings.

Most foundation walls are poured and tamped concrete. Some are built of concrete blocks. stone, or brick, by a mason. Where piers are used to support the sills the mason is called on to build them. If poured concrete piers are called for, the carpenter builds the forms in most cases. If there are many of them the forms may come in sections, either wood or metal, and concrete workers assemble them into forms with rods and bolts.

Brick may be used in very dry soils for interior basement partition walls. Stone walls are much stronger than brick walls, especially if the stones are uniformly flat and hard. Concrete block walls made of good portland cement concrete are suitable in small dwelling work. These blocks are well seasoned before being used. They have the advantage of hollow construction which can be reinforced with poured concrete, and do not necessitate form work.

One great objection to any built-up wall is in the use of concrete or mortar between the voids. This space at the meeting of these bricks, stones, or blocks form an ideal opening for moisture and water to enter into the basement. Hollow tile is often specified for walls in some localities.

Check over each detail of the concrete form construction. See that each wall of the form is in place and plumb. Be sure that proper runways and platforms have been built for the men to work. When concrete is mixed in a concrete mixer on the job it must be wheeled in wheelbarrows from the mixer, up a runway to the top of the forms and over platforms to the several places where it is poured into the forms. Each batch of green concrete must be worked in with a tamp so that no air pockets are formed. All of the forms must be filled at one time while the concrete is still green, so that the entire job will form one solid mass and dry uniformly. Anchor bolts must be placed in the wall as designated in the plans. If the whole job cannot be done at one time, a key must be used.

A concrete block foundation is generally built on a poured concrete footing. The blocks do not require a form, but each one must be set in with care for plumb and spacing. Stone or tile walls require great care in bonding.

After green concrete has been poured and allowed to set until it has become hardened, the forms and runways are removed. A good way to test concrete for firmness and quality is to attempt

Block foundation. Note horizontal and vertical reinforcements.

to scrape away a grain of sand or piece of gravel with the thumbnail or a sharp tool. If sand and gravel can be removed by this process, the concrete is either green or of poor quality. Remember that the foundation has to carry the full weight of the structure, and to do so it must be of good quality.

Building code requirements must be considered in each locality, as some cities prohibit the use of hollow tile for foundations, while others have certain restrictions. The cost of foundation walls of other than solid concrete is not considered in this text, as solid concrete walls are generally considered the best for dwellings.

Solid concrete construction is estimated (that is,

A concrete foundation after forms have been removed.

the cost) by the cubic yard. This simply means the finding of the number of cubic yards of mass in the walls, footings, bases, etc., and multiplying this by the cost per cubic yard for material and labor. This cost of course varies greatly with each changing locality and conditions of construction. Find the cubical contents of concrete required in the footings and walls of the house, add to it the labor costs, and keep in separate listing with the foundation form work estimates.

Concrete is an artificial stone made of cement, sand, and aggregate of broken stone or gravel, bonded by means of mixing with water, gradually hardening from a plastic state as it dehydrates.

Natural cements were used before artificial cements, but their use has practically ceased with the development of artificial cements. The ingredients of artificial cement—lime, silica, alumina, and iron oxide—are mined from the earth. They are mixed in close ratios. A good grade of portland cement is composed as follows: Lime 62 parts; silica 23 parts; alumina 8 parts; iron oxide, magnesia, and sulphuric acid 7 parts. The last three parts are considered as impurities.

Concrete for house foundations is mixed in the following proportions: 1 part cement, 2 parts sand, and 4 parts course aggregate. It is dishonest and unfair for a builder to use a poor mixture of concrete, as such can result in failure when the heavy structure is erected upon it.

Concrete may be mixed on the job or purchased ready to pour from the mobile mixer in which it is delivered. On the job mixing is done either by hand or in a mixing machine. If mixed by hand the following steps are performed in sequence: (1) Prepare platform; (2) spread on sand; (3) spread on cement; (4) mix with shovels and hoes; (5) mix in water; (6) mix in gravel; (7) mix till slush mixture is obtained.

To take away built forms, use a heavy claw hammer or wrecking bar. Try not to split the boards, and save as much as possible for future use. Carry the boards or sections away from the concrete work. If the forms are to be knocked down entirely, remove the nails from the pieces and stack in an orderly pile on one side of the building lot away from activities. In removing the forms from the walls do not pry against the concrete wall to the point of injuring it. Take care not to chip pieces from the top edges of the wall. If a foundation wall is very high or particularly hard to reach, a runway must be built. A ladder is often used in these situations.

A carpenter should be very careful to see that all points in good construction have been observed, as the foundation is the base of the superstructure. Often good carpentry work is ruined by poor foundation work. A foundation must be built so that it holds together and settles uniformly, otherwise uneven settling causes bad breaks in upper construction work.

Place sill anchor bolts as designated in plans.

Erecting Plywood Forms for Poured Concrete Foundation

Large paneled forms for a basement wall are erected in place for the pouring of concrete by locating the front wall of the foundation from the lot pins or batter boards. For an 8″ wall, measure in on the poured footing 9″ and strike a chalk line. Locate the rear wall of the foundation and measure in as for the front wall and chalk a line as shown in Fig. 1. Both front and rear lines must be parallel. The side walls of the foundation are measured in from the lot pins or batter boards in the same manner and cross-checked by the 6-8-10 method (see page 34) to insure squareness. The chalk line provides the inside lines for placing the plywood forms.

Start at the corners of the footing by placing one inside and one outside form corner at each corner. The outside corner is made up of two outside panels or fillers and one outside angle-iron corner complete with four clips. The inside corner is made up of two panels or fillers and one inside angle-iron corner with clips. This step is shown in Fig. 2.

Place the panels and fillers for the foundation around the outside of the footing to save time in handling. Start at one corner, in a counter-clockwise direction, and erect outside and inside forms simultaneously, as shown in Fig. 3.

As forms are set in place, tie rods are slipped in position and secured by locking levers and remain in the finished wall. Waling timbers or members are not needed to support the wall. The placing of forms and tie rods are shown in Fig. 4.

Fig. 5 shows a workman tapping the locking lever in place, thus making for a firm wall as it is erected.

As forms are locked in place, line-up rails are slipped on top of the forms, making for a positive alignment and rigidity, as illustrated in Fig. 6.

In approximately an hour and a half 120 feet of foundation wall can be set in place as shown

Fig. 1. Chalk line for plywood forms.

Fig. 2. Placing corner panels.

Fig. 3. Inside and outside forms erected simultaneously.

Fig. 4. Placing forms and tie rods.

Fig. 5. Tapping the locking lever.

Fig. 6. Aligning with lineup rails.

in Fig. 7, which is a completed foundation wall assembly.

With the completion of the forms concrete is poured as shown in Fig. 8.

As pouring progresses window bucks or frames for basement windows are set in place as shown in Fig. 9.

Within two hours the pouring of concrete is completed as shown in the illustration. Workmen watch the progress of pouring, having access to this operation on 2″ x 6″ scaffolding supported by the foot scaffolding brackets on the outside perimeter of the forms. See Fig. 10.

When the concrete is set, forms can easily be removed, cleaned, and oiled, and made ready for the next foundation erection and pouring, as shown in Fig. 11.

Fig. 9. Setting basement window frames.

Fig. 7.—A completed foundation wall assembly.

Fig. 10. Checking progress of concrete pouring.

Fig. 8. Pouring concrete into completed forms.

Fig. 11. Removing forms after concrete is set.

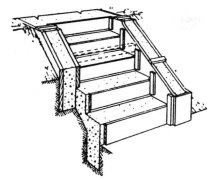

Steps supported on earth.

Part of form cut away to show construction.

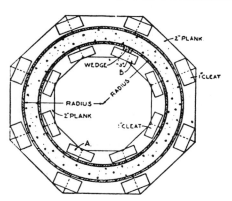

Plan of circular form.

6" GREATER THAN HEIGHT OF FORM.

3½"

Wedge.

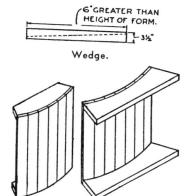

Inside form.   Outside form.

Suggestions for circular form.

Various Concrete Forms

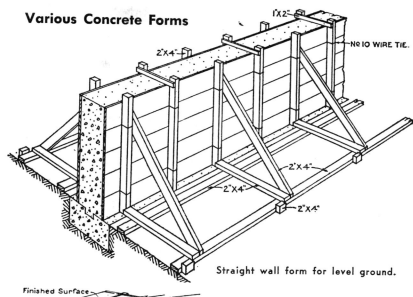

1"X2"

2"X4"

Nº 10 WIRE TIE.

2"X4"

2"X4"

2"X4"

Straight wall form for level ground.

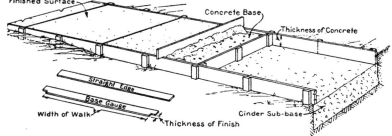

Finished Surface

Concrete Base

Thickness of Concrete

Straight Edge

Base Gauge

Width of Walk

Thickness of Finish

Cinder Sub-base

Walk forms.

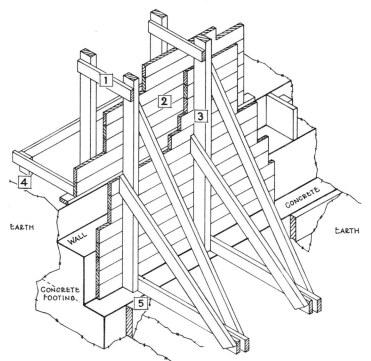

EARTH

WALL

CONCRETE FOOTING.

CONCRETE

EARTH

1. 1" x 3" y. p. stock.
2. 1" x 6" y. p. t & g stock.
3. 2" x 4" y. p. stock.
4. 1" x 3" y. p. stock.
5. 2" x 8" y. p. stock.

A built-up form for poured concrete.

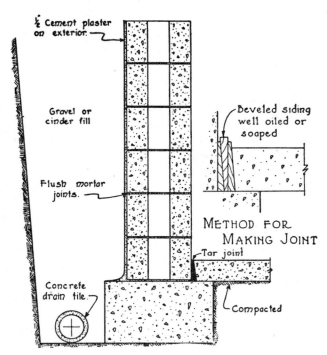

½ Cement plaster on exterior.

Gravel or cinder fill

Flush mortar joints.

Concrete drain tile.

Beveled siding well oiled or soaped

METHOD FOR MAKING JOINT

Tar joint

Compacted

A concrete-block basement wall protected against external water.

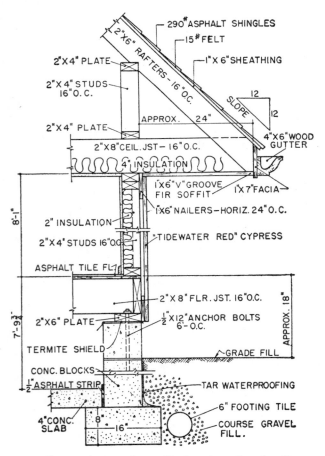

290# ASPHALT SHINGLES
15# FELT
1"X 6" SHEATHING
2"X 6" RAFTERS - 16" O.C.
2"X 4" PLATE
2"X 4" STUDS 16"O.C.
2"X 4" PLATE
SLOPE 12 / 12
APPROX. 24"
4"X 6" WOOD GUTTER
2"X 8" CEIL. JST - 16" O.C.
4" INSULATION
1"X6" V"GROOVE FIR SOFFIT
1"X 7" FACIA
2" INSULATION
1"X6" NAILERS—HORIZ. 24" O.C.
2"X 4" STUDS 16"O.C.
"TIDEWATER RED" CYPRESS
ASPHALT TILE FL.
8'-1"
2"X 8" FLR. JST. 16"O.C.
½"X12" ANCHOR BOLTS 6'-0.C.
2"X 6" PLATE
TERMITE SHIELD
GRADE FILL
APPROX. 18"
7'-9¾"
CONC. BLOCKS
½" ASPHALT STRIP
TAR WATERPROOFING
6" FOOTING TILE
4"CONC. SLAB
8"
16"
COURSE GRAVEL FILL.

Installation of 2" insulation blankets in wall and ceiling.

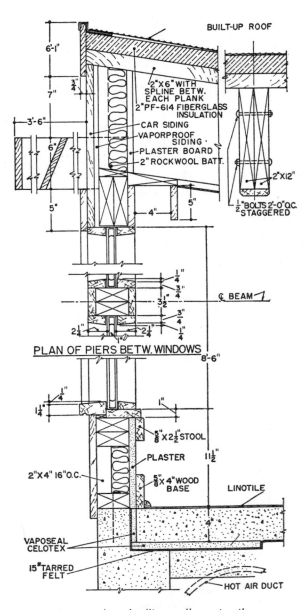

BUILT-UP ROOF
6'-1"
7"
¾"
3'-6"
6"
5"
2"X 6" WITH SPLINE BETW. EACH PLANK
2"PF-614 FIBERGLASS INSULATION
CAR SIDING
VAPORPROOF SIDING
PLASTER BOARD
2" ROCKWOOL BATT.
2"X 12"
½"BOLTS 2'-0"O.C. STAGGERED
5"
4"
5"
¼"
¾"
3½"
¾"
2¼"
2¼"
¼"
Ȼ BEAM

PLAN OF PIERS BETW. WINDOWS
8'-6"
¼"
1¼"
1"
1¼"
⅝ X2½ STOOL
PLASTER
11½"
2"X 4" 16"O.C.
⅝ X 4" WOOD BASE
LINOTILE
4"
VAPOSEAL CELOTEX
15# TARRED FELT
HOT AIR DUCT

Basementless dwelling wall construction.

Foundation and Framing Details for Foundation Walls

NOTE—For heating installations see Chapter 14— Heating Installations and Air Conditioning.

6

Introduction to Framing

NOTE—In considering the specific phases of framing in the following chapters, reference must be made when necessary to certain other chapters such as Heating Installations (including fireplaces) and Air Conditioning, Porch and Bay Framing, Stairs, Thermal Insulation and Moisture Barriers, and any other details that might not be dealt with specifically in a particular chapter on framing.

The accurate placing of girders, sills, joists, and subflooring is essential in floor framing to insure a strong and sturdy support for walls and roof. The framed floor must be plumb and level at all points. A good assembly of floor framing members is shown in the drawing below.

After the foundation is laid or poured, the girder is set in place. The sill members are chosen with care, placed in position on the foundation wall and anchored in place. Note the slight set-back of ¾″ for outside sheathing. End and header joists are then nailed into position as shown at the corner and at point 4, and these two members are held in a true vertical position with 10d nails toenailed into the anchored sill.

These members, the sill plate and end and header joists form a box sill used in the platform type of construction.

With the completion of the box sill the floor joists are set in place and lapped over the girder, as shown, with a minimum of 4″ for safety and nailing. Sixteen-inch center-to-center spacing is most commonly used in dwelling construction. Any joist member having a slight bow edgewise must be placed so that the bow or crown is on top. A crowned joist will tend to straighten out when the subfloor and normal floor loads are applied. The largest edge knots should be placed on top, so as to be the compression side of the bearing member.

Each joist is nailed to the header joist, or vertical member of the box sill, with two or three 20d nails as shown at point 3 and the header joist is nailed to the anchored sill with tenpenny nails 16 inches on center as shown at point 4. Joists are also nailed at the lap on the girder with no less than three 16d nails.

Double joists are used under all partitions and opening for stair wells and at chimneys.

Joists are also stiffened with solid, cross, or metal bridging about every eight feet of joist length.

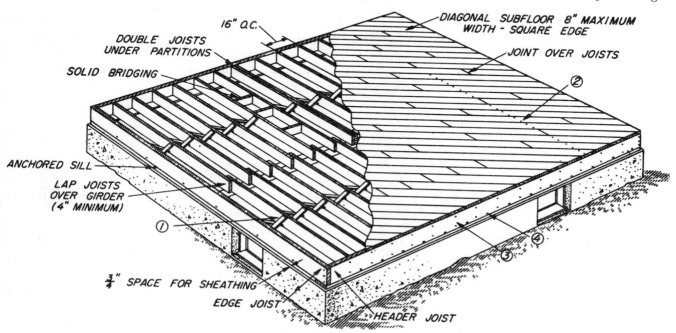

Assembly of floor framing members.

47

Solid bridging may be used as shown either straight-nailed or toenailed into joists to transfer heavy live and dead loads to adjoining joists.

Cross bridging, made of 1" x 3" material, is cut at an angle to fit diagonally between joists, as shown, each piece being nailed at the top with two 8d nails. Rigid metal bridging, with nailing flanges, often is used. Care must be taken with any type of bridging not to nail the bottom portion of the bridging until the subflooring is completely laid, then to nail with two 8d nails, as at the top of the bridge member.

After the joists are set in place and nailed at the sill and the girder lap and bridging members are set in place at the top portion of the joists, the sub-flooring is laid.

Subflooring stock should be no wider than 8" of tongued-and-grooved or square-edged material. Work is begun at one corner of the sill, laid diagonally, then nailed to each joist with two or three 8d nails. The illustration shows the subflooring laid diagonally. If subflooring is placed at right angles to the joists, the finish flooring must then be laid at right angles to the subflooring. Diagonally laid subflooring permits the finish flooring to be laid parallel or perpendicular to the run of the joists. All joints of the subflooring must meet at the center of the joists to provide a proper support for the ends of each subflooring board.

Plywood sheets may be used for the subflooring instead of tongue-and-groove or square-edge material. Thicknesses of five-ply plywood subflooring vary from 1/2" to 3/4" with all joists butted over the center of joists. If 1/2" five-ply plywood is used as subflooring, joists may be spaced 24" on center. When plywood is used as a base for parquet wood finish flooring (less than 25/32" thick), or for linoleum, composition, rubber, or ceramic tile, solid blocking must be installed under all edges of the plywood at right angles to the floor joists. If plywood is used for leveling purposes over old or other subflooring the minimum thickness should be 1/4" three-ply plywood.

Plumbing Up the Substructure

Each member of the floor construction must be accurately placed and in a true position when nailed. If the top of the foundation wall is a bit out of horizontal position the sill members are trued up with mortar beds before being bolted down. Each corner must be square. Each length of header joist checked for vertical and horizontal accuracy before being nailed. Each joist must be sighted for true level position and braced with

bridging or temporarily nailed strips as construction proceeds. Sighting for crown or bow must be made as each member is set in place. The sub-flooring must provide a level platform for the superstructure.

Plumbing Up and Bracing Wall Framing

Wall framing members include, primarily, the vertical and horizontal members of exterior and interior walls, such as the sole plate, the studding, and the top plate, which serve as a nailing base for wall covering materials and as a support for upper floors, ceilings, and roofs.

These typical wall framing members are shown in the drawing on page 49.

Wall framing lumber must be stiff, must hold nails well, and be free from warp and easy to work. The varieties of lumber best suited are the hemlocks, southern yellow pine, Douglas fir, white fir, and spruce. Grades vary from No. 1 to No. 2, well seasoned.

With the completion of the floor platform the stock for the sole plate, studding, and top plate is laid out on the floor, wall section by wall section, the window or door headers are set in place and each section is nailed with 16d nails. The sections are then raised, checked for true position, and braced, and the sole plate is nailed to the subfloor as shown at point 1. Note the placing of the temporary brace, from stud to floor, as shown in the drawing. This bracing can be done at several places as each wall section is erected.

Point 2 of the drawing indicates the place of nailing the under member of the double plate to the stud with two 16d nails. Point 3 indicates the place of nailing the stud to the sole plate with two 8d nails.

Any window or door opening requires double studding, as shown at point 4, which is held in a true vertical position with 10d nails placed about every 16" of length.

If the wall is built up on the floor platform the top member of the double plate is assembled as shown at point 5 and nailed in place with 10d nails about every 16".

Corner nailing, bracing, and erecting of studded walls is very important, whether the wall is framed, piece by piece, or assembled on the floor platform. Point 6 shows the method of lapping and nailing joining walls. Note the construction of the corner stud, the spacer blocks and the 1" x 4" let-in or gained-in braces running from the sole plate, to the approximated middle of the corner studding,

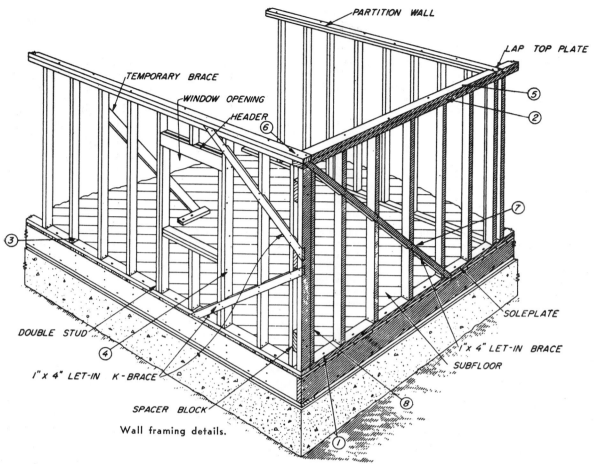

PARTITION WALL

LAP TOP PLATE

TEMPORARY BRACE

WINDOW OPENING

HEADER

⑤

②

⑥

⑦

③

SOLEPLATE

DOUBLE STUD

④

1"x 4" LET-IN BRACE

SUBFLOOR

1"x 4" LET-IN K-BRACE

⑧

SPACER BLOCK

①

Wall framing details.

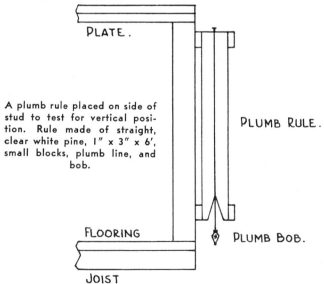

PLATE.

A plumb rule placed on side of stud to test for vertical position. Rule made of straight, clear white pine, 1" x 3" x 6', small blocks, plumb line, and bob.

PLUMB RULE.

FLOORING

PLUMB BOB.

JOIST

thence upward to the bottom portion of the upper member of the top plate.

On wall construction without window or door openings a let-in brace runs the full height of the studded wall as shown at point 7 and two 8d nails are used at each stud.

A partition wall joins the outside wall by the use of two outside wall studs at the place of meeting, and the top member of the partition wall laps into the top member of the outside wall.

As construction proceeds, the true vertical position must be checked at all times with a plumb bob and line or a plumb rule check as shown in the sketch. Any wall member which is out of vertical position must be brought back into true position, or if there is too much wind the member must be replaced.

Plumbing and Bracing Ceiling Joists, Rafters, and Gable Studding

The foundation walls carry, first of all, the framed floor platform; the framed platform carries the studded outside and inside framed walls; and finally the framed platform and framed walls must carry the framed roof and ceiling joists.

A simple form of gable roof construction is shown in this layout of typical members.

With the completion of the framing of all studded walls the ceiling joists are cut and nailed in place to hold together all wall construction and

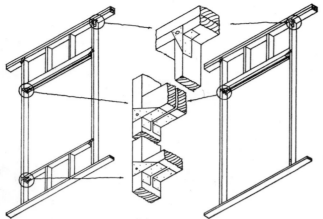

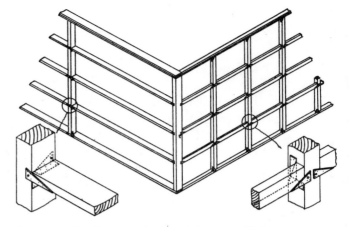

Framed openings in outside studded walls may be held plumb and true by the use of metal grip plates nailed at various corners of framed members. The metal grips hold the plate, lintel, studs, and header in true horizontal and vertical positions as shown in the enlarged details in the center of the illustration. This method of strengthening framed walls is used in addition to the conventional straight nailing and toenailing of framed members.

Large panels which may house windows, ventilators, or screens are reinforced and held plumb by the use of metal grip plates nailed at corners. These panels may be used separately or erected in large openings in outside framed walls.

to absorb the thrust of rafters which would otherwise tend to push out the exterior walls.

Ceiling joists run from outside walls to interior walls and are joined as shown in the illustration at point 12. Ceiling joists are toenailed to the wallplate with two 10d nails and lapped over the center partition and nailed to each other on each side with two 10d nails. This is indicated on the drawing below at points 1 and 2.

The laying out, cutting, and erection of rafters

is dealt with, in full, in another chapter in this book, but several points of interest can be mentioned about this roof layout in relation to floor, wall, and rafter framing.

At point 3 the ceiling joist is nailed to the rafter with two 10d nails when the lapping of the joist brings it in line with the face of the rafter.

As the rafters are erected, in pairs, against the ridge board and are seated on the top member of the wallplate, each rafter is toenailed, as indicated at point 4, with two nails. Nailing the rafters at the ridge board is done by face-nailing with 10d nails as indicated at point 5. Points 6 and 7 show additional placement of nails to further secure the rafter framing members.

Ends or cripple studs make up the wall framing in the gable end of the wall and run

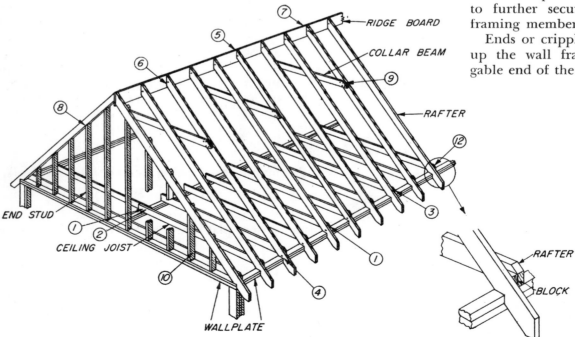

Roof framing details.

from the wall plate to the bottom edge face of the rafter and are notched, point 8, for a more secure support of the roof and wall.

The bottom end of the gable stud is toenailed into the top of the wallplate, point 10, with two 10d nails.

Additional stiffening and plumbing of the framed roof members are accomplished through the use of collar beams, point 9, which absorb and spread the roof load. If an attic space is finished, this collar beam becomes the carrying member for the attic ceiling.

Also temporary braces are placed at right angles to the rafters as plumbing and squaring of members is done and are removed as the roofers are nailed to the top edge face of each rafter.

GOOD FRAMING.

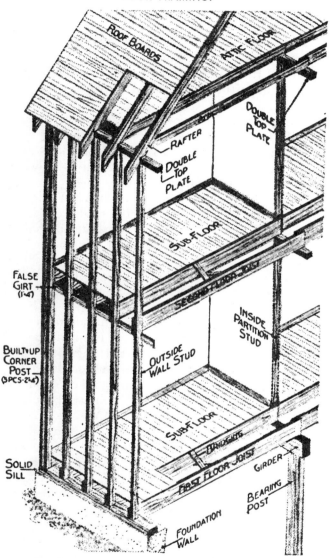

POOR FRAMING.

Because the balloon frame has qualities and advantages that cannot be found in other types, conscientious builders everywhere have striven to build 100% efficiency into this type of framing, with the result that today it is an eminently satisfactory frame from every standpoint.

Wall and corner studs, continuous from sill to plate, make for stiffness, corner braces and firestopping in the walls and floors for rigidity and fire-resistance, while, by reducing as well as equalizing as far as possible the amount of cross-sectional lumber subject to shrinkage in the inside and outside walls, the problem of plaster cracks and other ills traceable to shrinkage is largely solved.

Nor are these improvements of the kind that add greatly to the cost, in either time or material. In fact, the difference in the cost of a good balloon frame over that of a poor one is so small, when compared to the added efficiency, that it is surpris-

ing to find it so grossly misused. The drawing at the right shows common abuses in its construction—how even the best method of framing a house may be reduced to total inefficiency by cutting the corners and cheapening its construction. Unfortunately, many so-called balloon frame houses are constructed in this manner. The elimination of corner braces robs the structure of much of its rigidity. The omission of floor headers and firestops makes it readily susceptible to fire. The ready circulation of air between walls and floors is also responsible for serious heat losses in the finished house. A preindication of plaster cracks, squeaking floors, and numerous other house ills is apparent in this cheapened frame. The drawing at the left shows a balloon frame properly and efficiently built.

7

Sills and Girders

Sills

The concrete wall is the foundation on which all upper structure rests. The sill is the foundation on which all framing structure rests and it is the real point of departure from actual carpentry and joinery activities.

Sills are bases for wood or metal framing. Study the sills in the accompanying set of plans and refer to any other available plans. The illustrations show the typical methods of constructing sills for wood and metal framed houses.

After studying the house plans and learning the type of sill required, clean off the top of the foundation wall and see that each metal anchor bolt is ready for use. Secure good straight stock of the size required. Square off one end of the stock. Place bed plate on the foundation wall against the anchor bolts and mark off places where bolts are to enter the plate. Bore holes in this plate and then build up the sill as required. Use 20-penny common nails throughout. In making joints for the bed plate of header, use a lap joint as indicated, page 55. Build up the sill, place over bolts, securely fasten down, level off, shim up where necessary, and chop off any crown in the wood. Square all corners by use of the 6, 8, 10 method. (See page 34.)

The illustrations on the following pages give a graphic idea of some of the necessary operations.

If the plans and specifications call for a structural steel sill, build up according to plans.

Wooden or steel sills are built up on the job. Wooden sills usually consist of a bed member and an upright member called a header. Steel sills are of one piece, manufactured in certain widths ready for assembling on the job. Since these members are placed on top of the foundation wall and are the first members of the main frame, great care is taken in placing each part.

Wooden sills are estimated by taking the actual length needed to cover the top of the foundation wall. This length will equal the perimeter of the foundation wall wherever the sill member is required. Add 1 in number for every 10 members used because of squaring of stock and lap for joints.

If the bed plate and header are of the same size (2" x 8" or 2" x 10"), standard lengths of the stock can be ordered. If the entire perimeter is 185′, this length will be divided by 8 or 10, which will give the number of pieces required, plus the several added for squaring and joining.

Steel sills can be ordered by the length, size, and stock number of style designated in the specifications. The labor costs can be figured as about 20 hours for every 1,000 board feet of lumber and about 10 hours for every 1,000 linear feet of steel sill work.

There are several types of sills in use in modern house framing, the chief ones being: balloon frame sill, braced frame sill, box or western sill, and T sill.

Wooden sills are constructed of pine or oak wood. The bed plate should be anchored every 10′ or so by use of a ⅝" or ¾" anchor bolt about 18" long, which is set in the concrete foundation wall as it is being poured.

Sills generally have bearing under their entire length. The chief factors of a sill should be its resistance to cross-grain crushing and ability to withstand decay and insect attack. All wood has more resistance against crushing lengthwise or with the grain than it has in crushing across the grain. No. 1 common grade of Douglas fir can withstand a load of 1,100 pounds per square inch with the grain but only 325 pounds per square inch across the grain.

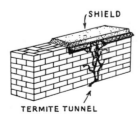

A metal shield protecting the foundation wall under the sill from termites.

Termite.

Termites superficially resemble ants in size, general appearance, and habit of living in colonies,

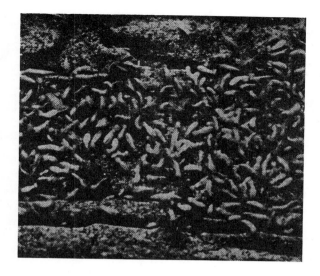

Worker termites—natural size.

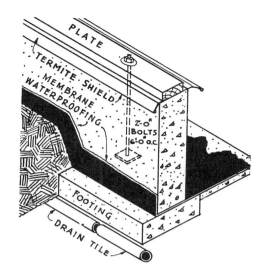

A metal termite shield between foundation and sill plate.

hence they are frequently called "white ants." These ants are blind and never expose themselves in the daylight, so they are seldom seen. Subterranean termites do not establish themselves in buildings by being carried in with lumber but by entering from ground nests after the building has been constructed. They nest in damp earth and live on cellulose or wood. They burrow through

poorly made masonry walls to get at wood members which they hollow out and weaken. If unmolested, they eat out the woodwork, leaving a shell of sound wood to conceal their activities, and damage may proceed so far as to cause collapse of parts of a structure before discovery.

To prevent this undermining, various methods are used. Sills may be treated with creosote or zinc chloride or penta solutions. Termite shields made of metal are sometimes used. Pieces of slate imbedded in cement are effective in preventing the spread of these pests.

There are about 56 species of termites known in the United States, but the two major species, classified from the manner in which they attack wood, are ground-inhabiting or subterranean termites, the most common, and drywood termites, found almost exclusively along the extreme southern border and the Gulf of Mexico in the United States.

Sill on concrete foundation.

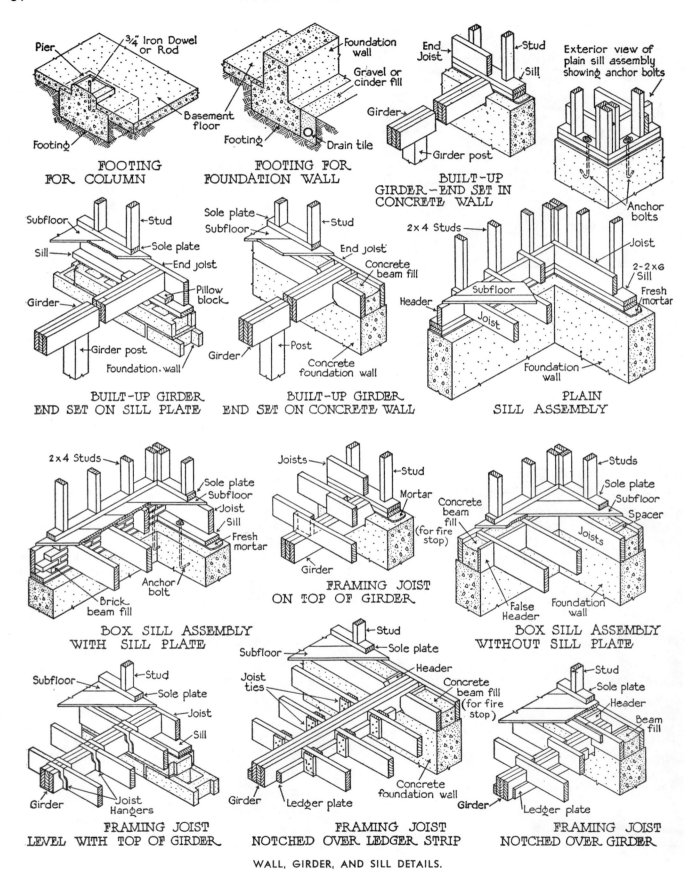

FOOTING FOR COLUMN

FOOTING FOR FOUNDATION WALL

BUILT-UP GIRDER—END SET IN CONCRETE WALL

Exterior view of plain sill assembly showing anchor bolts

BUILT-UP GIRDER END SET ON SILL PLATE

BUILT-UP GIRDER END SET ON CONCRETE WALL

PLAIN SILL ASSEMBLY

BOX SILL ASSEMBLY WITH SILL PLATE

FRAMING JOIST ON TOP OF GIRDER

BOX SILL ASSEMBLY WITHOUT SILL PLATE

FRAMING JOIST LEVEL WITH TOP OF GIRDER

FRAMING JOIST NOTCHED OVER LEDGER STRIP

FRAMING JOIST NOTCHED OVER GIRDER

WALL, GIRDER, AND SILL DETAILS.

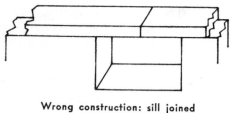

Wrong construction: sill joined over opening.

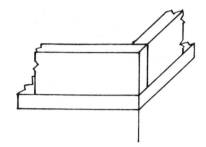

Sill framed at foundation corner.

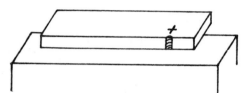

Hole marked for anchor bolt.

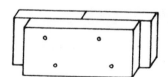

Backing of butt joint.

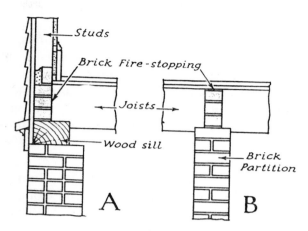

Studs

Brick Fire-stopping

Joists

Wood sill

Brick Partition

A   B

Sill construction detail.

Lap joint of bed plate.

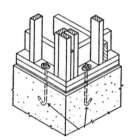

Anchor bolts (arrows).

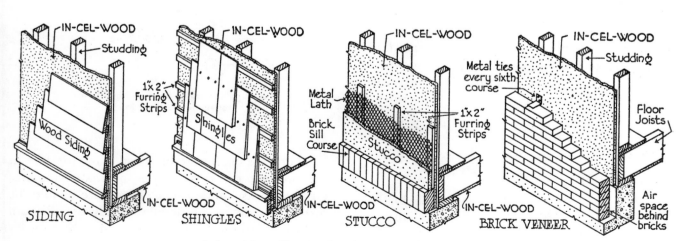

IN-CEL-WOOD
Studding
Wood Siding
IN-CEL-WOOD
SIDING

IN-CEL-WOOD
1"x 2" Furring Strips
Shingles
IN-CEL-WOOD
SHINGLES

IN-CEL-WOOD
Metal Lath
Brick Sill Course
Stucco
1"x 2" Furring Strips
IN-CEL-WOOD
STUCCO

IN-CEL-WOOD
Metal ties every sixth course
Studding
Floor Joists
Air space behind bricks
IN-CEL-WOOD
BRICK VENEER

L-shaped box sills using In-cel-wood insulating material.

Girders

Girders as well as sills comprise the foundation upon which all of the upper structure rests. Girders are needed to support floor joists wherever the width or length of the house make it impossible to use joists the length of the full span. The full span is considered to be from foundation wall to foundation wall.

Building code requirements limit a 2" x 10" long-leaf yellow pine joist, having a load limit of 66 pounds per square foot, to a span of about 18'. Since but few dwelling are as narrow as this, an intermediate bearing member known as a girder is needed.

Girders for dwellings are almost always specified as steel I-beams. An I-beam of 8" depth has a load strength of 8.08 tons if supported every 10'. It can readily be seen that a steel I-beam makes the ideal type of girder.

Girders can be built up of wood, too, if select stock is used. Be sure it is straight and sound. Square off ends of stock. If the girder is to be built up of 2" x 8" or 2" x 10" stock, place pieces on the sawhorses and nail together. Use the piece of stock that has the least amount of wind or warp for the center piece and nail other pieces on side of center stock. Use a common nail that will go through the first piece and nearly through the center piece. Square off the ends of the girder after the pieces have been nailed together. If the stock is not long enough to build up the girder the entire length, the pieces must be built up by staggering the joints, as illustrated on page 57.

If the girder supporting post is to be built up it is to be done in the same manner as described for the girder. Obtain the size of the metal dowel in the post footing and bore a hole in one end of the post to receive this dowel pin. Place the girder post in position and brace it until the girder is put in place.

If the girder is solid or built up, safe sizes are as follows:

Span	Width	Depth	Load
10'	4"	8"	1,988 lb.
6'	4"	8"	2,488 lb.

If a sheet-steel joist is used, a girder support is required over any span more than 18 feet. An I-beam girder, as described elsewhere, can be used with sheet steel joists as well as wood joists. If open truss steel joists are used, a span of 32 feet can be made. If clearspan truss joists are used, a span of 56 feet is permitted. If work other than wood girders or girder posts is done, the structural steel worker does the work.

Girders are built up or cut to size on the job. The cost of girders is based on the actual number of pieces needed, plus the labor, nails or other hardware. The cost of girder supporting posts will be the same as girders. The stock is listed piece by piece. The hardware is listed item by item. It will take about 20 hours of labor to erect every 1,000 board feet of girder or girder posts. Estimate the number of board feet of lumber and the hardware needed in the construction of the girders and girder posts for the house in the set of plans. The size is determined by the load to be borne.

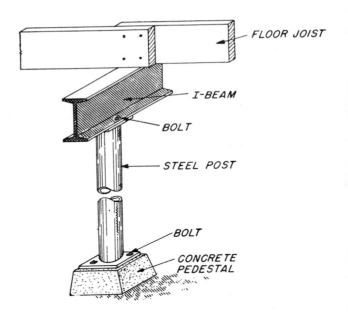

Lally column and I-beam girder of steel for support of floor joists.

There are various tables and data for use in determining the correct sizes of wood columns, girders, joists, and rafters. Reference should be made to standard handbooks. Study the diagram and calculate the loads on the girders and girder posts of the house shown in the blueprints.

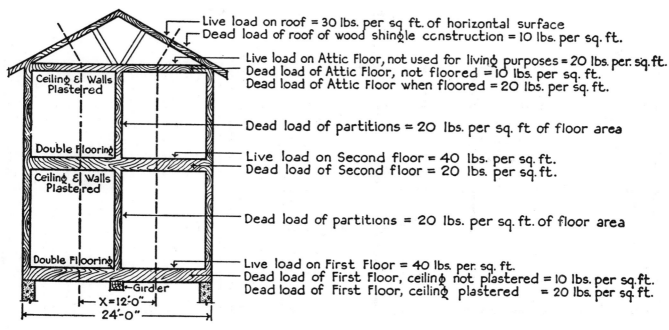

Live load on roof = 30 lbs. per sq ft. of horizontal surface
Dead load of roof of wood shingle construction = 10 lbs. per sq. ft.

Live load on Attic Floor, not used for living purposes = 20 lbs. per sq. ft.
Dead load of Attic Floor, not floored = 10 lbs. per sq. ft.
Dead load of Attic Floor when floored = 20 lbs. per sq. ft.

Dead load of partitions = 20 lbs. per sq. ft of floor area

Live load on Second floor = 40 lbs. per sq. ft.
Dead load of Second floor = 20 lbs. per sq. ft.

Dead load of partitions = 20 lbs. per sq. ft. of floor area

Live load on First Floor = 40 lbs. per sq. ft.
Dead load of First Floor, ceiling not plastered = 10 lbs. per sq. ft.
Dead load of First Floor, ceiling plastered = 20 lbs. per sq. ft.

FIGURING LOADS FOR HOUSE FRAMING.

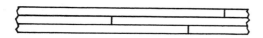

Plan view of girder showing method of staggering joints.

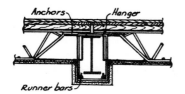

Beam furring and standard nailer joist.

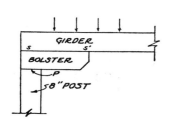

Hardwood bolster used to prevent crushing of girder.

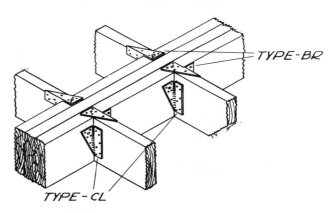

Girder construction for balloon framing.

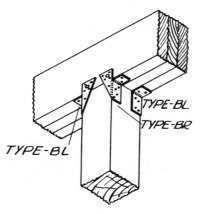

Built-up wooden beam fastened to supporting post with metal grips.

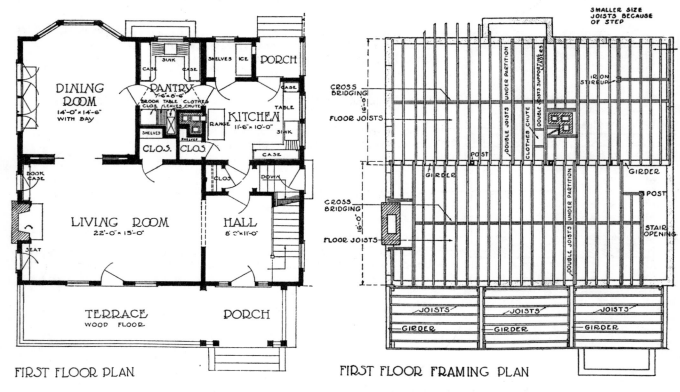

FIRST FLOOR PLAN   FIRST FLOOR FRAMING PLAN

A first-floor plan showing location of posts, girders, and joists.

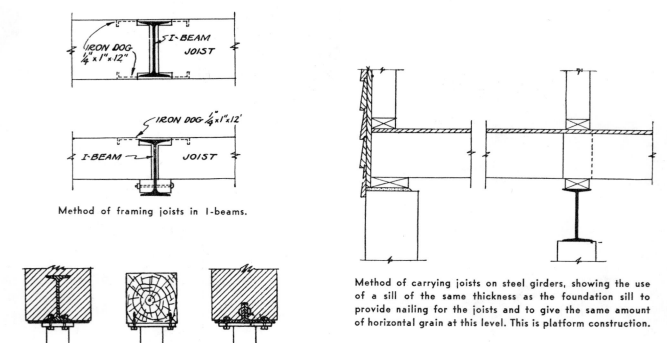

Method of framing joists in I-beams.

Showing the use of girder column and cap which
supports a wood girder.

Method of carrying joists on steel girders, showing the use
of a sill of the same thickness as the foundation sill to
provide nailing for the joists and to give the same amount
of horizontal grain at this level. This is platform construction.

SIZES OF BUILT-UP WOOD GIRDERS
FOR VARIOUS LOADS AND SPANS

Based on Douglas Fir 4-SQUARE
Guide-Line FRAMING

Load per Linear Foot of Girder	Length of Span				
	6'-0"	7'-0"	8'-0"	9'-0"	10'-0"
	Nominal Size of Girder Required				
750	6x8 in.	6x8 in.	6x8 in.	6x10 in.	6x10 in.
900	6x8	6x8	6x10	6x10	8x10
1050	6x8	6x10	8x10	8x10	8x12
1200	6x10	8x10	8x10	8x10	8x12
1350	6x10	8x10	8x10	8x12	10x12
1500	8x10	8x10	8x12	10x12	10x12
1650	8x10	8x12	10x12	10x12	10x14
1800	8x10	8x12	10x12	10x12	10x14
1950	8x12	10x12	10x12	10x14	12x14
2100	8x12	10x12	10x14	10x14	12x14
2250	10x12	10x12	10x14	12x14	12x14
2400	10x12	10x14	10x14	12x14	
2550	10x12	10x14	12x14	12x14	
2700	10x12	10x14	12x14		
2850	10x14	12x14	12x14		
3000	10x14	12x14			
3150	10x14	12x14			
3300	12x14	12x14			

Deflection not over 1/360 of Span—Allowable Fiber Stress 1,600 lbs. per sq. in.

The 6-in. girder is figured as being made with three pieces 2 in. dressed to 1⅝ in. thickness.

The 8-in. girder is figured as being made with four pieces 2 in. dressed to 1⅝ in. thickness.

The 10-in. girder is figured as being made with five pieces 2-in. dressed to 1⅝ in. thickness.

The 12-in. girder is figured as being made with six pieces 2-in. dressed to 1⅝ in. thickness.

NOTE—For solid girders multiply above loads by 1.130 when 6-inch girder is used; 1.150 when 8-in. girder is used; 1.170 when 10-in. girder is used; and 1.180 when 12-in. girder is used.

Instructions for Determining Girder Sizes

FIRST—Refer to diagram and using it as a guide, determine for each floor the length of joist spans that are to be supported by the girder. For the first floor it is equal to one-half the total distance from center line of girder measured both ways to either the next girder, the basement bearing partition, or the foundation wall, except when joists are continuous over this girder and broken over nearest support on each side, in which case it is equal to ⅝ this total distance. Use the same method for second and third floors and roof when part of that weight is to be supported by the girder through the bearing partition, struts, etc.

SECOND—Multiply the load per square foot, as indicated on the chart, for each of these floors and roof by the various spans, including 20 lb. per square foot of floor area for first- and second-story partitions. (In this case it is 2,880 lb.)

(First floor plus partitions.........70 lb. x 12 ft.—840 lb.)
(Second floor plus partitions.......80 lb. x 12 ft.—960 lb.)
(Attic floor, not floored............30 lb. x 12 ft.—360 lb.)
(Roof ....40 lb. x 18 ft.—720 lb.)

(Total ....2,880 lb.)

The total represents the load to be supported by the girder for each foot of its length.

THIRD—Determine length of girder span (distance between columns).

FOURTH—Refer to table, read down in column at left to load already determined, then across to column corresponding to length of span to be provided for. The figure at this intersection represents the size of girder required.

SIZES OF WOOD COLUMNS FOR
VARIOUS LOADS AND COLUMN HEIGHTS

Based on Use of No. 1 Common Douglas Fir

Load on Column (lbs.)	Length of Column					
	6'-0"	5'-0"	6'-6"	7'-0"	7'-6"	8'-0"
	Nominal Size of Column Required					
10,000	4x6 in.	4x6 in.	4x6 in.	4x6 in.	4x6 in.	4x6 in.
15,000	4x6	4x6	4x6	4x6	6x6	6x6
20,000	6x6	6x6	6x6	6x6	6x6	6x6
25,000	6x6	6x6	6x6	6x6	6x6	6x6
30,000	6x6	6x6	6x8	6x8	6x8	6x8
35,000	6x8	6x8	6x8	6x8	6x8	6x8
40,000	6x8	6x8	8x8	8x8	8x8	8x8
45,000	8x8	8x8	8x8	8x8	8x8	8x8
50,000	8x8	8x8	8x8	8x8	8x8	8x8
55,000	8x8	8x8	8x8	8x8	8x8	8x8

Instructions for Determining Column Sizes

FIRST—Use the total load per linear foot of girder obtained when determining girder sizes.

SECOND—Determine length of girder span being supported by column (see diagram, this is equal to one-half total distance from column measured both ways to next column or bearing wall, except when the girder is continuous over this column and broken over the column or bearing wall on each side, in which case it is equal to ⅝ this total distance).

THIRD—Multiply the length of this span in feet by load per linear foot.

FOURTH—Refer to table. Read down in column at left to load already determined, then across to column corresponding to length of column (distance from concrete footing to under side of girder). The figure at this intersection represents the size of column required.

The very next job for the carpenter or joiner to perform, after the sills have been built, is the job of erecting the girder supporting posts and the girder or girders. Study the details in the set of plans and erect the type of girder required. Follow the details as shown in the set of plans relative to the size and method of placing or building up girders.

NOTE—For fireplace and chimney details see Chapter 14.

8

Floor Joists

Floor joists are the framed members on which the floor is placed. They form the backbone of the platforms known as floors. Observe the framing details in the set of plans which pertain to the floor joists. Note the method of framing at the sills, chimney, fireplace, and any other opening or well. Select the floor joists stock with care, being sure each piece is straight and sound. Obtain from the set of house plans the length of the joists. Use the first joist cut of each length for the pattern in marking off similar lengths.

Wood joists are generally spaced 16" apart, center-to-center measure. The location of each joist should be marked on the sill and on the girder. Place pieces of stock of equal length in place on the sill and girder. Do not nail until all joists of equal length are in place. If there is a bow or crown in any joist, place the crown on the top. If the widths of joists vary, trim off where needed. This trimming can be done by the use of a hatchet.

If structural steel joists are used, place each in position as shown in the plan. Sheet-steel joists can be spaced about 24" or 36" apart center to center, according to the span.

After wood joists have been placed and properly sized they should be nailed in position by 20d. common nails. Straight-nail joists wherever possible. A spacing strip, made of a long narrow piece of stock with markings every 16", may be used to help hold the joists in place. All headers, stair wells, and any irregular framing are framed according to the special details worked out in the set of plans.

When joists are used over a long span they have a tendency to sway from side to side. In order to overcome this tendency to sway and to make these carrying members more rigid, a series of braces are inserted at regular intervals. These braces are known as bridging, which is inserted in rows about 8' center to center. If bridging is made of wood stock it is usually 1" x 3" material. Obtain a pattern of bridging stock by placing a piece of material in position as shown in the details. The saw cut will form the correct angle. Nail the top of the

bridging with 6d or 8d nails but do not nail the bottom of the bridging until the rough floor has been laid. This is in order to keep the bridging from pushing up any joist which might cause an unevenness in the floor.

Joists placed in a bathroom may have to be braced to carry the extra load of fixtures.

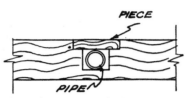

Piece let in joist which supports bathroom floor and conveniences.

Structural steel joists are braced with metal bridging.

Floor joists are estimated by the actual count of the number required. To obtain this number, one must study the framing plan, as each plan has its individual problem in framing. This applies to both wooden joists and steel joists. One might divide the butt side of the sill by the distance the joists are placed on centers and consider this the number of joists to use. To this number, however, must be added the special sizes or additional full lengths for opening headers, trimmers, etc. The hardware will be about 24 lb. of spikes, 20d, for every 1,000 board feet. The number of pieces of structural steel fittings can be estimated by the piece. The amount of labor for structural steel joist erection will be about half of that of other joist erection.

Bridging is estimated by the linear feet of stock used. Each set of cross bridging takes about 4' of 1" x 3" stock. A man can cut and nail about 1,000 linear feet of bridging stock in an hour. 8d common nails are used. Add this bridging estimate to the other estimates of the quantity estimate of the house. Structural steel bridging is estimated by the piece. This bridging requires no nailing, as each piece is bent over the joist. A man can work up this bridging at about twice the speed of wood bridging.

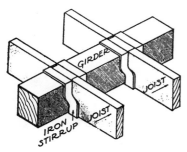

Joists hung on girder with
iron stirrups.

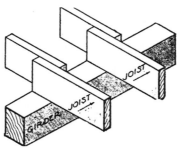

Joists lapped on top of girder.

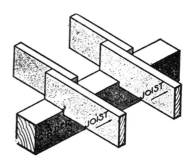

Joists sized down and lapped
over girder.

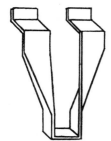

Joist hanger or stirrup.

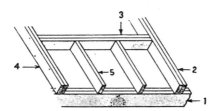

Header, trimmer and tail joists:
1, 3, header; 2, 4, trimmer; 5, tail.

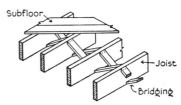

Floor joist bridging.

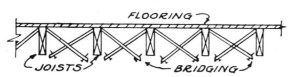

Bridging loose at lower end until subfloor
is nailed into position.

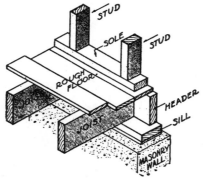

Joist framed into header on sill.

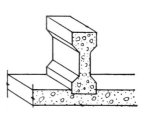

Pre-cast concrete joist.

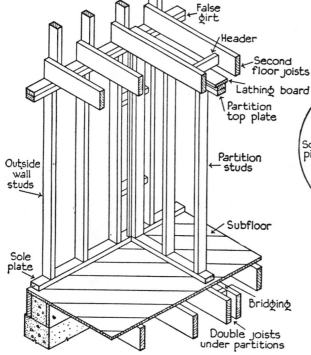

Framing for non-bearing partition.

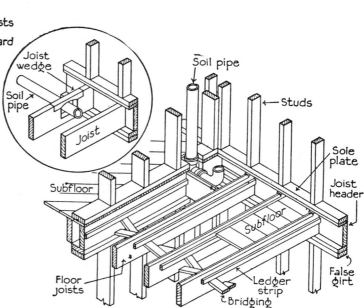

Framing joists under bathroom.

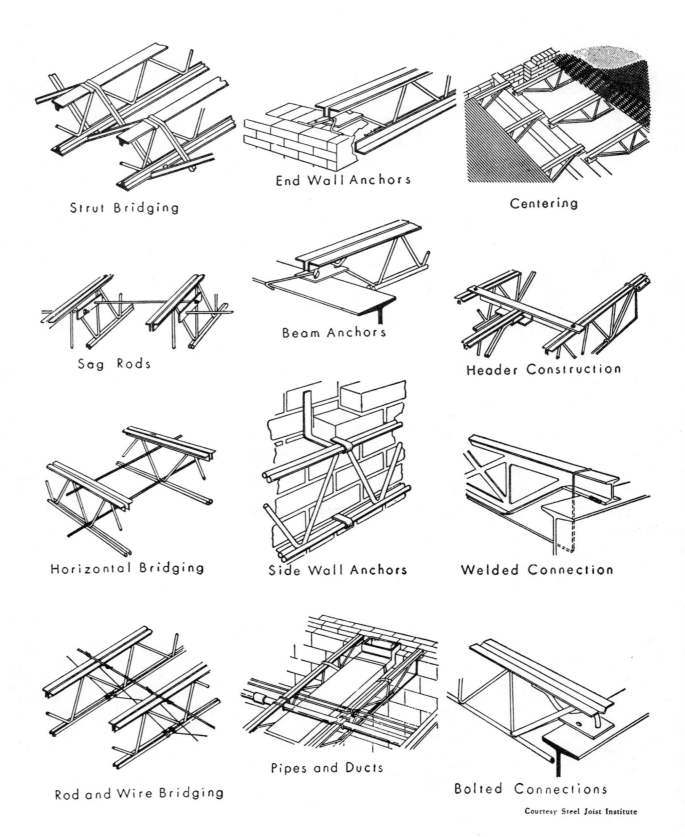

Strut Bridging

End Wall Anchors

Centering

Sag Rods

Beam Anchors

Header Construction

Horizontal Bridging

Side Wall Anchors

Welded Connection

Rod and Wire Bridging

Pipes and Ducts

Bolted Connections

Courtesy Steel Joist Institute

INSTALLATION OF STEEL JOISTS.

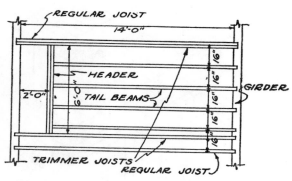

Showing use of trimmer and header joists.
Tail beams or short joists may be larger.

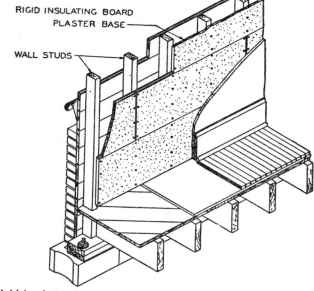

Rigid insulating board used as base for plaster. An application
sometimes used as shown here, where insulating board is applied
between finish floor and sub-floor.

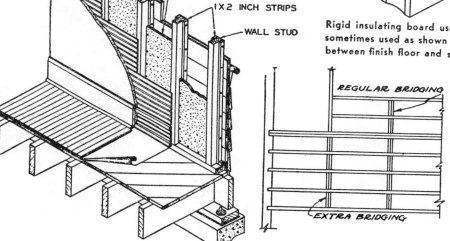

Rigid insulating board applied between wall studs.

Showing use of extra
bridging to support trim-
mer when it is placed
more than two feet from
regular bridging.

JOIST
FRAMING

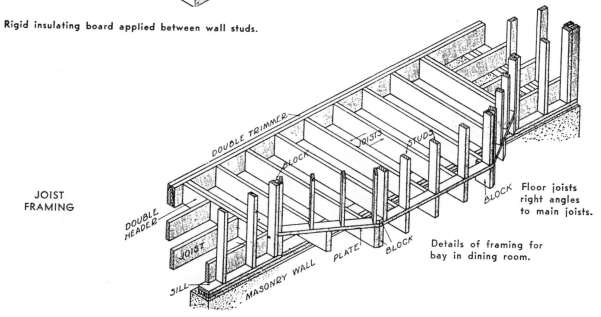

Floor joists
right angles
to main joists.

Details of framing for
bay in dining room.

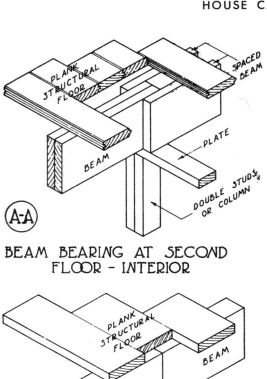

BEAM BEARING AT SECOND FLOOR - INTERIOR

(A-A)

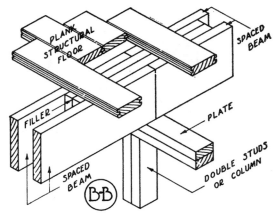

BEAM BEARING AT SECOND FLOOR - INTERIOR

(B-B)

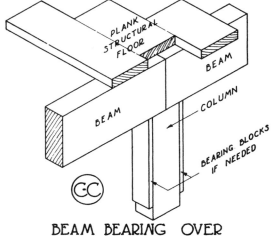

BEAM BEARING OVER BASEMENT POST

(C-C)

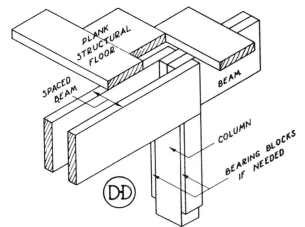

BEAM BEARING OVER BASEMENT POST

(D-D)

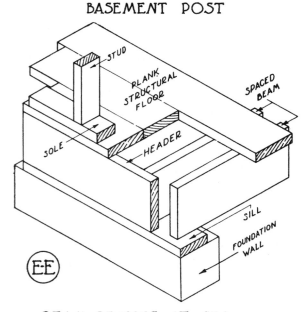

BEAM BEARING AT SILL

(E-E)

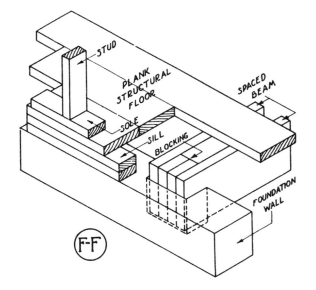

BEAM BEARING AT SILL

(F-F)

FRAMING DETAILS OF PLANK AND BEAM SYSTEM.

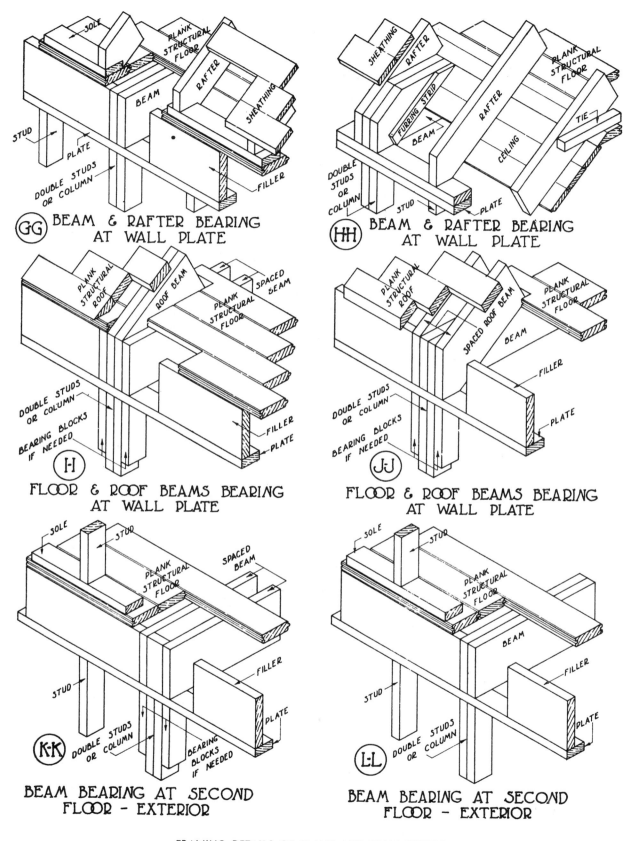

BEAM & RAFTER BEARING AT WALL PLATE (GG)

BEAM & RAFTER BEARING AT WALL PLATE (HH)

FLOOR & ROOF BEAMS BEARING AT WALL PLATE (I-I)

FLOOR & ROOF BEAMS BEARING AT WALL PLATE (J-J)

BEAM BEARING AT SECOND FLOOR - EXTERIOR (K-K)

BEAM BEARING AT SECOND FLOOR - EXTERIOR (L-L)

FRAMING DETAILS OF PLANK AND BEAM SYSTEM.

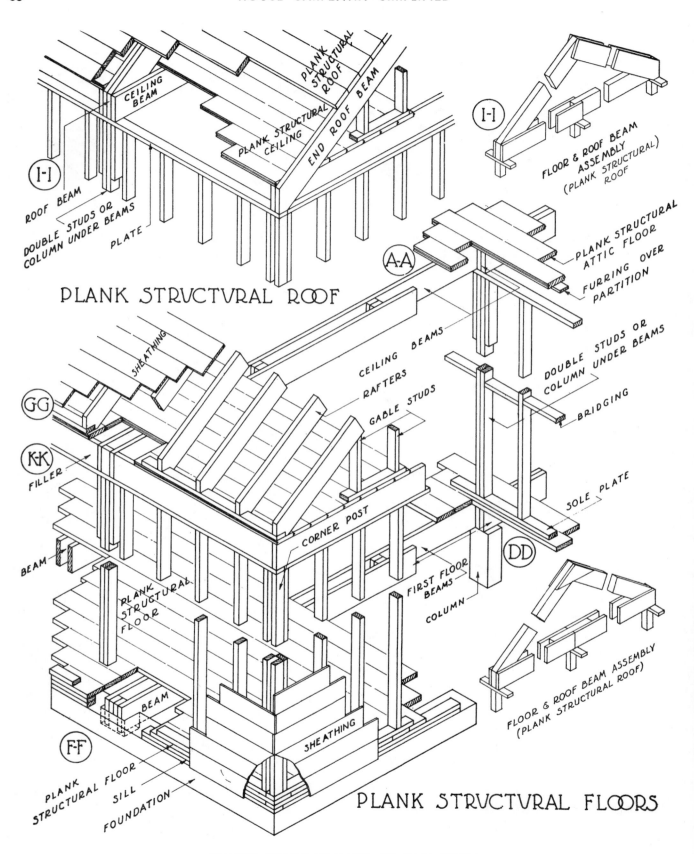

PLANK STRUCTURAL ROOF

PLANK STRUCTURAL FLOORS

FRAMING DETAILS OF PLANK AND BEAM SYSTEM.

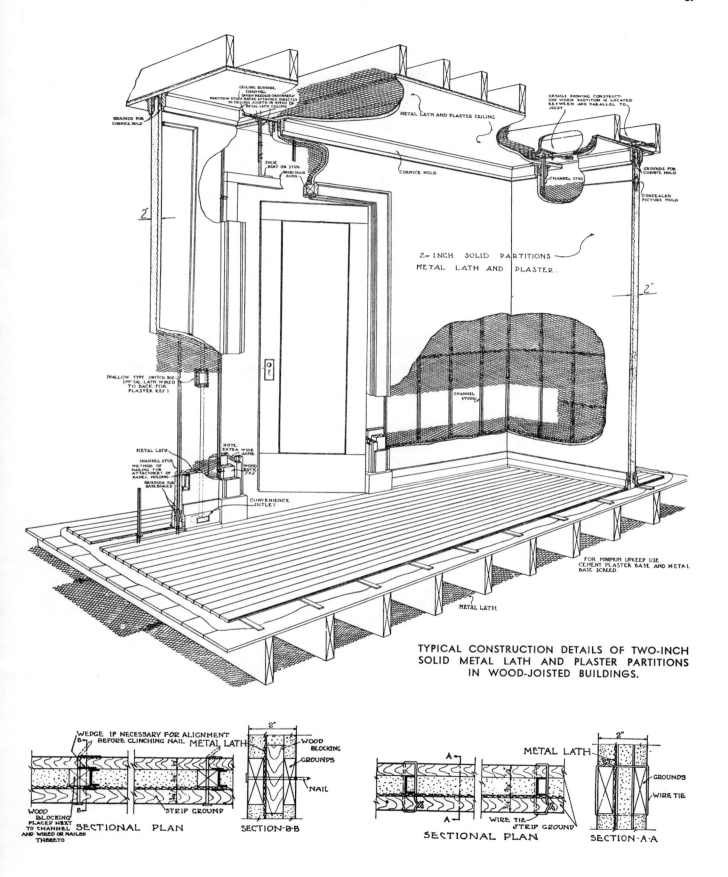

GROUNDS FOR CORNICE MOLD

CEILING RUNNER CHANNEL
(WHEN NEEDED ORDINARILY
PARTITION STUDS MAY BE ATTACHED DIRECTLY
TO CEILING JOISTS OR WIRED TO
METAL LATH CEILING)

METAL LATH AND PLASTER CEILING

DETAILS SHOWING CONSTRUCTION WHEN PARTITION IS LOCATED BETWEEN AND PARALLEL TO JOIST

2"

3 HOLE BENT ON STUD
WOOD DOOR BUCK

CORNICE MOLD

GROUNDS FOR CORNICE MOLD

CHANNEL STUD

CONCEALED PICTURE MOLD

2- INCH SOLID PARTITIONS
METAL LATH AND PLASTER.

2"

SHALLOW TYPE SWITCH BOX
(METAL LATH WIRED TO BACK FOR PLASTER KEY)

CHANNEL STUDS

METAL LATH
CHANNEL STUD METHOD OF NAILING FOR ATTACHMENT OF PANEL HOLDING
GROUNDS FOR BASE BOARD

NOTE EXTRA WIDE JAMB
WOOD BUCK 2 X 2

CONVENIENCE OUTLET

FOR MINIMUM UPKEEP USE CEMENT PLASTER BASE AND METAL BASE SCREED.

METAL LATH

TYPICAL CONSTRUCTION DETAILS OF TWO-INCH
SOLID METAL LATH AND PLASTER PARTITIONS
IN WOOD-JOISTED BUILDINGS.

WEDGE IF NECESSARY FOR ALIGNMENT
BEFORE CLINCHING NAIL   METAL LATH

B

2"
WOOD BLOCKING
GROUNDS
NAIL

WOOD BLOCKING PLACED NEXT TO CHANNEL AND WIRED OR NAILED THERETO

B

STRIP GROUND

SECTIONAL PLAN

SECTION-B-B

METAL LATH

A

A

WIRE TIE
STRIP GROUND

SECTIONAL PLAN

2"
GROUNDS
WIRE TIE

SECTION-A-A

9

Subflooring

The floor joists form a framework for the subfloor. This floor is called also the rough floor and may be visioned as a large platform covering the entire width and length area of the building. Two layers or coverings of flooring material, subflooring and finish flooring, are placed on the joists. This practice has many advantages, among which are: It makes for better insulation, stronger construction, and a finer and more pleasing finish; hardwood can be used as the finish flooring; also other materials, such as linoleum, rubber, cement, brick, glass, tile, or cork can be used.

Clear the top of the floor joists of all material except the nailing or spacing strips used to hold joists in place. Check the joists for proper spacing, twist, or wind. Place several pieces of rough tongue-and-groove flooring stock on the joists in such a manner as to furnish a temporary walk. Do not nail these pieces down on the joists.

Select a sound, straight piece of flooring to begin with and place this piece flush with the edge of the sill header. Nail down with 8d common nails. This piece can be held by nails driven vertically, as a piece of shoe stock will hide these nails. All succeeding pieces should be held by nails driven at a slant at the tongue side of the stock. This method is called toenailing.

If the specifications require the flooring to be laid diagonally to the floor joists, begin at the extreme edges of two sill headers which form a corner of the house and nail the flooring. Select short pieces of stock at first, nail in place, and saw off flush with the outside face of the sill header. Place each additional piece of flooring, fitting the groove over the tongue and toenail in place. Nail at each joist.

Study the framing details carefully as the work progresses. Allow for any openings, such as stair wells, chimney openings, or clothes chute, as designated.

Check all joists for uniformity of level surface. Sight from width side of joists for any joist having excessive crown or upward bulge. Use a long straightedge to test levelness, and then remove excessive crown by chopping with a hatchet. Straighten any joist having excessive wind.

Floors laid on structural-steel joists may be nailed directly to the joists in the same manner as wooden floors are nailed to wooden joists. Join all flooring over joists, never without a support.

In light frame construction there is no need to use subflooring thicker than 25/32nds of an inch. This is the thickness of dressed 1" lumber, according to American Lumber Standards.

Subflooring may be placed in either of two ways, squarely across the joists or diagonally across the joists. The subflooring laid squarely across the joists is much more economical of labor with all except end-matched material. It has the disadvantage, however, that the finish floor can be laid only at right angles to the subflooring and parallel with the joists. Diagonal subflooring is troublesome to lay, with the exception of the end-matched type, because of the necessity of cutting all ends to fit diagonally over the joists, which require two or more cuts for every board, each of which is longer than a square cut. With end-matched lumber this is not necessary, as the pieces may be butted wherever the joints occur, whether between joist support or not. The tongue at the ends and edges of such joists give sufficient strength, according to the tests of the Forest Products Laboratory, to support any reasonable weight, especially when supplemented by the finish floor.

A diagonal subfloor further gives choice of laying the finish floor in either direction, parallel to or at right angles to the joists. It is possible, therefore, to arrange the finish floor to run in one direction in one room and in another direction in the next, should that be desired.

There should be two 8d nails in each piece of subflooring up to 6" in width at every joist, and three or more in every piece over 6" in width.

Flooring is sold by board measure and comes in designated thicknesses and widths but often in random lengths. Calculate the actual area to be covered. For the following widths add the corresponding percentage for waste:

For 6" flooring add 15% for waste.
" 4" " " 20% " "
" 3" " " 25% " "

NOTE 1—For radiant heating installations see Chapter 14.

NOTE 2—See also Chapter 30—Thermal Insulation and Moisture Barriers.

Laying a subfloor of fir plywood on concrete slab.

Plywood panels, known in the trade as "2.4.1," are placed in position in a flooring system devised by Steinkamp. Joists used in this system are Junior Beams, lightweight steel structurals, to the top of which are attached 2 x 4's to form a 4-foot-square grid. The plywood panels are 1⅛ inches thick and provide a rigid flooring on which vinyl, plastic tile, hardwood, or wall-to-wall carpeting can be placed.

Concrete Slabs on Ground

The primary function of a basement conventionally was to provide a space for a central heating plant and for the storage and handling of bulk fuel and ashes. The basement also provided a space for laundry and other utilities. With the wide use of liquid and gas fuels the need for fuel and ash storage space has been greatly reduced. Often, too, space can be compactly provided on the ground floor level for the heating plant, laundry, and other utilities, hence the need for a full basement is greatly reduced.

A common type of floor construction for basementless houses is a concrete slab over a suitable foundation. To eliminate cold and uncomfortable floors, collection of condensation, and loss of heat through the floors, certain basic requirements must be met in the construction of concrete floor slabs

Laying a subfloor of masonite on diagonally laid boards.

Thick fir plywood subfloor underlayment panel is used for this remodeling job. In this case blocking is supported with lumber strips along lower side of floor girders.

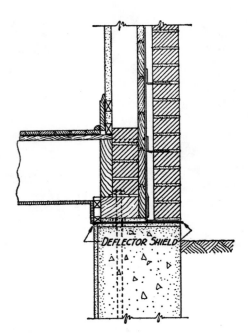

Subflooring in brick veneer wall.

laid directly on the ground. A few requirements are: Establish the finish floor level high enough above the natural grade level so that the finished grade will provide good drainage away from the foundation walls; remove all debris, topsoil, stumps, and organic matter, and tamp soil to prevent loose pockets; install sewer, water, gas, and oil supply

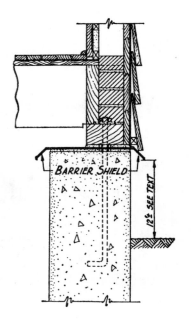

Subflooring in framed walls.

lines and other subsurface work before pouring slabs; fill the space between the soil level and the under side of the slab with no less than 4″ of well-tamped coarse gravel or crushed rock; lay a vapor barrier over the gravel to prevent soil mixture from working through the slab; install rigid insulation around the perimeter of the wall; reinforce the slab with wire mesh; and top dress the slab, before it hardens, with 1 part of cement and 3 parts of sand, not less than 1″ thick.

NOTE—In addition to the following see also Chapter 14—Heating Installations and Air Conditioning (Radiant Heating) and Chapter 30—Thermal Insulation and Moisture Barriers.

Fig. 1 shows an independent slab and foundation. The insulation is located on the outside of the foundation wall. Sleepers for the finish floor are 2″ x 2″ members pressure-treated with preservative and embedded in the concrete slab.

Fig. 2 shows the insulation placed on the inside of the foundation wall with the vapor barrier below the slab and on top of the gravel fill. A seal of hot tar is placed on top of the rigid insulation at the meeting of the foundation wall and slab.

Fig. 3 shows peripheral warm-air heating ducts placed in floor slab with a permanent vapor barrier on both sides of the rigid insulation. The vapor barrier is also carried under the concrete slab.

Fig. 4 shows radiant heating pipes for circulating hot water embedded in the slab of independent foundation wall and concrete floor slab. Note the seal of tar at the sole plate, the thick gravel fill, and 3″ slab of insulation concrete in addition to the vapor barrier.

Fig. 5 shows the wall and floor construction of a basementless house when the floor is not of the slab type. The conventional sill and floor joists supports the subfloor and finish floor. The foundation wall is ventilated by openings, screened at the outside. Note the vapor barrier on the well-tamped ground, the insulation between the joists just below the subfloor and the vapor barrier between the finish floor and subfloor.

Insulation for floor slabs must have a high resistance to heat transmission, permanent durability when exposed to dampness and frost, and high resistance to crushing due to floor loads, weight of the slab, or expansion forces. This insulation also should be immune to fungus and insect attack and should not absorb or retain moisture.

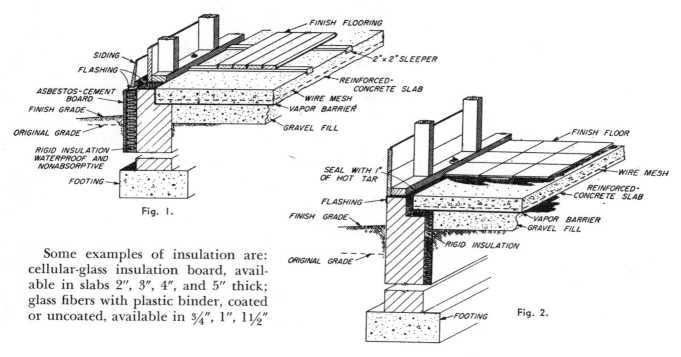

Fig. 1.

Fig. 2.

Some examples of insulation are: cellular-glass insulation board, available in slabs 2″, 3″, 4″, and 5″ thick; glass fibers with plastic binder, coated or uncoated, available in ¾″, 1″, 1½″

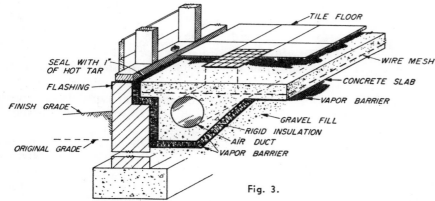

Fig. 3.

and 2″ thicknesses; wood or plant fiber boards, available in ½″, 25/32″, 1″ and its multiples of thicknesses; insulating concrete made of 1 part cement and 6 parts expanded mica aggregate; and concrete made with lightweight aggregate such as expanded slag, burned clay, or pumice, using 1 part cement to 4 parts of aggregate.

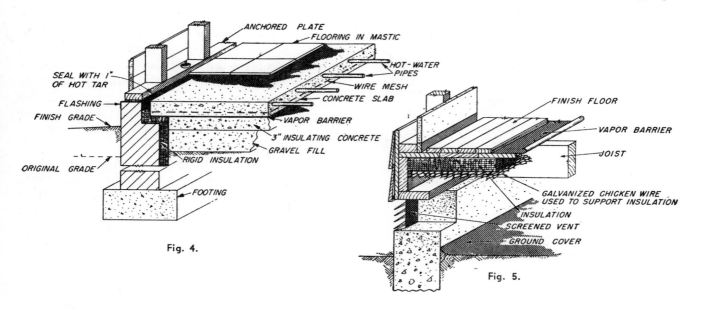

Fig. 4.

Fig. 5.

10

Outside Framed Walls

The foundation walls of a building form bearing walls for the upper structure and an enclosure for the basement. Outside walls rest directly on the foundation walls, with sills acting as anchors for them, and form bearing walls for the roof. The upper-story walls and enclosures, for the entire inner construction also are carried by the bearing walls.

From the set of house plans obtain the requirements for the framing of the outside walls. If the corner posts are not assembled and raised with the outside studded walls, they should be assembled and erected by finding the length of the corner posts, from the framing details, and cutting the stock to proper lengths. Nail pieces together with 12d or 16d nails, using the method required. Erect the post at the corner of sill, and plumb and brace it securely.

The corner posts may be framed with outside studded walls before the wall is raised in place. Plumb and brace the entire wall after it is raised. Use the spirit level and plumb bob to test the corner posts and plate.

Individual members of the studded wall may be raised one at a time. If this method is used, note the length of studs, and cut and place ready for nailing. Find the distance the studs are to be placed on centers and mark this distance on the extreme edge of the flooring above the sill. If a shoe plate is placed on the flooring before the studs are in place, nail down this shoe plate and toenail each stud to the shoe plate. Brace the studs temporarily and nail the plate number to top of studs. If a shoe plate is not used, nail studs to flooring by toenailing and place plate on top of studs.

If the studded wall is assembled on the subfloor or away from the structure, space each stud 16" center to center, nail shoe, ribband strip, and top plate to the studs, and raise in section and nail securely to sill or subfloor.

Brace all erected walls securely, keeping in mind always that framing timber is quite heavy and that wind exerts pressure on open framework.

If the framing details of the set of house plans do not give the information regarding the size of the window and door openings, the following general rules can be used. Obtain the width of the glass used in the sash and add $10\frac{5}{8}$" to this as an over-all width of the rough window opening. Obtain the length of the glass (if two sashes are used, double this amount) used in the sash and add 12" to this as an over-all height of the rough window opening.

In allowing an opening for a casement sash or window opening an allowance of 8" must be added to the width of the glass size and 10" must be added to the height of the glass size.

In allowing an opening for a door, add $6\frac{1}{4}$" to the width of the door and 4" to the height of the door. This rule applies to both outside and inside doors, French doors, or any other type of door not having a side light sash. Doors or sashes with special side lights or framing must be dealt with as special cases, using the general rules stated as a help in figuring out the special framing to allow for openings. Methods used in framing porches, bay windows, and other types of attached construction will be dealt with in Chapter 19.

In framing structural-steel walls one must refer to the plans, note the location of the studs, and erect them individually. Allowances for door and window openings are made according to the details.

The carpenter and joiner frames the wood or metal frames of a house. These parts consist in the main of wood or steel and hardware. Such items as nails, screws, glue, bolts, and fastenings may be included in hardware.

In previous assignments instructions were given to keep the several estimates in record form. There are many forms on the market used in estimating construction costs.

The cost of studded walls may be estimated by the count. Allow one stud for every 12" of length

(*Continued on page* 78)

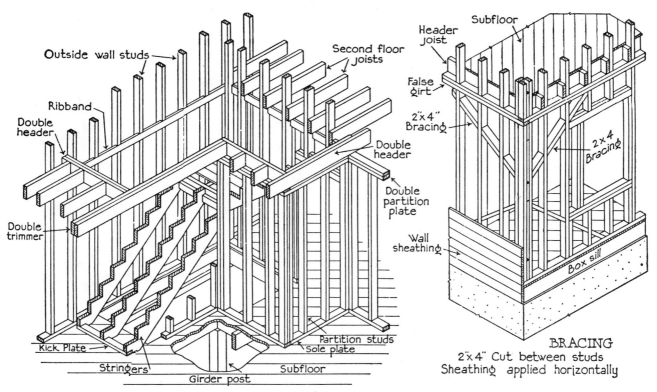

FRAMING FOR OPEN STAIRWAY

BRACING
2"x 4" Cut between studs
Sheathing applied horizontally

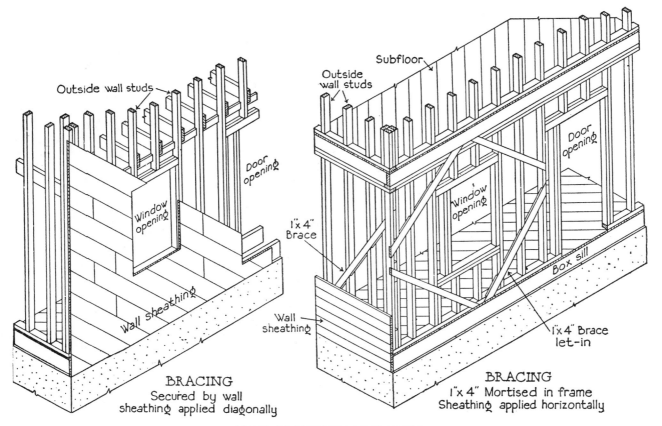

BRACING
Secured by wall
sheathing applied diagonally

BRACING
1"x 4" Mortised in frame
Sheathing applied horizontally

STANDARD METHODS OF FRAMING.

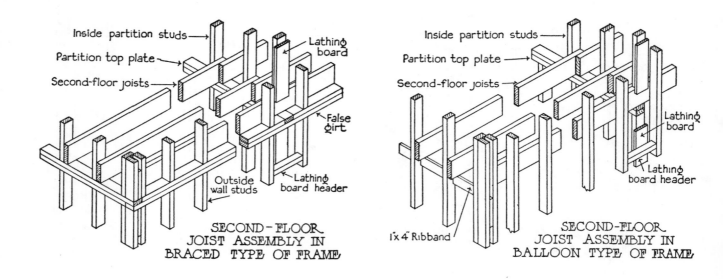

Inside partition studs →
Partition top plate →
Second-floor joists →
Lathing board
False girt
Outside wall studs
Lathing board header

SECOND-FLOOR
JOIST ASSEMBLY IN
BRACED TYPE OF FRAME

Inside partition studs →
Partition top plate →
Second-floor joists →
Lathing board
Lathing board header
1"x 4" Ribband

SECOND-FLOOR
JOIST ASSEMBLY IN
BALLOON TYPE OF FRAME

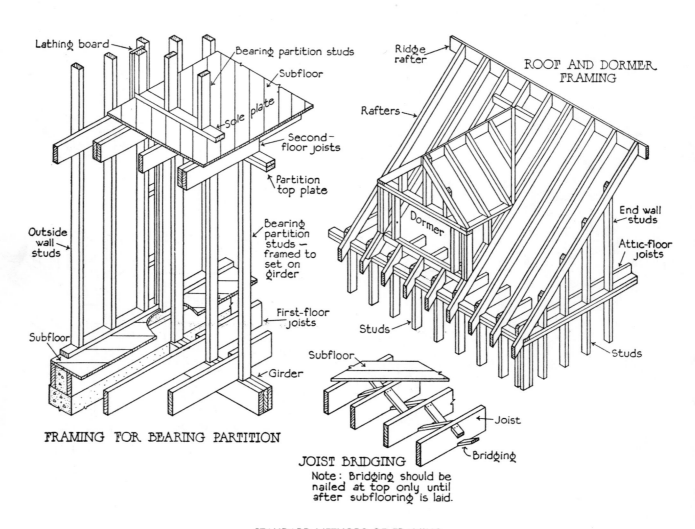

Lathing board →
Bearing partition studs
Subfloor
Sole plate
Second-floor joists
Partition top plate
Bearing partition studs — framed to set on girder
Outside wall studs
First-floor joists
Subfloor
Girder

FRAMING FOR BEARING PARTITION

Ridge rafter
ROOF AND DORMER FRAMING
Rafters →
Dormer
End wall studs
Attic-floor joists
Studs
Studs

Subfloor
Joist
Bridging

JOIST BRIDGING
Note: Bridging should be
nailed at top only until
after subflooring is laid.

STANDARD METHODS OF FRAMING.

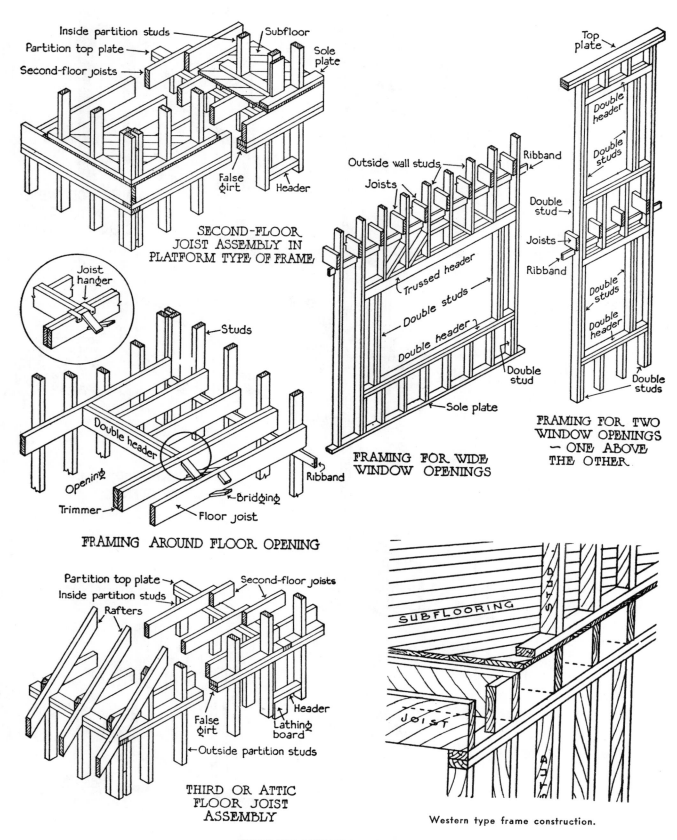

Inside partition studs
Partition top plate
Second-floor joists
Subfloor
Sole plate
False girt
Header

SECOND-FLOOR
JOIST ASSEMBLY IN
PLATFORM TYPE OF FRAME

Joist hanger

Studs
Double header
Opening
Trimmer
Bridging
Floor joist
Ribband

FRAMING AROUND FLOOR OPENING

Outside wall studs
Joists
Ribband
Trussed header
Double studs
Double header
Double stud

Sole plate

FRAMING FOR WIDE
WINDOW OPENINGS

Top plate
Double header
Double studs
Double stud
Joists
Ribband
Double studs
Double header
Double studs

FRAMING FOR TWO
WINDOW OPENINGS
— ONE ABOVE
THE OTHER

Partition top plate
Inside partition studs
Rafters
Second-floor joists
False girt
Header
Lathing board
Outside partition studs

THIRD OR ATTIC
FLOOR JOIST
ASSEMBLY

SUBFLOORING
JOIST

Western type frame construction.

STANDARD METHODS OF FRAMING.

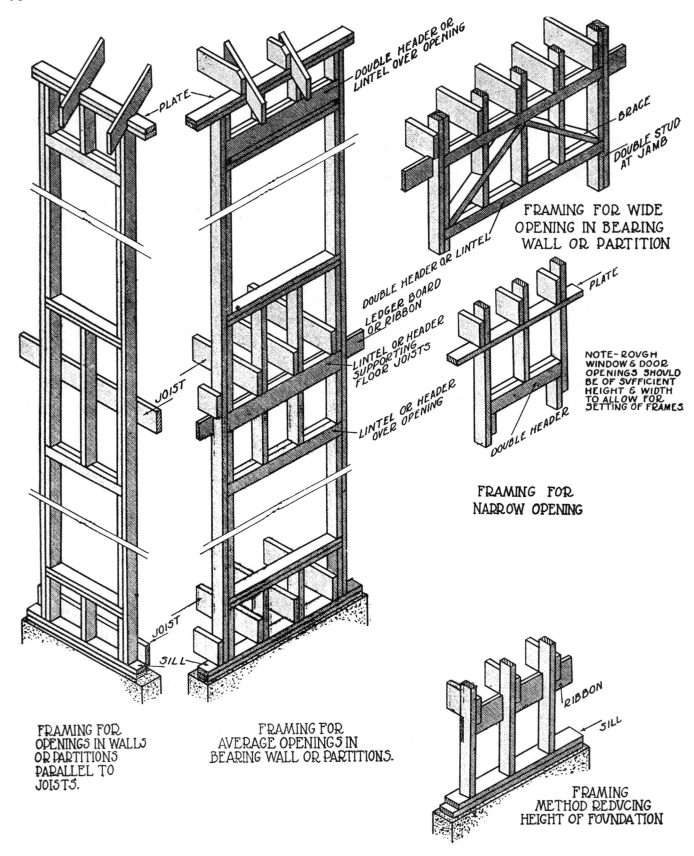

PLATE

DOUBLE HEADER OR
LINTEL OVER OPENING

BRACE

DOUBLE STUD
AT JAMB

FRAMING FOR WIDE
OPENING IN BEARING
WALL OR PARTITION

DOUBLE HEADER OR LINTEL

LEDGER BOARD
OR RIBBON

LINTEL OR HEADER
SUPPORTING
FLOOR JOISTS

JOIST

LINTEL OR HEADER
OVER OPENING

PLATE

NOTE- ROUGH
WINDOW & DOOR
OPENINGS SHOULD
BE OF SUFFICIENT
HEIGHT & WIDTH
TO ALLOW FOR
SETTING OF FRAMES

DOUBLE HEADER

FRAMING FOR
NARROW OPENING

JOIST

SILL

FRAMING FOR
OPENINGS IN WALLS
OR PARTITIONS
PARALLEL TO
JOISTS.

FRAMING FOR
AVERAGE OPENINGS IN
BEARING WALL OR PARTITIONS.

RIBBON

SILL

FRAMING
METHOD REDUCING
HEIGHT OF FOUNDATION

STANDARD METHODS OF FRAMING.

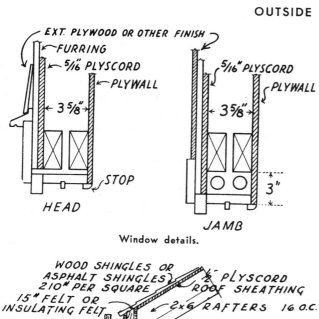

EXT. PLYWOOD OR OTHER FINISH
FURRING
5/16" PLYSCORD
PLYWALL
3 5/8"
STOP

HEAD

5/16" PLYSCORD
PLYWALL
3 5/8"
3"

JAMB

Window details.

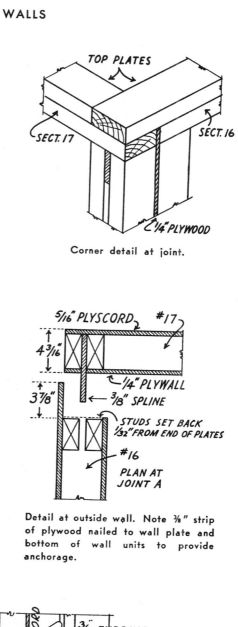

TOP PLATES

SECT. 17   SECT. 16

2 1/4" PLYWOOD

Corner detail at joint.

5/16" PLYSCORD   #17
4 3/16"
1/4" PLYWALL
3 7/8"   3/8" SPLINE
STUDS SET BACK 1/32" FROM END OF PLATES
#16
PLAN AT JOINT A

Detail at outside wall. Note 3/8" strip of plywood nailed to wall plate and bottom of wall units to provide anchorage.

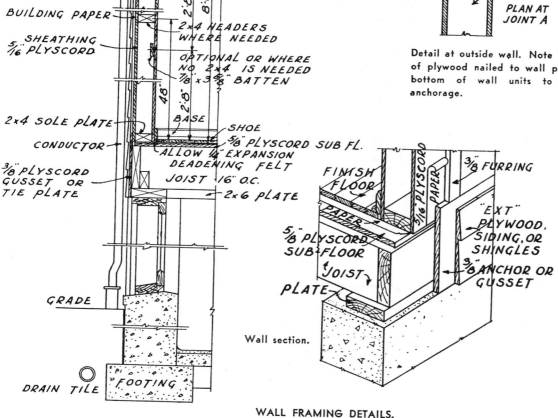

WOOD SHINGLES OR ASPHALT SHINGLES 210" PER SQUARE
15" FELT OR INSULATING FELT
FIR GUTTER
1 1/8 x 8" FRIEZE
5/16" PLYSCORD BELT COURSE
CONDUCTOR
3/8" FURRING STRIPS
"EXT" PLYWOOD OR BEVEL SIDING OR SHINGLES
BUILDING PAPER
SHEATHING 5/16 PLYSCORD
2x4 SOLE PLATE
CONDUCTOR
3/8 PLYSCORD GUSSET OR TIE PLATE
GRADE
DRAIN TILE
FOOTING

1/2" PLYSCORD ROOF SHEATHING
2x6 RAFTERS 16 O.C.
2x4 PLATE "X"
2x6 OR 2x8 C.J.
1/4" PLYWALL
2'8"
8'0"
STUDS 16 O.C.
2'8"
2x4 HEADERS WHERE NEEDED
OPTIONAL OR WHERE NO. 2x4 IS NEEDED
7/8 x 3 5/8" BATTEN
2'8"
48"
BASE
SHOE
5/8 PLYSCORD SUB FL.
ALLOW 1/4" EXPANSION
DEADENING FELT
JOIST 16 O.C.
2x6 PLATE

FINISH FLOOR
3/16 PLYSCORD
PAPER
3/8 FURRING
PAPER
5/8 PLYSCORD SUB FLOOR
JOIST
PLATE
"EXT" PLYWOOD, SIDING, OR SHINGLES
3/8 ANCHOR OR GUSSET

Wall section.

WALL FRAMING DETAILS.

(Continued from page 72)

of wall, either outside or inside. In this way, if studs are placed 16″ center to center, this will allow a sufficient number to be used at corners, windows, and doors. It will take about 32 hours to frame 1,000 B. M. of studding. Steel studs are estimated by count, taking off the count from the set of plans. The erecting time is the same as in wood framing. Hardware and fastenings are calculated according to the plans.

Estimate the material and time required to erect the outside walls of the house in the set of house plans. Keep this in a permanent record form.

Split-Level Framing

Framing a dwelling to vary from the conventional practices of two floor levels by arranging rooms at four levels is accomplished by the use of a straight rectangular plan and a bearing partition running the entire length of the house through the center.

The floor plan *A* outlines show the arrangements of rooms. The recreation room is at the lowest level. A crawl space is excavated under the living room, dining room, and kitchen, while the patio and garage are at grade level.

The cross-sectional framing elevation *B* on page

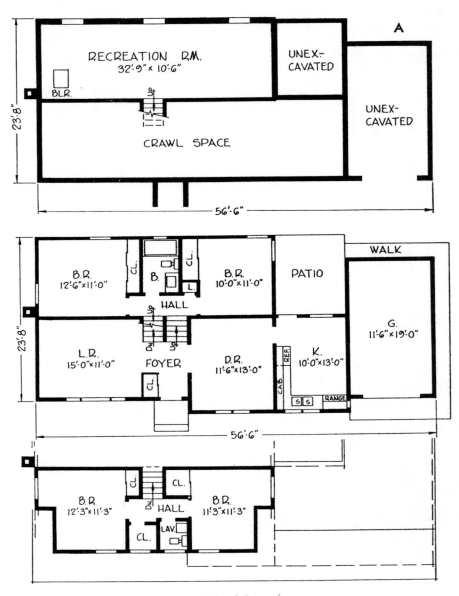

A split-level floor plan.

Outside framed wall assembly of split-level room arrangement.

81 shows the four floor levels, namely: recreation room level; living room, dining room and kitchen levels; rear bedroom and bath levels; and front bedrooms floor level. In this section can be seen

An outside framed wall showing window and door framing, diagonal subflooring, stair well, and method of framing inside partition wall to outside wall.

the four- and eight-foot studding, stairway and cantilever projection at bay and roof overhang.

Points to observe in making split-level framing relatively simple are: Adopt a simple, straight, rectangular plans of floors; avoid jogs, L-shapes or irregular perimeters; have a minimum of bearing partitions; use standard lumber lengths and avoid cutting into framing.

All joists are 2 x 8's, 12' long, set in place without cutting, with one exception, the 14' joist at the kitchen - dining room bay. Floor-to-ceiling closet doors are used, thus eliminating framed openings. Baseboard radiation is used to avoid cutting into studding at walls. The stair sections are simple and interchangeable.

This simplified method of framing a split-level structure is done by crews of two to four carpenters who are schooled in each step of procedure, namely: precutting the studs, jack studs, headers, cripples, etc., and nailing together subassemblies; installation of center partitions and first- and second-floor joists; laying subfloor; applying sheathing; installing windows and doors; applying outside wall covering.

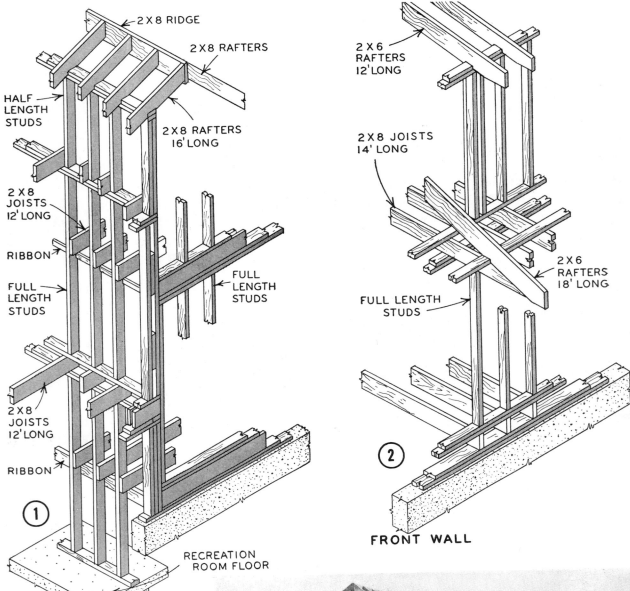

2 X 8 RIDGE

2 X 8 RAFTERS

HALF LENGTH STUDS

2 X 8 RAFTERS 16' LONG

2 X 8 JOISTS 12' LONG

RIBBON

FULL LENGTH STUDS

FULL LENGTH STUDS

2 X 8 JOISTS 12' LONG

RIBBON

①

RECREATION ROOM FLOOR

CENTER BEARING PARTITION

2 X 6 RAFTERS 12' LONG

2 X 8 JOISTS 14' LONG

2 X 6 RAFTERS 18' LONG

FULL LENGTH STUDS

②

FRONT WALL

The photograph showing the outside wall framing is taken from the left-hand side of the house with the living room in the foreground. Detail 1 shows the center bearing partition members and method of continuous framing. Detail 2 shows the framing members just beyond the bay and at the right-hand portion of the house.

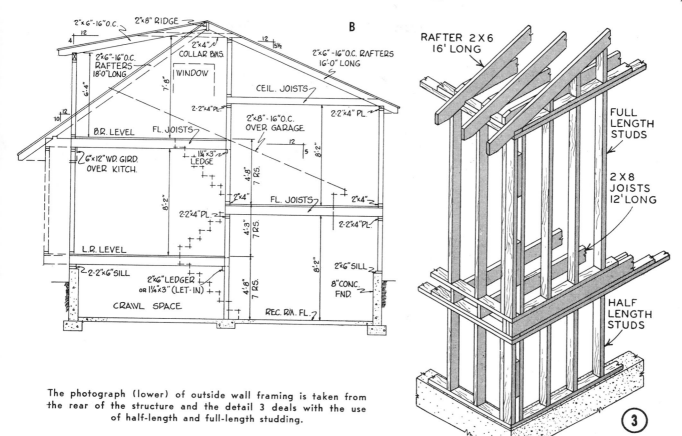

Detail B labels:
2"x6"-16"O.C.
2"x8" RIDGE
B
2"x4" COLLAR BMS.
2"x6"-16"O.C. RAFTERS 18'-0" LONG
WINDOW
2"x6"-16"O.C. RAFTERS 16'-0" LONG
CEIL. JOISTS
2-2"x4" PL.
B.R. LEVEL
FL. JOISTS
2-2"x4" PL.
2"x8"-16"O.C. OVER GARAGE
2-2"x4" PL.
6"x12" WD. GIRD. OVER KITCH.
1¼"x3" LEDGE
2"x4"
FL. JOISTS
2"x4"
L.R. LEVEL
2-2"x4" PL.
2-2"x4" PL.
2-2"x6" SILL
2"x6" LEDGER OR 1¼"x3" (LET-IN)
2"x6" SILL
8" CONC. FND.
CRAWL SPACE
REC. R/R. FL.

RAFTER 2X6 16' LONG
FULL LENGTH STUDS
2 X 8 JOISTS 12' LONG
HALF LENGTH STUDS
③ REAR WALL

The photograph (lower) of outside wall framing is taken from the rear of the structure and the detail 3 deals with the use of half-length and full-length studding.

11

Inside Framed Walls

The outside walls of a house are a support for the roof and an enclosure for the entire inner construction. The inside walls are partitions or divisions for the several rooms inside the house. Inside walls may or may not support other parts of the structure.

Studded partition walls are framed on the floor and raised in place in much the same manner as the outside studded walls. Walls may be framed piece by piece too. However, in any case great care must be taken to allow for all door, entry, or special openings in the walls. See that the free or lower end of all bridging is nailed in place before any walls are erected. Inside walls of structural steel are set in place piece by piece, each piece bolted in place following the specifications on the plans. Refer to the illustrations in the previous chapters, particularly those shown in Chapters 6 and 10.

All framed walls, either outside or partition, have openings allowed for doors, windows, and other types of passages. The size of the openings is estimated or calculated from the size of the door or window, etc., to be housed in the opening. In allowing for an opening in the framed studded wall to house a door, the following items are considered. List and add the widths.

    a. Width of door—3' outside door, 2' 6" inside doors.

    b. Twice width of outside casing trim—2 x 4½".

    c. This equals 3' plus 9" or 3' 9" between studs for opening.

    d. There is, however, one extra stud placed on each side of the single stud opening, which will reduce the width of the opening by 2" x 1⅜" and give a clear distance between doubled studs of 3' 6¼" for door and frame.

    e. Length of door—7' outside doors, 6' 8" inside doors.

    f. Add ¾" for rough floor, ¾" for finish floor, ½" for threshold, 1" for door jamb and 1" for lugs. This will be 4" in all.

    g. Add the 4" to 7' which will give the total clear space from floor joist to bottom of door header.

In other words, add 6¼" to the width of the door and 4" to height of door to obtain the inside width and height of the framed opening.

In allowing for an opening in the framed studded wall to house a window, the following items are considered. List and add the widths.

    a. Width of glass in sash—a two-light window or sash having each light of glass 28" x 34" in size.

    b. 28" plus 2" plus 2" is 32" (2" for stiles of sash).

    c. Add to this the width of outside casings—2 × 4" is 8".

    d. This totals (32" plus 8") 40". This is the distance from center to center of the single studs.

    e. Stud placed on each side will reduce the width by the thickness of one stud since the distance is from c. to c.

    f. This will be 40" less ½ of 2¾" (1⅜"), which is 38⅝".

    g. Twice length of glass for a double-hung sash—34" × 2 is 68".

    h. To this add thickness of window-frame sill 2", window-frame head jamb 2", space for lugs 2", plus 6" for lower and upper sash rails and meeting rails, total addition 12".

    i. 68" plus 12" equals 80".

    j. If there are muntins in sash, add ¼" for each one.

In other words, add 10⅝" to width of glass and 6" to each single height of glass to obtain clear space to allow for a sash and window frame.

In estimating inside and outside studded walls no allowances are made for openings. The studs are estimated by count, allowing one for every 16" of length to be walled. Corners are counted as two or three, depending on the type of corner post used.

Bay-window framing is estimated as any outside studded wall. Openings for windows are estimated as any ordinary window.

Make a diagram of a window and of a door opening as described above. Place all necessary dimensions on each sketch. The illustrations will help to make clear the foregoing discussions.

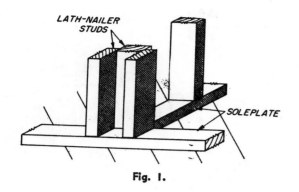

Fig. 1.

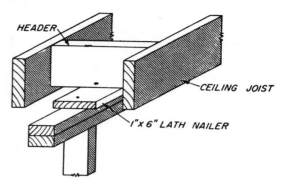

Fig. 4.

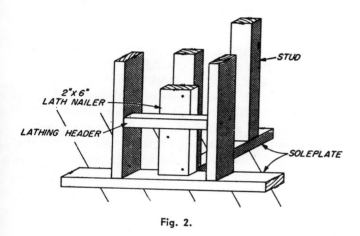

Fig. 2.

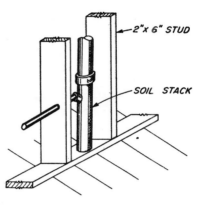

Fig. 5.

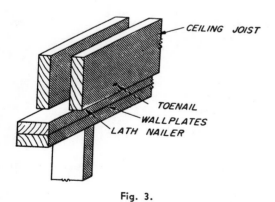

Fig. 3.

Framed walls are basically the horizontal and vertical members which serve as a nailing base for wall-covering stock or materials and as supports for upper floors, ceilings, and roofs. Conventional wall framing is of 2″ x 4″ stock, spaced 16″ on centers. This framing must provide good nail-holding power, must be easily worked, warp-free, and sturdy. Floor framing is of 2″ x 8″ or 2″ x 10″ stock, placed 16″ on centers, and must have the same qualities as wall framing or studding.

Spacing and adjusting wall and floor framing members for lathing, piping, and conveniences requires great care. Fig. 1 shows how a nailing base for lath is obtained by the placing of studding at an interior wall intersection.

Fig. 2 shows the placing of lath nailers by the use of additional nailer members at a wall intersection.

Fig. 3 illustrates the use of two ceiling joists on either side of a wall plate to form a purchase for lath.

Fig. 4 shows the use of a 1″ x 6″ member housed over double wall plate members to support a header between regularly spaced ceiling joists.

One of the walls of a bathroom is used for the soil stack and stack vent for the water closet. If a 4″ cast-iron bell pipe is used for a stack, a 2″ x 6″ studding must be used to control the pipe hubs as shown in Fig. 5.

(Continued on next page)

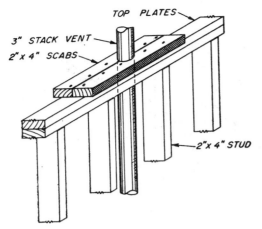

Fig. 6.

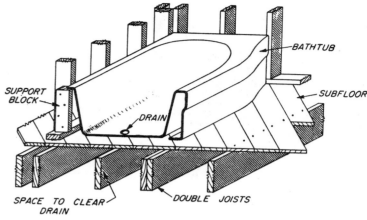

Fig. 7.

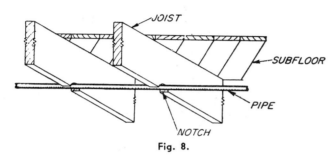

Fig. 8.

(Continued from page 83)

If 3″ galvanized pipe is used for a soil stack, which is often done in one-story houses, the stack wall may be of 2″ x 4″ studding but reinforced at the plates with scab members as shown in Fig. 6.

Joist and stud framing, for heavy bathroom fixtures, such as a bathtub, must be so arranged to carry the load without deflection. Fig 7 shows the doubling of joists at the outer edges of the tub and

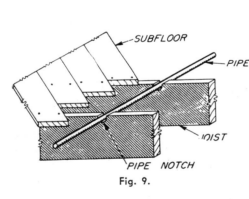

Fig. 9.

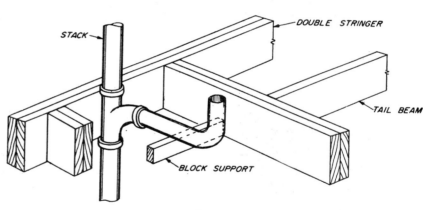

Fig. 11.

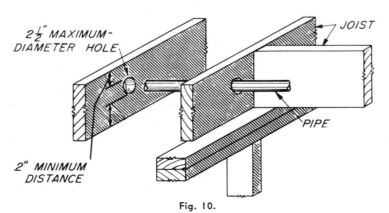

Fig. 10.

the placing of supporting blocks on the sole plate to support the housed edge of the tub.

The notching or cutting of framed stock must be done with care. Fig. 8 shows how a service pipe is let in to a joist, at the bottom of the member, with the notch not more than one-sixth of the joist width and near the end of the joist span.

Fig. 9 shows a service pipe notched into the upper part of a joist and just below the subflooring.

If a soil stack is run horizontally into a vertical stack, joist headers are used to frame an opening as indicated in Fig. 10. Note the support of a block placed below the horizontal stack member and attached to the doubled joist members.

Service pipe holes may be drilled into joists, as indicated in Fig. 11, provided the hole is no greater than 2½" in diameter and the edge of the hole is not less than 2" from the top or bottom edge of the joists.

NOTE—For details of framing for fireplaces or other heating or air-conditioning installations see Chapter 14.

Plank-and-Beam Framing System for Dwelling Construction

The plank-and-beam system for the construction of floors, walls, and roofs in today's houses is uniquely adaptable to the modern design trends toward one-story structures, large glass areas, mod-

ular coordination, open-space planning, and natural finish of materials.

It is characterized by the concentration of structural loads on fewer and larger-sized pieces than those in conventional construction, resulting in rapid on-site assembly. Duel function of materials and the use of planks continuous over two or more spans result in further economy.

Adapted from heavy timber construction, the plank-and-beam system is used for floor and roofs in combination with ordinary wood stud or masonry walls, or with curtain wall construction with skeleton frame.

Fig. 1, showing interior wall, roof, and exterior wall framing, illustrates the general principles and basic simplicity of the system. The similarity to structural steel framing practices is striking. High-quality materials and careful workmanship are inherent requirements. Simplicity of assembly extends even to inexpensive construction of the roof overhang which is necessary in many parts of the nation to keep the summer sun from the large glass areas.

Fig. 2 shows how a plank-and-beam built roof is applied to masonry wall construction. Assuming the width of the house to be 24' with either a flat or low-pitched roof, the 14' length planks automatically provide an approximate 2' overhang.

Figs. 3a and 3b, at the roof assembly illustrate the simplicity of construction which eliminates lookouts, soffit, facia, moldings, or

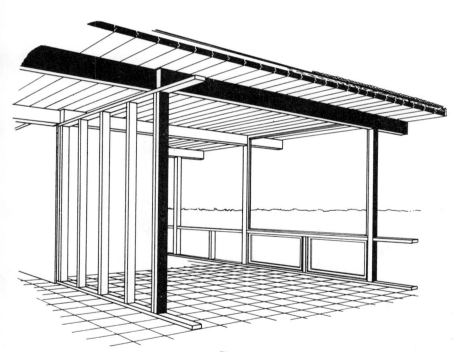

Fig. 1.

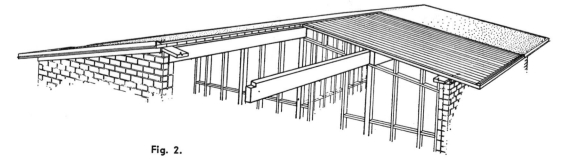

Fig. 2.

eave vents. The insulation, roofing, and gravel are stopped by a simple wooden member, covered with metal to provide a drip.

Planning a house on a modular basis is a proven money saver because materials are used with a

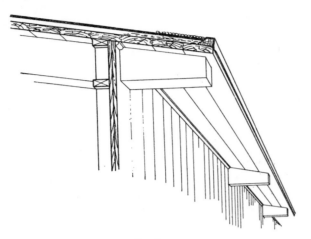

Fig. 3a.

minimum amount of cutting and fitting. A module is a size of one part taken as a measure for regulating the proportions of others. The plank-and-beam system fits naturally with modular design. For example, if an 8' spacing for beams and columns is used, 16' planks can be continuous over

two spans, and 4' x 8' sheets of drywall and plywood will fit without cutting. If 2' x 6' or 2' x 8' tongued-and-grooved planking are used over wide beam spacing, it eliminates the use of ceiling joists, bridging, lath and plaster or drywall construction. The plank and beams may be finished on the ground before erection.

The isometric drawing, Fig. 4, shows a typical wall section, 40' in length, with window and door

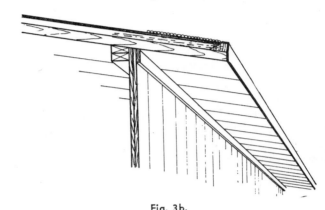

Fig. 3b.

openings. The studs are placed on 24" centers. The floor-to-ceiling height is 8'. There are no lintel beams or crippled studs. A nailing strip must be provided on the underside of the planking in order to receive the interior finish and the exterior sheathing and siding.

Reference should be made to other details in the plank-and-beam system in Chapter 8—Floor Joists.

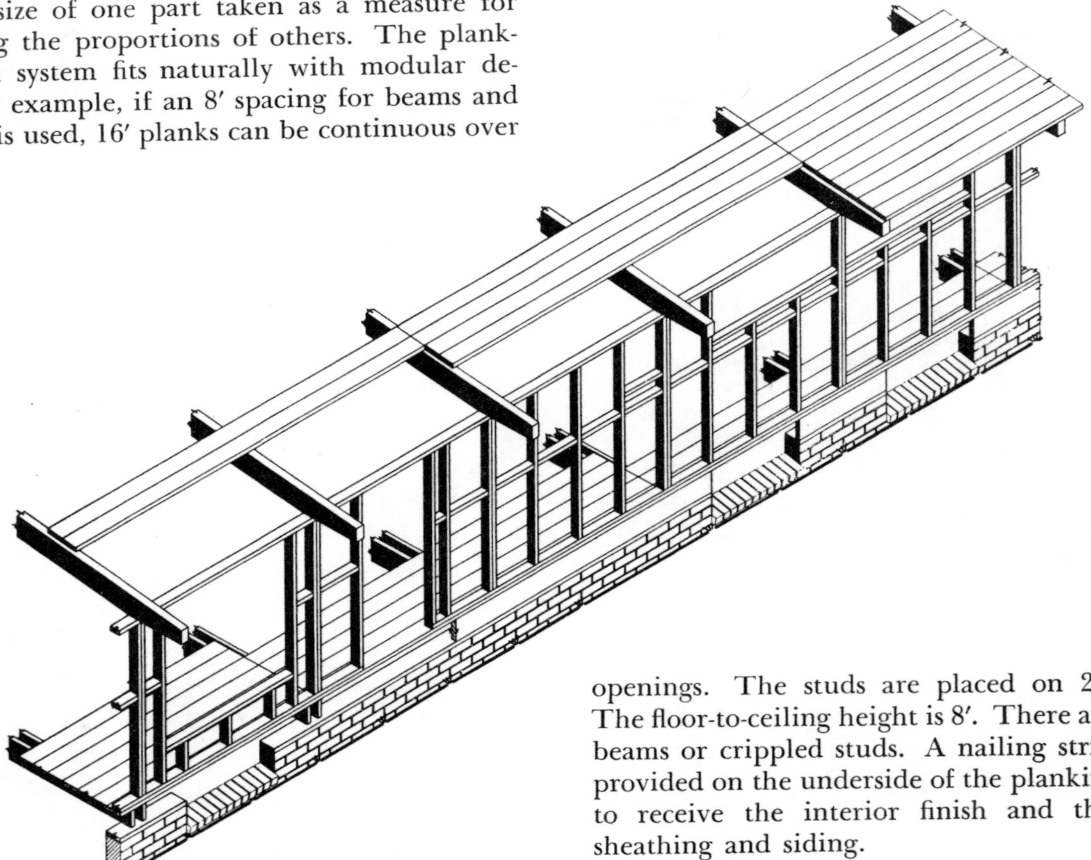

Fig. 4.

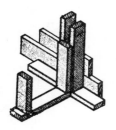
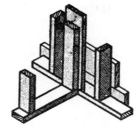
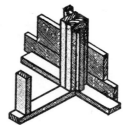

METHODS OF FRAMING STUDS AT PARTITION CORNERS

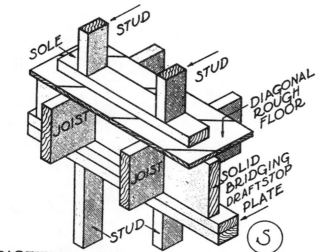

PARTITION AT RIGHT ANGLES TO JOISTS
WESTERN FRAME

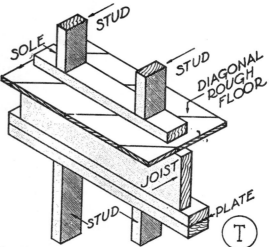

PARTITION PARALLEL WITH JOISTS
WESTERN FRAME

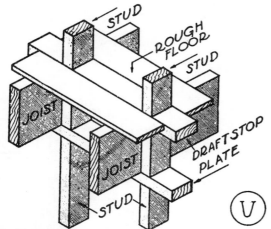

PARTITION AT RIGHT ANGLES TO JOISTS
BALLOON AND
BRACED FRAME

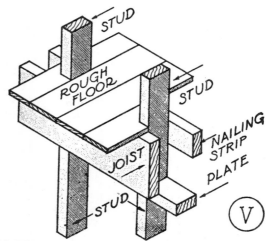

PARTITION PARALLEL WITH JOISTS
BALLOON AND
BRACED FRAME

METHODS OF FRAMING STUDDED WALLS.

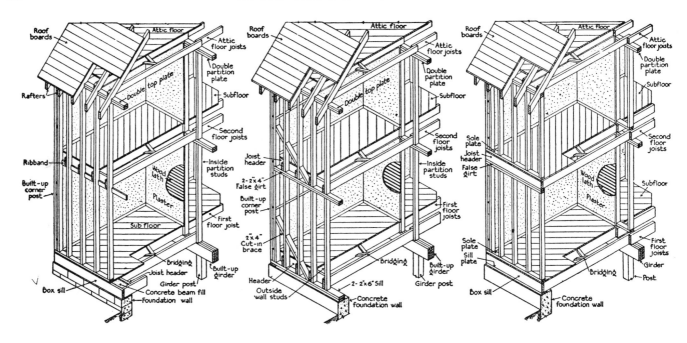

THE BALLOON FRAME

This type of frame has many things to recommend it. The one-piece studs, extending the full height of the wall and tied together by the ribband at the second floor line reduce to a minimum the shrinkage factor. It is strong and rigid but requires careful fire-stopping.

This frame is more efficient when the interior studding is set directly on top of girders or bearing partitions.

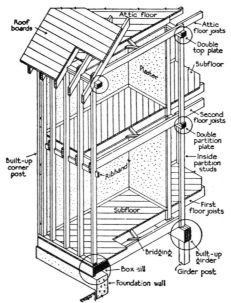

DETAIL OF METHOD FOR SECURING BALANCED SHRINKAGE

THE MODERN BRACED FRAME

This type of frame is an outgrowth of New England solid timber post and girth construction. Built-up members are used today very largely and with equal satisfaction. Instead of heavy posts set eight or ten feet apart, walls are built with 2 x 4 in. studs set 16 in. on centers. The second floor is carried on a double 2 x 4 in. girth. Diagonal bracing is inserted at the corners. This type has several commendable features. It is simple to build and has good provision for fire-stopping both at sill and second-floor line. 2 x 4 in. cut-in bracing, as illustrated, may also be used with other types. ~

THE FRAME provides the network to which the other materials are fastened and the strength and rigidity required to support the loads put upon it and preserve the materials with which it is built. Three distinct types of frames are shown by Figs. 1, 2 and 3. Numerous combinations of these types are frequently employed.

BALANCED SHRINKAGE

The total thickness of horizontal lumber in the framing of outside and inside walls on each floor should be equalized as nearly as possible to eliminate uneven shrinkage.

FIRE-STOPPING

Fire safety in a dwelling is increased by preventing the circulation of air in the walls between floors or between rooms. An effective method is shown in the drawing to the right.

THE PLATFORM FRAME

The Platform Frame is extensively used. It is similar in principle to Braced Frame but has boxed sill construction at each floor line. This makes for greater shrinkage but it is equalized on each floor when a similar type of construction is used under bearing partitions.

This frame is more efficient when the interior studding is set directly on top of girders or bearing partitions.

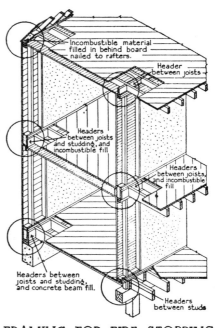

FRAMING FOR FIRE-STOPPING

SEVERAL STANDARD METHODS OF FRAMING.

12

Ceiling Joists

Ceiling joists are erected in much the same manner as floor joists. In a structure of two or more stories the ceiling joists become the floor joists of the floor above.

Study the framing details of the set of plans. If the structure is but one story in height the ceiling joists will not be broken in their span from plate to plate or partition plate, depending on the width of the building. It will be necessary, however, to frame in an opening for the chimney scuttle or well hole.

Check over-all measurements for accuracy, and partition walls for plumb. Determine various lengths of joists to be used. Trim to uniform size all joists resting either on plate or ribband strip. Study the illustrations on the following pages.

If the framing details require a double header and a double carrying joist, then frame according to these requirements. If the structure is to have a second story proceed with the partition wall and second-floor ceiling joists as directed for the first floor. Provisions must be made for nailing second-story flooring along the partition walls that run parallel to the joists.

Where windows or doors occur in outside walls or partitions, a part of some studs must be cut out. It therefore is necessary to introduce some form of a header over the doorway to support the lower ends of studs that have been cut. In like manner, there is a similar member, termed the *rough sill*, at the bottom of window openings.

Headers may be divided into two classes, the *nonbearing* and the *load-bearing*. The nonbearing headers occur in walls which are parallel to the joists of the floor above and carry only the weight of the framing immediately above. Load-bearing headers occur in walls which carry the ends of floor joists. If they rest on plates or ribbands immediately above the opening, they must support the weight of the floor or floors above.

Header sizes will be determined according to whether they are load-bearing or not. Unless the opening in a nonbearing partition is more than three feet wide, a single 2″ x 4″ is satisfactory as a header. This size is sufficiently strong and eliminates the likelihood of plaster cracks due to expansion or shrinkage. It often happens, however,

that trim inside or outside is so wide as to prevent satisfactory nailing over openings with a single 2 x 4. In such cases it is necessary to double the header to provide a nailing base for trim.

On load-bearing partitions or walls the header should be doubled even over narrow openings,

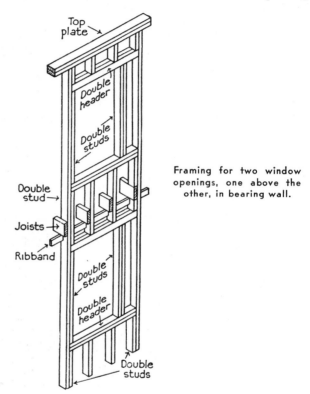

Framing for two window openings, one above the other, in bearing wall.

especially if a short stud occurs near the center of the header. The header rests on the studs.

If the 2 x 4's placed over the openings are one above the other in this construction, they should be adequately spiked together to properly support the load. If the 2 x 4's used as a header, instead of being laid horizontally, are placed vertically side by side, the spiking will not be quite so important, since each piece will offer greater resistance to bending than when laid flat. It should be noted, however, that the two 2 x 4's laid on edge will together measure only $3\frac{1}{4}″$ when laid flat, instead of $3\frac{5}{8}″$. Consequently, it will be necessary to insert small pieces of lath between the 2 x 4's in order to make the header line up with the studs.

(Above) Ceiling joists and adjacent framed members: A series of 2″ x 6″ ceiling joists extending from one outside wall to a partition and another series extending from a partition to the opposite wall. The various framed and temporary members are: 1, door header; 2, corner studding; 3, cripple stud; 4, double plate; 5, ceiling joists; 6, temporary brace and catwalk; 7, roof rafters; 8, temporary brace for rafters; 9, ridge board.

(Left) Ceiling joists and exterior and interior wall framing: This photograph shows the same ceiling joists and adjacent framed members as revealed in the first photograph but taken from a different position. Note the overlapping of the joists on the interior framed partition in the foreground of this picture. Subflooring has been laid diagonally while the exterior wall sheathing has been placed on the exterior wall studding in a horizontal position.

Ceiling joists and picture-window framing: Ceiling joists, 2″ x 6″ in size, and of 2″ x 12″ window headers. Note the precise method of toenailing the joists into a double header and the diagonally laid subflooring and sheathing boards. Various members are: 1, subflooring; 2, scaffolding and supports; 3, window header; 4, double studding at window opening; 5, double header to support ceiling joists; 6, ceiling joists; 7, exterior wall sheathing; 8, rafter; 9, roof boards.

Ceiling joists and roof-framing assembly: An illustration of carefully framed rafters, ceiling joists, and outside wall studding. The several members are: 1, ceiling joist splice plate; 2, outside wall stud; 3, double plate; 4, gable stud header; 5, gable stud; 6, ceiling joist; 7, rafter truss; 8, common rafter; 9, louver casing; 10, plumb cut at rafter edge.

REAR ELEVATION

LEFT SIDE ELEVATION

0   5   10   15   20
SCALE IN FEET

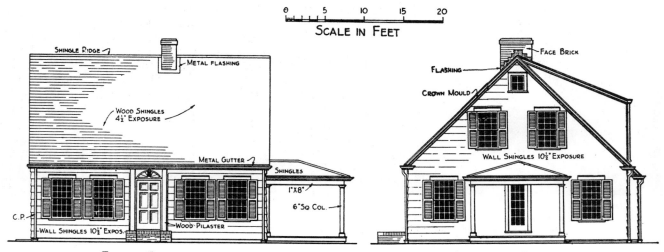

FRONT ELEVATION

RIGHT SIDE ELEVATION

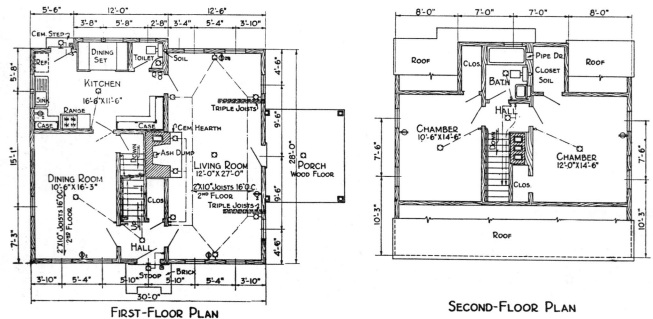

FIRST-FLOOR PLAN

SECOND-FLOOR PLAN

ELEVATIONS AND FLOOR PLANS.

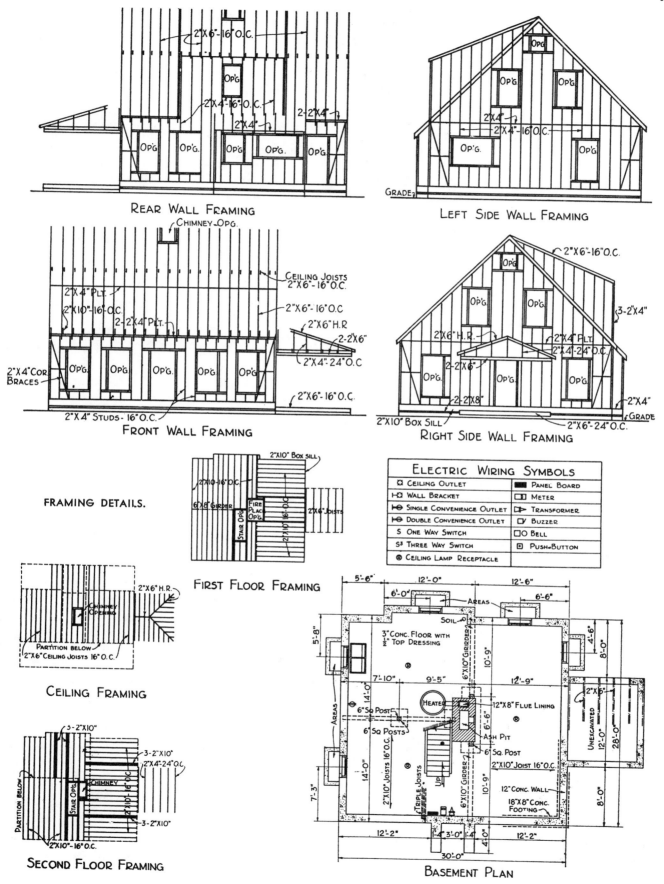

REAR WALL FRAMING

LEFT SIDE WALL FRAMING

FRONT WALL FRAMING

RIGHT SIDE WALL FRAMING

FRAMING DETAILS.

FIRST FLOOR FRAMING

CEILING FRAMING

SECOND FLOOR FRAMING

ELECTRIC WIRING SYMBOLS

Symbol	Name	Symbol	Name
Ceiling Outlet		Panel Board	
Wall Bracket		Meter	
Single Convenience Outlet		Transformer	
Double Convenience Outlet		Buzzer	
S One Way Switch		Bell	
S³ Three Way Switch		Push-Button	
Ceiling Lamp Receptacle			

BASEMENT PLAN

13

Roof Framing

In dwelling construction roofs should combine beauty and utility. Careful workmanship is required to achieve this, since roof framing offers some difficult problems in construction. This chapter presents typical roof framing problems as clearly as possible.

Refer to the set of house plans and note the type of roof designed for the building. The following illustrations show a gable roof in perspective and in elevation.

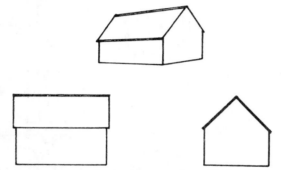

Perspective, front and side elevation of a gabled roof house.

One sheet of the plans usually shows the roof framing details and gives the following information:

    a. Width of building from outside edges of plates or sheathing.

    b. The size (thickness and width) of stock to be used as rafters and ridge material.

    c. The pitch of the roof.

    d. The scale used in making the drawings.

    e. The number and different kinds of rafters to be used, such as common, hip, valley, hip jack, valley jack or cripple jack rafters.

    f. Type of scuttle, if any; type of chimney; and type of dormer framing.

    g. Any other construction details on or dealing with the roof.

Obtain from the set of plans all possible items of information about the roof. Be certain to know the name and location of each item illustrated in the framing details.

The following steps of procedure deal with the framing of a gable roof. For detailed information about the procedure in framing a hip, gambrel,

mansard, etc., type of roof refer to the subsequent studies.

Obtain the carpenter's steel framing square and hold it in both hands. Hold the larger part in the left hand and the smaller part in the right hand. The part held in the left hand is called the body, beam, or blade, and is the larger and longer part. The part held in the right hand is called the tongue and is the smaller or shorter part.

The two parts, the blade and the tongue, come together or are held in place at a corner, or heel, or at an angle equal to one-fourth of a circle. This angle is one-fourth of 360 degrees, or 90 degrees. It is also a right angle.

Obtain a carpenter's pencil and carefully sharpen it to a flat, wedge-shaped point. Read the following steps taken to lay off a common rafter and then follow each step carefully.

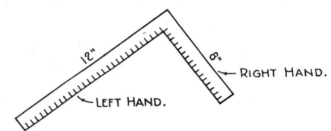

Hold the steel square as shown above.

Obtain a piece of 2″ x 8″ or 2″ x 10″ stock, random length, and place it on the sawhorses. Lay the stock with the width flat on the horses. Take the steel square and place the blade against the edge of the stock and the tongue across the width of the stock. Hold the tool firmly in place with one hand and mark a line with the pencil across the face of the width of the stock at the outside edge of the tongue.

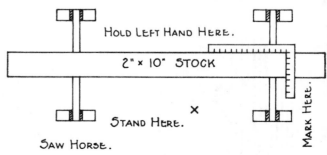

Marking off one end of the rafter stock for squaring.

Mark the other end of the stock in like manner after measuring the required length. The length can be marked off with two-foot rule, the steel line, or the steel square. When making a great many markings with the rule or steel square be certain to make each marking accurate.

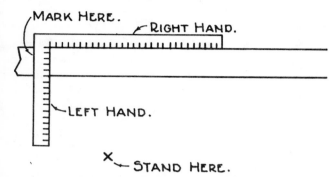

Mark off other end of the rafter stock for squaring.

After marking is made, place square carefully to one side, obtain a crosscut saw and cut off the ends of the stock on the outside of the pencil lines.

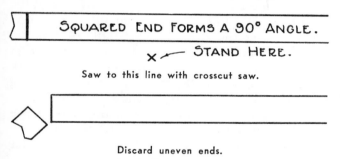

SQUARED END FORMS A 90° ANGLE.

×— STAND HERE.

Saw to this line with crosscut saw.

Discard uneven ends.

In actual practice the uneven ends of a rafter will be removed when the pattern for the rafter has been laid out and the slant cut has been made. The foregoing is given in order to acquaint the apprentice with the use, feel, and importance of the steel square and to give practice in the use of the ruler or measure in laying out distances.

Refer again to the house plans and note the figure or drawing indicating the rise per foot of run of the common rafter. This information is generally shown on the plans in the following manner.

The illustration shows the rise of the rafter is 8" and the run of the rafter is 12". Take the steel

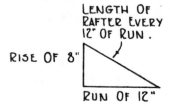

LENGTH OF RAFTER EVERY 12" OF RUN.

RISE OF 8"

RUN OF 12"

Graphic information found on roof layout of house plans.

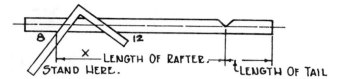

LENGTH OF RAFTER

LENGTH OF TAIL

STAND HERE.

square and locate number 12 on the tongue and number 8 on the blade. Hold the square as shown in the illustration at the left. Move figures 8 and 12 over the width face of rafter until each figure is over the edge nearest you. Note the position in the illustration. Make a short pencil mark as indicated in the following illustration.

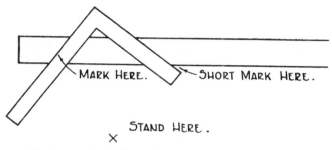

MARK HERE. SHORT MARK HERE.

STAND HERE.

The first marked-off position of cut for common rafter.

Move the steel square over to the right until the figure 8 on the square is over the first mark made by the figure 12. Repeat these marks as many times as there are whole feet (12") in the run of the rafter. The run of the rafter is half of the span of the rafter, or half the distance the rafter is to extend before it rests against the common rafter placed on the other side of the building. The following illustration shows how the successive markings are made. Continue to mark off the 8 and 12 markings, until the number of whole feet in the run are reached.

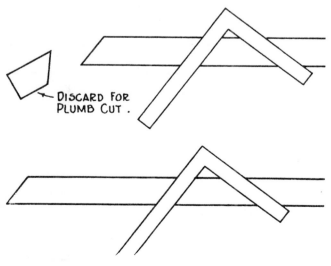

DISCARD FOR PLUMB CUT.

Successive marking for whole feet in run of rafter.

The plumb cut is the first slanting line made at the first figure 8 which is to be cut, as indicated when the whole rafter is laid out. The several markings are made for the number of whole feet of run of the common rafter. Then, if there are any fractions of an inch in the run, these inches, or the distance less than 12 inches, must be measured from the last mark along the edge of the rafter nearest you and the slanting line. This will form the seat cut. The following illustration shows the placing of the last whole number mark and the method of moving over the number of inches, always less than 12, to find the place to mark the first slanting line for the seat cut.

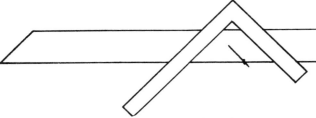

Marking off the fraction of a foot of run for seat cut.

The slanting line, so marked, will take on a slant opposite that of the plumb line—the line first marked at the extreme left-hand side. This line forms the first line of the layout of the seat cut.

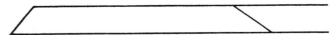

The seat cut or first cut of bird's-mouth cut.

With the blade against the edge of the stock and the tongue at right angles to the face of the rafter, mark a line intersecting the last line made. This will give the center of the width of the rafter.

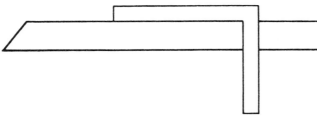

Mark off the center of the width of the rafter.

Marking off the center width of the rafter will produce a cross mark as shown in the following illustration.

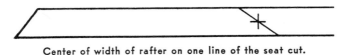

Center of width of rafter on one line of the seat cut.

Move the square to the right and make a slanting line across the face of the rafter, along the left side of the square (8″) which intersects the center of the rafter at the point just previously made.

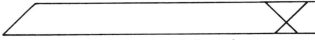

Layout of seat cut or bird's-mouth cut.

The seat cut can then be cut along these lines. This is not done, however, until the entire pattern of the common rafter is laid out. The following illustration shows the common rafter with the portion removed, which thus forms the seat cut.

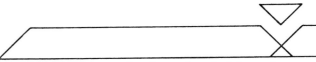

Forming the seat cut and removing stock by sawing.

The last mark to make on the common rafter is the slanting mark for the tail cut, the portion of the rafter extending beyond the seat cut. This slanting line is in the same direction as that of the plumb cut. It can be made by moving the framing square along the distance or length of the tail piece, and scribing or marking along the edge of the square at the figure 8. However, one may mark on the other side of the rafter pattern by placing the square in the position as shown in the following diagram. This is done when the rafter piece is not long enough to support the square when moving it along so that the slanting line, under figure 8, may be marked while the rafter piece supports the square.

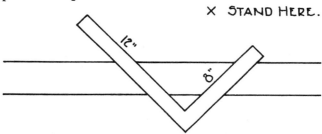

Position taken for final mark for the tail length cut.

After the slanting line for the tail cut is made, the complete rafter pattern is laid out except a short cut made on the plumb-line cut for a distance of half the thickness of the ridge piece. The ridge piece runs along the center of the meeting places of the common rafters and provides a nailing piece for all the common rafters which rest against it. The following illustration shows the cut allowed for half the thickness of the ridge piece, together with the seat cut and the tail cut.

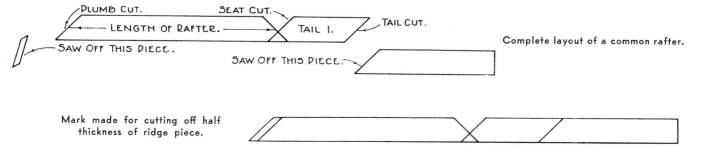

Complete layout of a common rafter.

This final illustration shows the complete pattern for laying off the cuts on a common rafter. Note that the plumb cut, the seat cut, and the slant cut are in the same position and on the same slant. Note that the length of the rafter is from the plumb cut to the seat cut. This is the portion of the rafter running from the ridge to the plate on the top of the outside studded wall. The tail length is the overhang of the roof from the outside wall to the eave and represents the overhang of the roof from the side of the outside wall of the building. This pattern can now be cut and marked as a pattern and used for laying off the other common rafters of like length.

Ceiling joists and rafters may be estimated by actual count or by the square. Reading again the method used in estimating first-floor joists, this method can be used for second floor joists for either steel or wooden members. In estimating joists by the square it is found that 126 board feet of 2″ x 8″ material will be required if placed 16″ cc and can be built up in about 20 hours. 2″ x 10″ joists placed 16″ cc will require 160 board feet to the square and can be built up in about 24 hours.

Rafters for gable roofs can be estimated by the count or square. In estimating by the count, the length of the plate on which the rafters rest can be divided by 16″, or by the number of inches the rafters are placed cc. In estimating by the square one can use 100 board feet of 2″ by 6″ stock every square if placed 16″ cc. This will take 24 hours to build up.

Estimate the number of rafters and time required to build up the framed roof of either a wooden-framed or a steel-framed roof. Draw the illustrations of the rafter layout of a house in the accompanying set of plans or any other rafter layout. Refer to layouts in this chapter.

In the first part of this chapter detailed steps are given in the framing or laying off of a common rafter by the use of the steel square. This study will deal with all other common uses of the steel square.

———

INTRODUCTORY DESCRIPTION OF THE STEEL SQUARE. The steel square consists of three parts: the *body,* the *tongue,* and the *heel.* The body is 24″ long and about 2″ wide. The tongue is 16″ or 18″ long and about 1-1/2″ wide. The heel is the outside corner formed by the meeting of the body and the tongue.

PROJECT: Hold the steel square in the hands, with body in the left hand and the tongue in the right hand. Make a small sketch of the square naming the three parts, place of left hand and of right hand and position of standing.

THE STEEL SQUARE, ITS RELATION TO ANGLES AND DEGREES. To repeat, the steel square (body and tongue) is in the form of a right angle, or 1/4 of a circle. A circle contains 360 degrees. If the body of the square is placed on a table with the tongue swung above vertically, the body would form the base, the tongue the altitude and the line (an imaginary one connecting the ends of the tongue and body) would form the hypotenuse of a right-angle triangle.

PROJECT: Place on table as designated. Locate the base, altitude, and hypotenuse. Make a small sketch of the square, naming the base, altitude, and hypotenuse. Sketch the three remaining right angles and place a circle around entire four angles. Designate degrees in entire circle and in each right angle.

THE DIVISIONS OF THE INCH FOUND ON THE OUTER AND INNER EDGES OF THE FACE AND BACK OF SQUARE. If the steel square (Stanley 100) is held with the body in the *left* hand and the tongue in the *right* hand, the observer will find the following scales:

Front of square—

On the body—outside edge—inches and 1/16″
On the body—inside edge—inches and 1/8″
On the tongue—outside edge—inches and 1/16″
On the tongue—inside edge—inches and 1/8″

Now if the square is held with the body in the *right* hand and the tongue in the *left* hand, the following scales will be observed:

Back of square—

On the body—outside edge—inches and 1/12″
On the body—inside edge—inches and 1/32″
On the tongue—outside edge—inches and 1/12″
On the tongue—inside edge—inches and 1/10″

PROJECT: Hold the steel square in your hands as described so that the face is toward you. Observe scales on body and tongue. Make a sketch of the square and indicate the scales found on the face. Likewise make another sketch and indicate the scales found on the back of the square. All measurements on the outer edge begin at the heel; on the inner edge, at the interior angle.

THE HUNDREDTH SCALE. There is, most generally, on the back of the square a small table showing the inch divided into 100 equal parts. This enables the user to obtain any part of an inch, such as 1/100, 1/50, 3/100, 1/25, 1/20, 3/50, 7/100, etc.

PROJECT: Hold the body of the square in the right hand and the tongue in the left hand. In the corner of the heel there is a scale, 1″, divided into equal parts. Obtain a divider, take off spaces or units of measure from this scale, and draw lines, one each, the following lengths: 1/25″, 1/2″ 4/100″. 76/100″, 98/100″, 13/100″, 10/100″, 35/100″ and 1/50″.

THE ESSEX BOARD MEASURE. There is, most generally, on the back of the square a large series of tables, the use of which will enable one to obtain the number of board feet in any given piece of stock. These tables are called the Essex board measure. The inch markings along the outer edge of the square which are above the board-measure tables are used with the tables. Calculations are begun with a board 1″ thick and 12″ wide.

PROJECT: Place the tongue of the square in the left hand and the body in the right hand. Locate series of board measure tables along entire length of body. Follow these steps to use the tables:

a. Locate 12″ mark on outer edge of body.
b. Under this mark locate figure representing the length of the board for which the board measure is desired.
c. Along the outer edge on the same scale of inch graduations locate the figure representing the width of the board.
d. Drop down from this figure to line having the length figure under 12″ mark and this figure will give the board measurement of the stock.

PROJECT: Find the board measure of the following pieces of stock: one piece, 1″ x 11″ x 8′; two pieces 1/2″ x 51/2″ x 4′; one piece 13/4″ x 15″ x 22′; five pieces, 23/4″ x 8″ x 16′; one piece, 2″ x 10″ x 12′.

THE OCTAGON SCALE. There is, most generally, a scale on the face of the tongue. By use of this scale one can construct an eight-sided figure. This scale is called the octagon scale.

PROJECT: Place the tongue of the steel square in the right hand and the body in the left hand. Locate the octagon scale along center of tongue. Follow these steps to use this scale:

a. Draw a square 6″ to a side.
b. Produce bisectors through base and sides.
c. By use of a divider, take as many units from the scale on the square as there are inches in the width of the figure.
d. Lay off this length on both sides of the four points of intersection of bisectors passing through four sides of figure.
e. Connect points obtained to form eight-sided figure.

THE BRACE SCALE. There is, most generally, on the back of the tongue of the square a scale which gives the exact length of common braces.

PROJECT: Place the tongue of the square in the left hand and the body in the right hand. Locate the brace scale or brace measure along the center of tongue. If base and altitude are known, the length of the hypotenuse or brace can be found on the brace table. Follow these steps to use this scale:

a. What is length and height of brace? Locate these two figures on scale.
b. Opposite these two figures is given the length of brace.
c. Lay off brace, on paper or 2″ x 6″ stock, having the following units for each brace: 39-39, 48-48, 18-24, 33-33, 24-24.

TYPES OF ROOFS: The gable, gambrel, and lean-to roofs are the ones most generally used in house construction. It is good to be able to illustrate several types of roof shapes.

PROJECT: Sketch, in perspective, the several types of roofs shown below in orthographic.

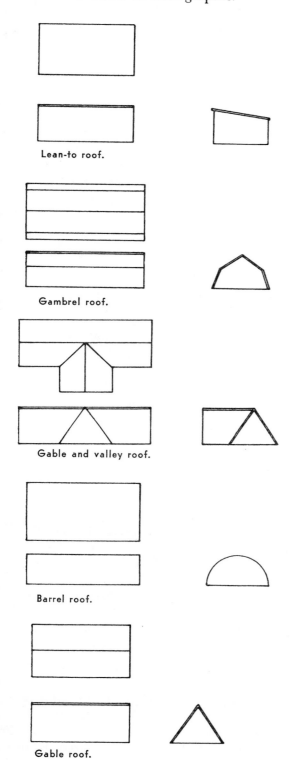

Lean-to roof.

Gambrel roof.

Gable and valley roof.

Barrel roof.

Gable roof.

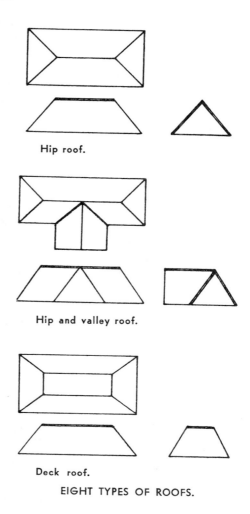

Hip roof.

Hip and valley roof.

Deck roof.

EIGHT TYPES OF ROOFS.

ROOF TERMS. A simple gable roof has several important parts which are mentioned in this roof framing discussion. The parts and terms are illustrated on page 100.

PROJECT: Given the width of the building as 24' 6", the pitch as 1/4, find the run, rise, and length of a common rafter from center of ridge to outside of plate. Add an additional 18" of length to the rafter for the length of the tail overhang.

WHAT IS MEANT BY PITCH OF ROOF. In addition to learning some typical types of roofs and typical roof terms it is important to learn exactly what is meant by roof pitch.

The illustration on page 100 shows the more important roof pitches. Note the rise per foot of roof run is merely the vertical distance in relation to the horizontal distance expressed to give an idea of the slant of the roof. Note that *pitch* means merely the slant height of the roof and is always obtained by dividing the span or building width by the **rise**.

PROJECT: Illustrate a roof with a span of 24′ 0″ and have one-fourth pitch. Show the rise of the roof. Draw to center lines. What is meant by pitch, span, and rise per foot of run, and what are the most common pitches of roofs?

TYPES OF RAFTERS. Before learning how to mark off and cut various types of rafters it is important to learn the names and shapes of several typical roof members.

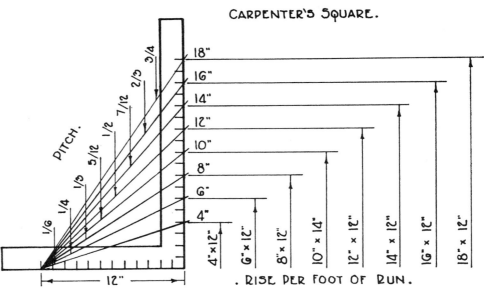

CARPENTER'S SQUARE.

The carpenter's square and roof pitches.

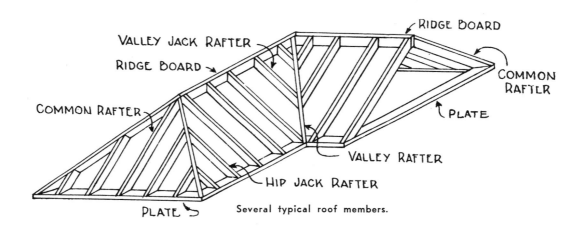

Several typical roof members.

PROJECT: From the above drawing, which is done in oblique, draw the top view (plan) and label each different rafter as shown above.

TYPES OF RAFTER CUTS. After learning the names and shapes of several typical roof members, it is important to learn the typical types of rafter cuts. The following illustration shows three types of rafter cuts: heel, plumb, and side. These cuts are known by many other names, but a little thought will show their basic relations one with another, regardless of name.

PROJECT: From the drawing, which is done in oblique, draw the top view (plan) and the side view. Label each different rafter cut.

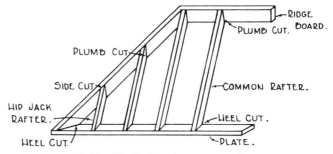

A hip, hip jack and common rafter.

LENGTH-PER-FOOT-OF-RUN. The term *length per foot of run* means simply this: The slant distance in a combination of horizontal and vertical directions, or the length in space acquired by an over and up movement. If, in the case of the common rafter, we imagine the run to be the base of a right-angled triangle, the rise to be the altitude, and the length to be the hypotenuse, we can state this: Base is always 1' of run, altitude always rise per foot of run and hypotenuse always length per foot of run.

PROJECT: Construct a true right-angle triangle, making the base 12″ or properly scaled down to fit on drawing paper. Refer to page 99, make the pitch of this triangle one-third, complete the hypotenuse or length per foot of run, and complete the rise per foot of run. What is the length of the rafter?

TRUE LENGTH OF A COMMON RAFTER. Controversy need not arise over a definite understanding of the *true length* of a rafter, for it is agreed that the true length of a common rafter is the shortest distance between the outer edge of the plate and a point on the center line of the ridge. This true length may be thought of as the hypotenuse of a right-angled triangle or as the measuring line which runs parallel to the top edge of the rafter. A common mistake is in thinking the true length of a rafter is measured on a line extending from the top of the plate to the top of the ridge.

PROJECT: Produce the end view of a gable rafter showing plate common rafter, and ridge. On this drawing show the correct measuring line for a common rafter.

APPLYING THE SQUARE TO FIND THE LENGTH OF A COMMON RAFTER. (This has been explained.)

LENGTH OF COMMON RAFTER AS GIVEN ON THE SQUARE. In addition to the use of the steel square in finding the length of a common rafter, the table on the square may be used. Obtain a steel square, find the face of the body. Refer to the series of rafter tables. The first table given is *length of main rafters per foot of run*. To find the length of a common rafter per foot of run, obtain the rise of the roof per foot of run. This will be given in inches. On the face of the square obtain the figure in the inch line equal to the figure of the rise per foot of run. On the first line under this inch figure will be found a figure which will be the length of the common rafter per foot of run. Multiply this figure by the run of the building, which produces the length of the rafter from ridge to plate. Deduct one-half thickness of ridge board and true length is found.

PROJECT: Find the length of a common rafter having a rise of 8″ per foot of run on a building 24' wide. What is the length of the rafter? What is the true length?

Hip rafter. Forms the intersection of an external roof angle.

Jack rafter. Spans the distance from a wall plate to a hip or from a valley to a ridge.

Common rafter. One having the top cut supported by the ridge and the bottom or seat cut resting on the wall plate.

Cripple jack rafter. Extends from a valley rafter to a hip rafter at an angle of 90 degrees to the ridge board.

Curb rafter. The upper rafter of a mansard roof.

False rafter. A framing member forming the gable.

Hip jack rafter. A shortened common rafter with the seat cut resting on the wall plate and the cheek cut resting against the side of the hip rafter.

Hip valley cripple jack rafter. One framed between a hip and valley, having two beveled cheek cuts but no seat cut.

Ornamental, exposed rafter. One framed in an open cornice.

Valley rafter. Forms and supports the valley in an intersecting roof. It has a beveled plumb cut at the upper end and a seat cut at the lower end.

Valley cripple jack. One framed between the short end and supporting valley rafter having a cheek cut, at opposite angles, on each end.

Valley jack rafter. Forms part of a valley having a top cut fastened to the ridge and a bottom cheek cut fastened to the side of the valley rafter.

OTHER CUTS ON COMMON RAFTERS. In addition to the plumb-line cut and seat cut on a full-length common rafter there are shortened common rafters or jack rafters taking a bevel or hip cut instead of the side or bevel cut and the other, the length cut, the usual ridge plumb cut. The heel cut or plate cut or bird's-mouth cut of a jack rafter is obtained in the same way as for the full-length common rafter. The plumb cut or ridge cut of jack rafter is obtained the same way as for the full-length common rafter.

However, there are two differences between the cuts on a common rafter and those on a jack rafter. One is which is shorter than a full-length common rafter.

The side or bevel cut is obtained by referring to the rafter table on the face of the square. The line 'side cut of jacks use the marks' will give the figure to use with 12 on the square. If the rise per foot of run of the roof is 8″ refer to the figure in this line under 8. This is 10, and with 10 on outside of square and 12 on outside of square (tongue), lay off bevel cut.

PROJECT: Lay off the side or bevel cut on a common jack rafter leaving a rise of 8″ per foot of run.

Lay off the seat cut. The length of a common jack rafter is found by using the table placed on the steel square. If jack rafters are placed 16″ cc use the line 'difference in length of jacks 16″ centers'. In the inch line on edge of square find the figure indicating the rise per foot of run of common rafter and under this figure in the 'difference in length of jacks 16″ centers' line find the figure indicating the length of the first jack rafter. For each succeeding jack rafter add this figure once. Lay off the length of the jack rafter. For any length deduct one-half the diagonal thickness of the hip or valley rafter.

LOCATION OF HIP AND VALLEY RAFTERS. Refer to types of rafters and learn the appearance and location of hip and valley rafters.

To find the length of a hip rafter one takes the constant 17″, instead of 12″, on the framing square.

SIDE CUTS ON HIP AND VALLEY RAFTERS In addition to the method of laying off and cutting a hip rafter as stated in "location of hip and valley rafters" there is another cut known as the side or bevel cut to be made when a hip rafter frames itself into a ridge. Refer to the face of the steel square and in line of rafter tables under inch mark (rise per foot of run) find a figure. Use this figure on body of square and 12″ on tongue of square to lay off the side cut.

PROJECT: Place side cut on hip rafter.

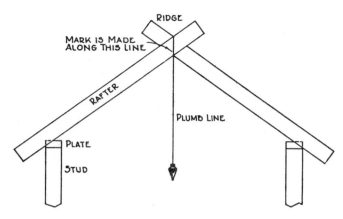

Showing two rafters with plumb line indicating place of ridge cut.

RIDGE DEDUCTION FOR HIP OR VALLEY RAFTERS. The ridge deduction for a hip or valley rafter is the same as for a common rafter except that half the diagonal thickness of the ridge must be used instead of half the actual thickness.

PROJECT: Deduct for ridge piece on rafter (hip or valley) as laid off and framed in the above sections on location of hip and valley rafters, and on side cuts on hip and valley rafters.

NOTE—For roof framing for air-conditioning installation, see Chapter 14—Heating Installations and Air-Conditioning.

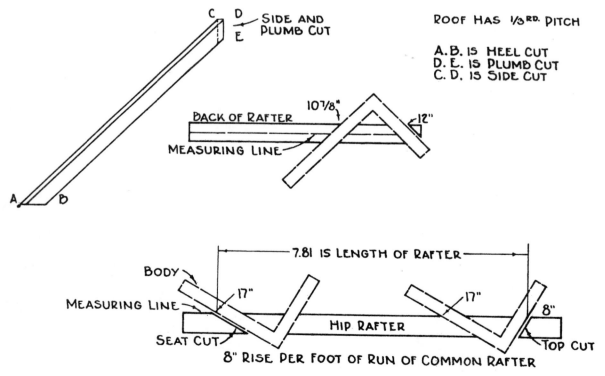

ROOF HAS 1/3RD. PITCH

A.B. IS HEEL CUT
D.E. IS PLUMB CUT
C.D. IS SIDE CUT

RIDGE DEDUCTIONS FOR HIP OR VALLEY RAFTERS.

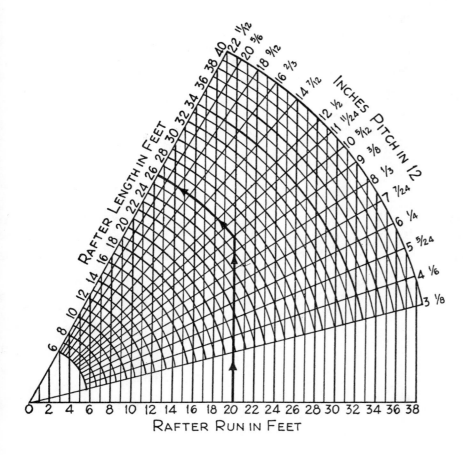

To find the rafter length when its run and pitch are known, follow the vertical line from the run to its intersection with the radial line of the pitch. From the intersection follow the curved line to the length. The diagram also may be used to determine the run when the length and pitch are known, or to determine the pitch when the length and run are known. Example: For a run of 20 feet and a pitch of 10 in 12, the length of the rafter is read directly from the diagram as 26 feet.

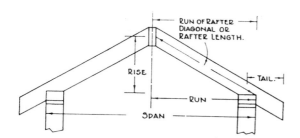

Principal items in gable roof construction.

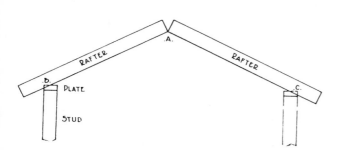

Common rafters brought together at "A" indicating need of a plumb cut.

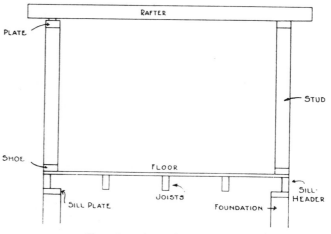

Elevation of simple shed roof.

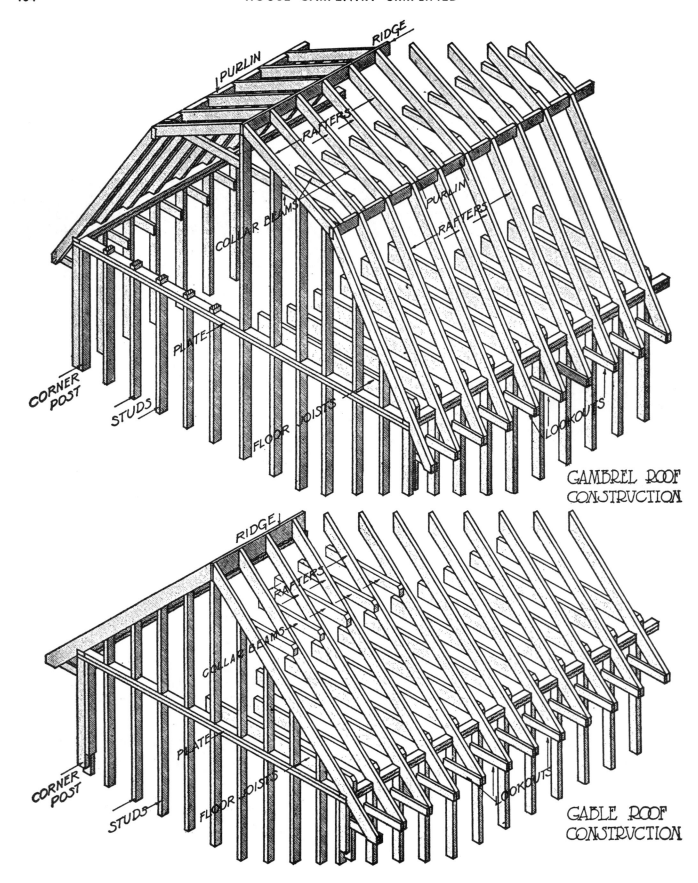

GAMBREL ROOF
CONSTRUCTION

GABLE ROOF
CONSTRUCTION

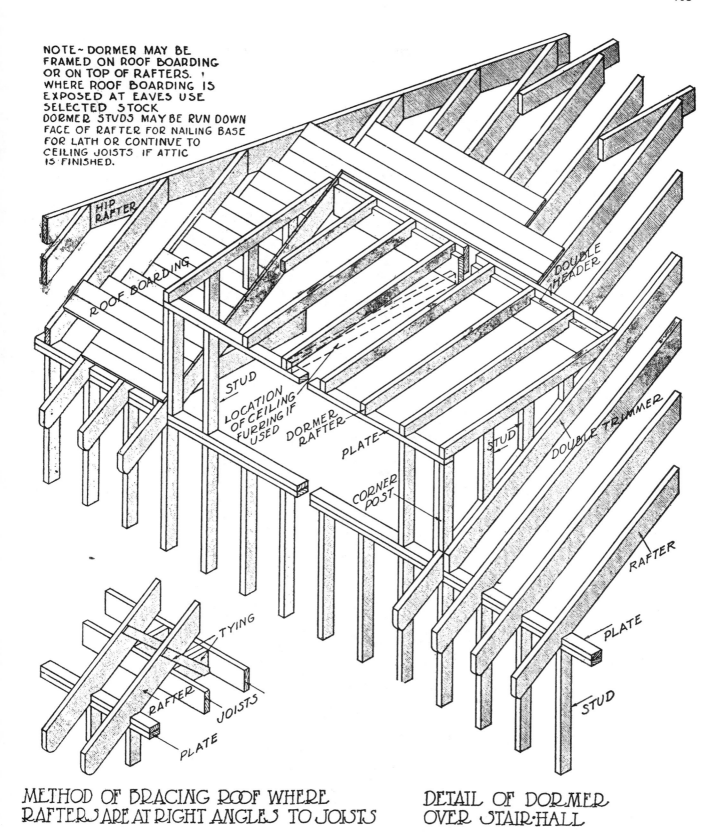

NOTE~ DORMER MAY BE
FRAMED ON ROOF BOARDING
OR ON TOP OF RAFTERS. '
WHERE ROOF BOARDING IS
EXPOSED AT EAVES USE
SELECTED STOCK
DORMER STUDS MAY BE RUN DOWN
FACE OF RAFTER FOR NAILING BASE
FOR LATH OR CONTINUE TO
CEILING JOISTS IF ATTIC
IS FINISHED.

HIP RAFTER

ROOF BOARDING

DOUBLE HEADER

STUD

LOCATION OF CEILING FURRING IF USED

DORMER RAFTER

PLATE

DOUBLE TRIMMER

CORNER POST

STUD

RAFTER

PLATE

STUD

TYING

RAFTER

JOISTS

PLATE

METHOD OF BRACING ROOF WHERE
RAFTERS ARE AT RIGHT ANGLES TO JOISTS

DETAIL OF DORMER
OVER STAIR·HALL

DORMER FRAMING OVER STAIR HALL.

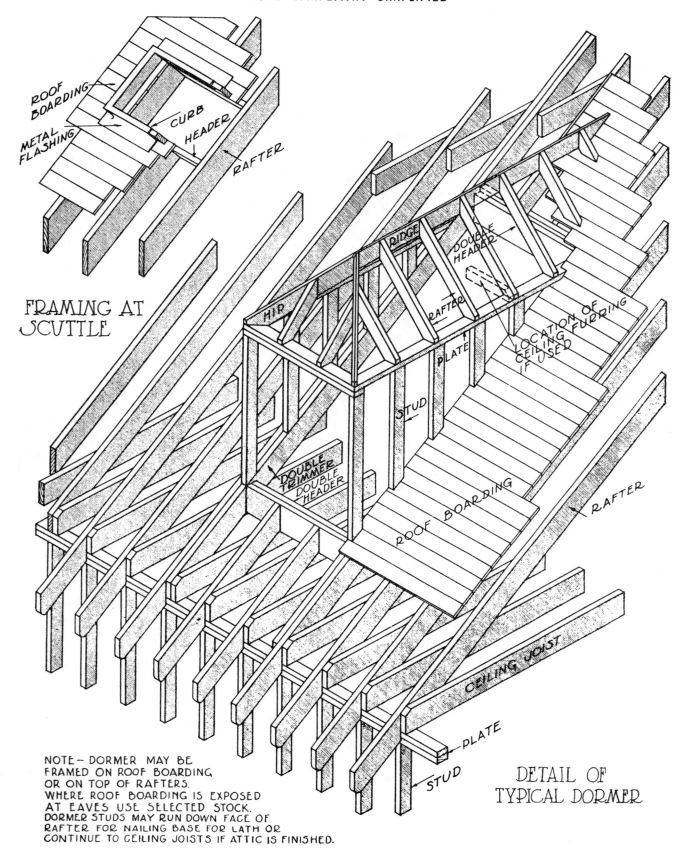

ROOF BOARDING

METAL FLASHING

CURB

HEADER

RAFTER

FRAMING AT SCUTTLE

RIDGE

DOUBLE HEADER

HIP

RAFTER

PLATE

STUD

LOCATION OF CEILING FURRING IF USED

DOUBLE TRIMMER

DOUBLE HEADER

ROOF BOARDING

RAFTER

CEILING JOIST

PLATE

STUD

DETAIL OF TYPICAL DORMER

NOTE— DORMER MAY BE
FRAMED ON ROOF BOARDING
OR ON TOP OF RAFTERS.
WHERE ROOF BOARDING IS EXPOSED
AT EAVES USE SELECTED STOCK.
DORMER STUDS MAY RUN DOWN FACE OF
RAFTER FOR NAILING BASE FOR LATH OR
CONTINUE TO CEILING JOISTS IF ATTIC IS FINISHED.

DETAILS OF DORMER FRAMING.

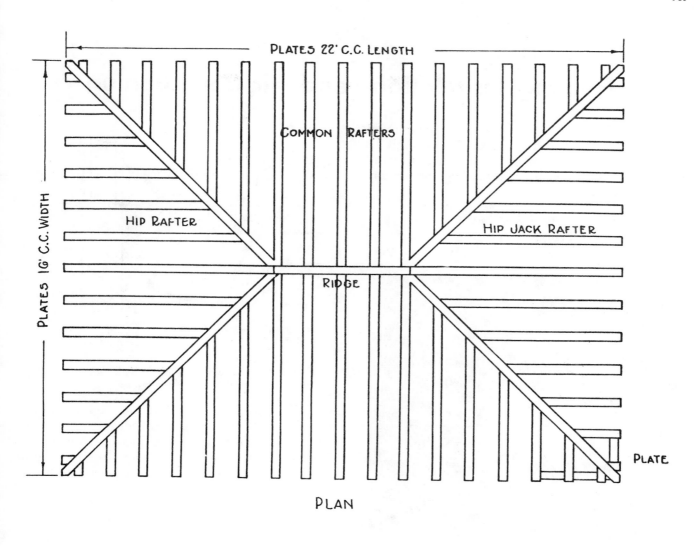

PLAN

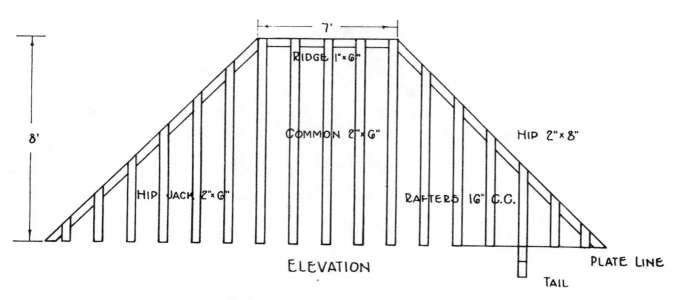

ELEVATION

PLAN AND ELEVATION OF A HIP ROOF SHOWING RAFTER LAYOUT.

14

Heating Installations and Air Conditioning

Elements of this chapter of course require reference to various other chapters of the book. This grouping here has been made in order to avoid multiplicity of presentation of heating and air-conditioning details.

Radiant Heating

The major problem in the heating of a basementless house is to obtain warm, draft-free conditions

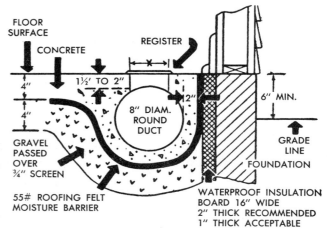

A sectional view of a method of placing a perimeter heating duct in a basementless house.

Ceiling radiant heating installation.

near the floor. Regardless of the type of heating to be used, the first step in this direction in a slab-on-ground type of house is to provide some type of insulation under the floor or along the foundation wall. As a minimum, this insulation should be one inch in thickness. It should prevent direct contact of concrete floor slab and foundation, and should extend down along the foundation to at least 12 inches below the grade level or under the floor for a mini-

A typical floor heating coil installation. The serpentine coil is made of ¾-inch black iron pipe on 12-inch centers. Joints are welded. Gravel fill is covered with weatherproof membrane. L-type insulation is used along exposed edges of floor. Pipes are ready to be covered with sand aggregate cement. Cement should enclose pipes with at least 1¼ inch over top of pipe.

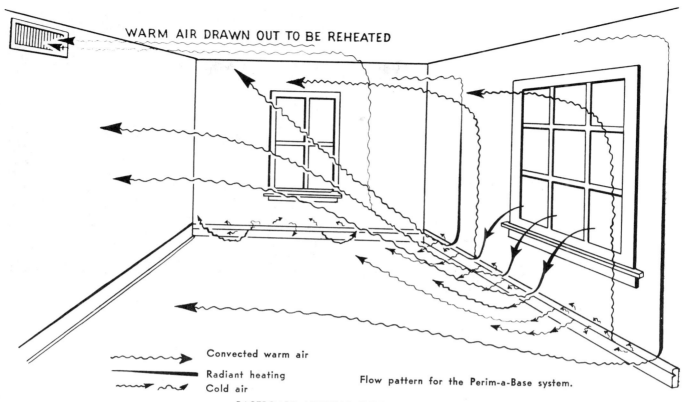

WARM AIR DRAWN OUT TO BE REHEATED

~~~~~~→ Convected warm air

——→ Radiant heating

~~~~~→ Cold air

Flow pattern for the Perim-a-Base system.

BASEBOARD HEATING INSTALLATION.

Trane hot water baseboard convector with continuous opening: (1) Dirt seal prevents heat-stain on the walls. (2) One-piece back for easy installation. (3) Reverse curve at base replaces usual quarter round for easier housekeeping. (4) and (5) The fin-and-tube heating coil is suspended on hangers that permit free expansion with resulting fuel economy and silent operation. (6) Snap-on front. (7) Free-swinging dampers are optional, can be snapped on later, are held by a damper spring.

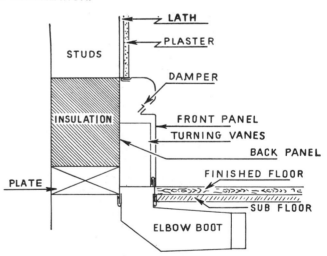

Typical installation of Perim-a-Base system.

mum distance of two feet. It is also advisable to provide a waterproof membrane under the entire floor area. For crawl space houses, especially if the crawl space is ventilated, the under side of the floor should be insulated.

Baseboard radiation consists of long, low units roughly approximating the conventional wooden baseboard in size and appearance. The units are designed so that hot water or steam can be circulated through them.

In a well-built house, baseboard heating, properly designed and installed, will guarantee warm floors and uniform, draft-free heat in all types of homes including slab-on-ground or crawl space basementless construction.

Fireplaces

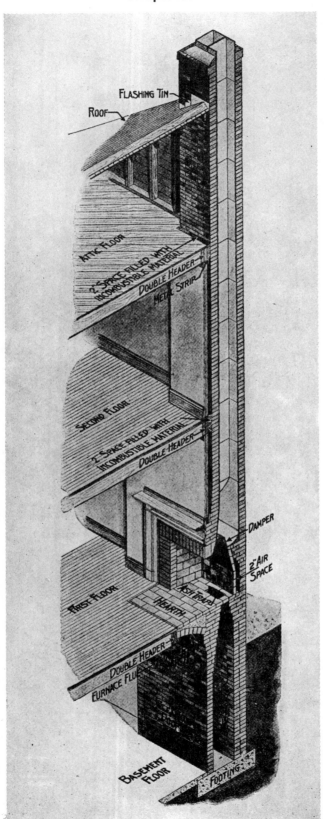

A properly built fireplace and chimney.

Rustic used-brick fireplace has separate openings for family room and living room, using same stack, acting as a room divider.

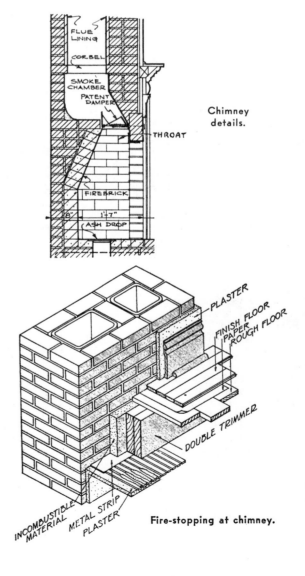

Chimney details.

Fire-stopping at chimney.

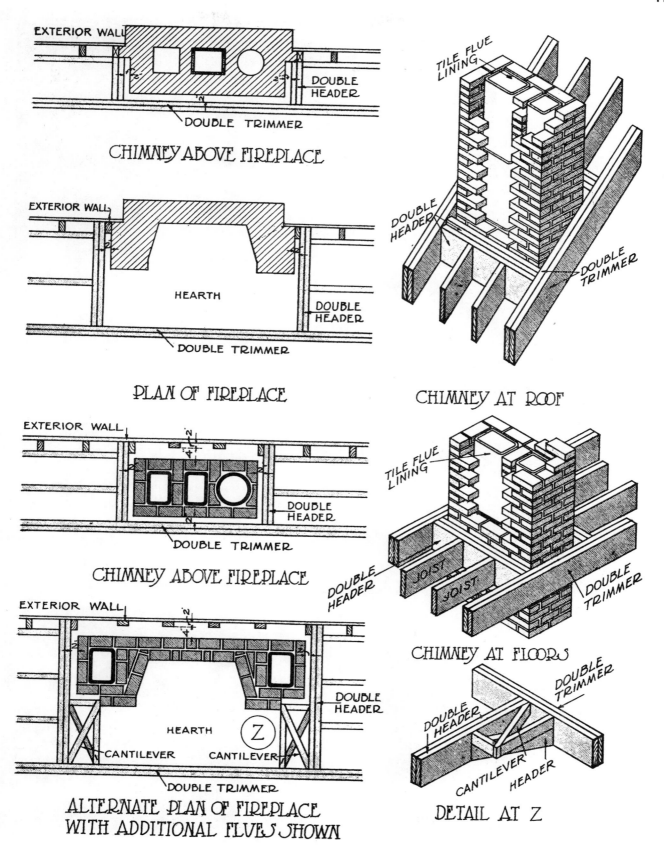

CHIMNEY ABOVE FIREPLACE

PLAN OF FIREPLACE

CHIMNEY ABOVE FIREPLACE

ALTERNATE PLAN OF FIREPLACE
WITH ADDITIONAL FLUES SHOWN

CHIMNEY AT ROOF

CHIMNEY AT FLOORS

DETAIL AT Z

FIREPLACE AND CHIMNEY FRAMING DETAILS.

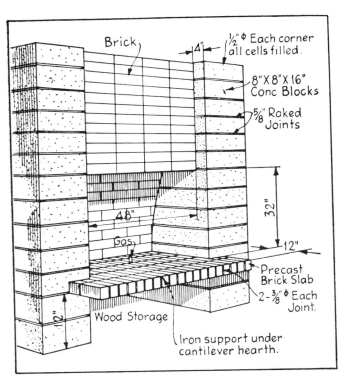

Cantilevered hearth.

The hearth slabs are made in one piece, with ⅜-inch steel reinforcement in the mortar joints, then set in place. The steel goes the entire depth of the hearth slab and also crosswise between the ends of the brick. The weight of the brick and steel supports the cantilevered portion, so that three or four persons could jump on it without damaging it.

Building the hearth slab: Units must be wet until a small dry egg is left in center when the brick is cut in two. In using common brick, submerse it totally from two to five minutes.

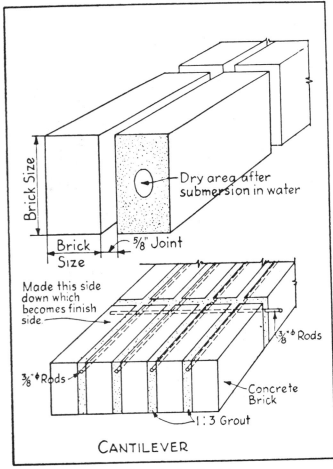

Building the hearth slab.

These two fireplaces were built by Alfred L. Tank, a Los Angeles mason contractor.

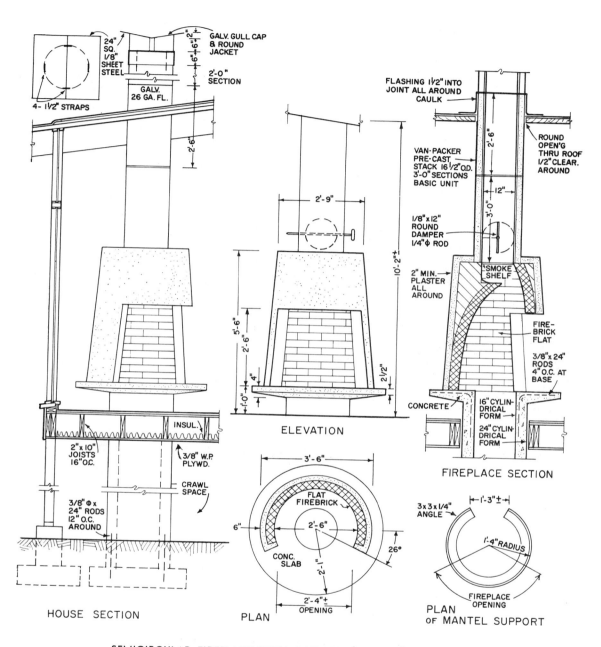

SEMICIRCULAR FIREPLACE WITH CAST CYLINDRICAL FOUNDATION.

With the availability of packaged chimneys and fireplaces, the design, construction and placement of today's fireplaces are limited only to the imagination of the designer. This fireplace, unusual in both appearance and construction, utilizes a pre-cast stack.

The fireplace features a circular reinforced concrete foundation. Two concentric Sonotube forms were used in construction. Support for the fireplace extends up through the insulated crawl space.

The fireplace was designed by Seattle architect Zema Baumgardner.

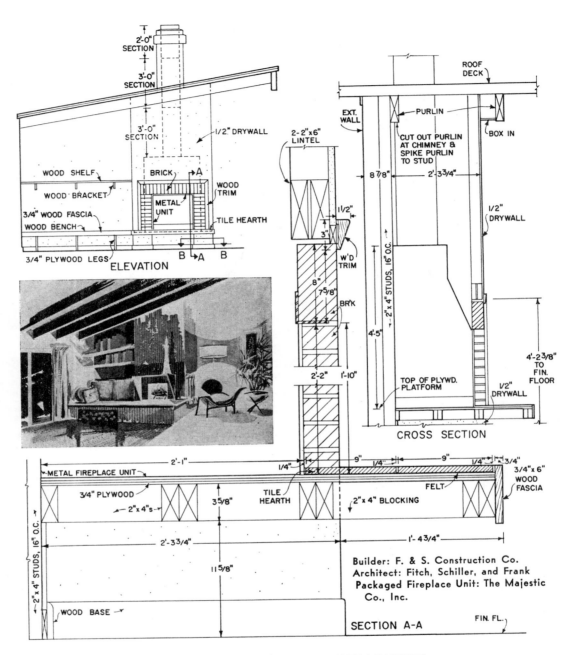

ELEVATION

CROSS SECTION

SECTION A-A

Builder: F. & S. Construction Co.
Architect: Fitch, Schiller, and Frank
Packaged Fireplace Unit: The Majestic Co., Inc.

PACKAGED FIREPLACE, BUILT CUSTOM FASHION.

Fireplaces have generally been expensive items in the construction of homes. Part of the cost was due to the heavy supporting structure necessary to carry its weight.

Now, with prefab chimneys and fireplaces, you can get fireplaces in homes at a lower cost. In the corner fireplace shown here, the metal unit was used as a basis, with the exterior built around it.

Each item used further developed the custom appearance.

The sketch shown varies slightly from the construction details. It shows 1/4-inch wood paneling instead of the 1/2-inch plasterboard indicated. The line of the hearth extends across to the wall coinciding with the edge of the built-in bench. The detail indicates the bench receded. The differences are interesting as possible alternate treatments.

Contemporary Fireplace Design.

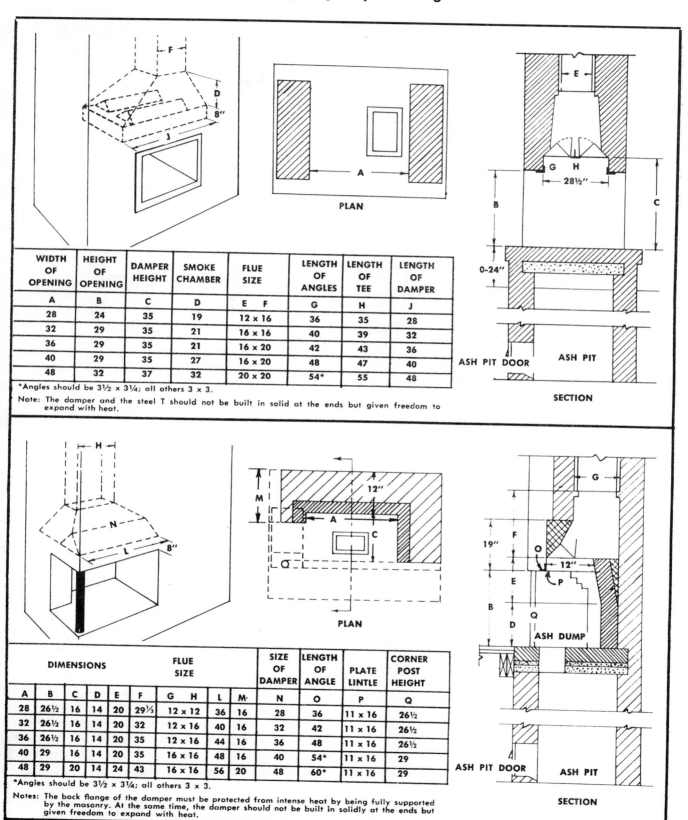

WIDTH OF OPENING	HEIGHT OF OPENING	DAMPER HEIGHT	SMOKE CHAMBER	FLUE SIZE		LENGTH OF ANGLES	LENGTH OF TEE	LENGTH OF DAMPER
A	B	C	D	E	F	G	H	J
28	24	35	19	12 x 16		36	35	28
32	29	35	21	16 x 16		40	39	32
36	29	35	21	16 x 20		42	43	36
40	29	35	27	16 x 20		48	47	40
48	32	37	32	20 x 20		54*	55	48

*Angles should be 3½ x 3¼; all others 3 x 3.

Note: The damper and the steel T should not be built in solid at the ends but given freedom to expand with heat.

PLAN

ASH PIT DOOR   ASH PIT

SECTION

DIMENSIONS						FLUE SIZE				SIZE OF DAMPER	LENGTH OF ANGLE	PLATE LINTLE	CORNER POST HEIGHT
A	B	C	D	E	F	G	H	L	M.	N	O	P	Q
28	26½	16	14	20	29⅓	12 x 12		36	16	28	36	11 x 16	26½
32	26½	16	14	20	32	12 x 16		40	16	32	42	11 x 16	26½
36	26½	16	14	20	35	12 x 16		44	16	36	48	11 x 16	26½
40	29	16	14	20	35	16 x 16		48	16	40	54*	11 x 16	29
48	29	20	14	24	43	16 x 16		56	20	48	60*	11 x 16	29

*Angles should be 3½ x 3¼; all others 3 x 3.

Notes: The back flange of the damper must be protected from intense heat by being fully supported by the masonry. At the same time, the damper should not be built in solidly at the ends but given freedom to expand with heat.

PLAN

ASH PIT DOOR   ASH PIT

SECTION

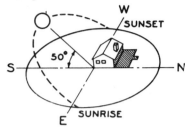

Orient the house so that major glass areas are to the north or south. Shield the west wall with a garage or carport when possible.

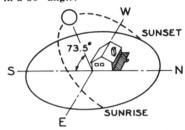

Position of the sun at noon on March 21st and September 21st in a latitude of 40° N. (Indianapolis, Ind.) results in a 50° angle.

Position of the sun at noon on June 21st in the same latitude (40° N.) results in a 73.5° angle.

ORIENTATION OF HOUSE.

Fences or tall hedges are good protection for east and west walls when the sun is low.

Canvas awnings can reduce the heat load on glass areas as much as 75%.

Trellis work with vines provides a "plant awning" in summer and allows winter sunshine to enter house.

Trees which shed their leaves provide shade in summer yet permit the winter sun to help warm the house.

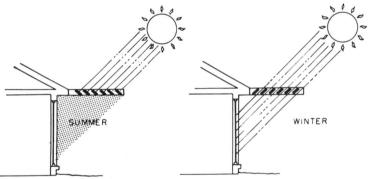

Overhangs with adjustable louvres provide accurate control throughout the year as they may be closed for summer shading and opened in the winter to take full advantage of the warm rays of the sun.

SHADING DEVICES.

Air-Conditioning Installation

An entire dwelling may be air-conditioned by the installation of a duct system between the ceiling joists and rafters. The conventional methods of framing a gable roof or a hip roof need not be altered for the proper and efficient installation of a duct system.

The perspective sketch, Fig. 1, shows the placing of the ducts and unit in a framed dwelling on conventional gable roof construction.

The cross section, Fig. 2, details the unit and a

portion of the supply and return ducts installed in the gable end of a roof and indicates the method of supporting by the ceiling joists. Note how the louver is housed into the outside wall of the gable end of the dwelling. Metal or wooden grilles of any design may be used and must be as open as possible to exchange the greatest amount of condenser air. No air conditioner will work well without adequate dissipation of the heat discharged from its condenser. The flush type of grille has a minimum size of 23″ high and 55″ wide and is so located that the bottom of the grille aligns with the base of the air conditioner.

Fig. 1

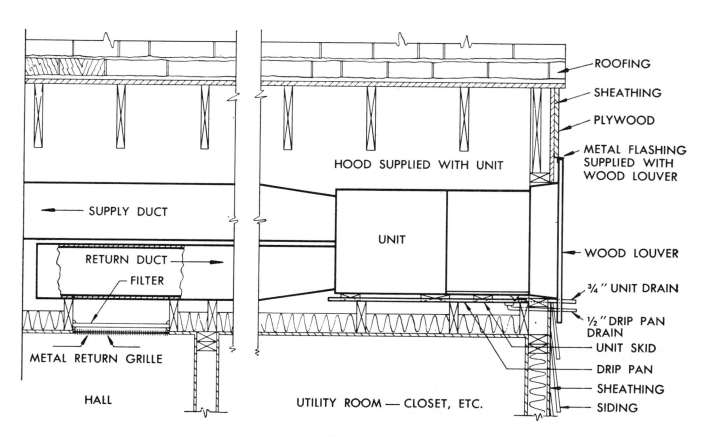

ROOFING

SHEATHING

PLYWOOD

METAL FLASHING
SUPPLIED WITH
WOOD LOUVER

HOOD SUPPLIED WITH UNIT

SUPPLY DUCT

UNIT

WOOD LOUVER

RETURN DUCT

FILTER

¾ " UNIT DRAIN

½ " DRIP PAN
DRAIN

UNIT SKID

DRIP PAN

METAL RETURN GRILLE

SHEATHING

SIDING

HALL

UTILITY ROOM — CLOSET, ETC.

Fig. 2

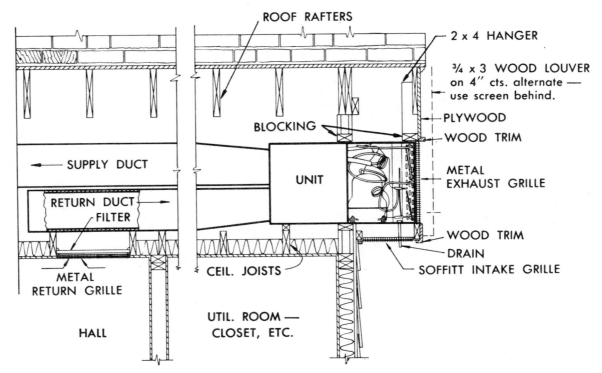

ROOF RAFTERS

2 x 4 HANGER

¾ x 3 WOOD LOUVER
on 4″ cts. alternate —
use screen behind.

PLYWOOD

BLOCKING

WOOD TRIM

SUPPLY DUCT

UNIT

METAL
EXHAUST GRILLE

RETURN DUCT
FILTER

WOOD TRIM

DRAIN

SOFFITT INTAKE GRILLE

METAL
RETURN GRILLE

CEIL. JOISTS

HALL

UTIL. ROOM —
CLOSET, ETC.

Fig. 3

Fig. 4

Fig. 5

The cross section, Fig. 3, shows the placing of the unit when the gable end of the roof is extended up to 24″ beyond the outside wall of the house. The air conditioner is then mounted in a balanced position in the outside wall. Air enters the condenser through the bottom on either side of the unit as well as through the louver. Note the conventional framing of the roof framing members and the ceiling and wall framing cross sections. In this type of installation an insulated baffle is placed around the unit so that air circulation does not enter the attic proper. If the unit is not placed against the grille, baffles also must be located around the air discharge end to prevent recycling of hot air back into the condenser coils.

The sketch, Fig. 4, shows the wall construction of a gable end when the air conditioner is housed in line or flush with the outside walls.

Variations of end gable construction, where the wall of the gable overhangs the main wall, are shown in the sketch, Fig. 5.

The cross section, Fig. 6, details the installation of the unit and ducts in a house of hip roof design and shows the roof framing details of the dormer as well as the main roof.

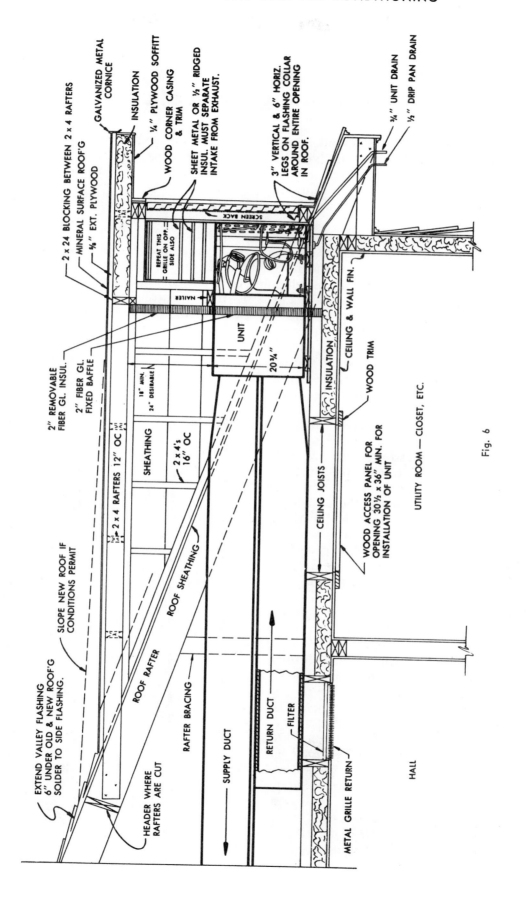

Fig. 6

15

Sheathing of Walls

With the completion of the outside and inside studded walls, one of the next important jobs in the construction of a house is boxing up, sheathing, or covering the framed walls. Illustrations show in detail how various types of sheathing boards are placed.

Before applying wooden boards or sheathing on studded walls, stack the sheathing stock, tongued-and-grooved shiplap or wide board material near the sides of the walls to be covered. Then select several straight and sound pieces of stock and square one end. Measure from exact corner of corner post along one side of the wall by placing a piece of stock in position and mark off on the stock the greatest length to the center of a stud. Square off and saw stock to size. This piece can be used as a pattern on all stock that is about the same length.

Place the stock at the bottom of the sill, directly above the foundation wall and nail in place. Use 8d nails and face-nail the sheathing with two nails at each stud. Check the pieces with the level for horizontal position and draw the stock down securely at all places. Do not bruise the tongue or groove of the stock. Remember that the sheathing is a tight casing of wood for the protection of the occupants of the structure and should be placed on the studded walls with this thought in mind.

Continue to place the stock in position and face-nail each piece with two nails at each stud. Join the stock only in center of stud where joint is required. Sheathe around the studded walls, working up as one goes around the building. When a door or window opening is reached, allow all stock to project slightly, nail stock securely and saw off flush with exact edge of opening. Sheathe the entire outside walls to the very top of the plate. The rafter length is figured to include the thickness of the sheathing stock and it is necessary that the sheathing stock be placed flush with the top of the plate member at all places.

Sheathing may also be placed on diagonally or in a combination of diagonal and horizontal positions, depending on the specifications and requirements set forth in the set of house plans. Steel-framed walls are covered with sheathing in much the same manner as wooden framed walls.

If tongued-and-grooved stock that has been used in concrete form construction is used, see that it is clean and free of concrete and earth. Use sound stock free of knots or rot.

Other types of covering for outside walls are wood-fiber board, masonite, gypsum, corkboard, celotex, etc.

A very interesting situation arises when one estimates diagonal or horizontal sheathing. The question is, which method will take more stock?

In estimating sheathing the following rules should be observed. In estimating horizontal sheathing find the area of the walls to be covered and add 1/10th of this area for waste in cutting. Disregard any openings unless it be a very large one, larger than doors or windows.

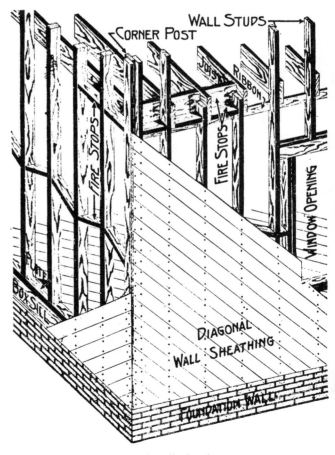

Diagonal wall sheathing.

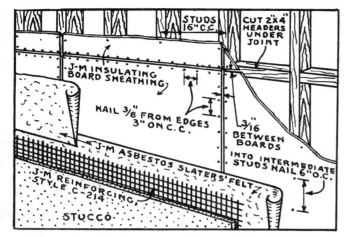

Application of insulating-board sheathing as exterior sheathing under stucco.

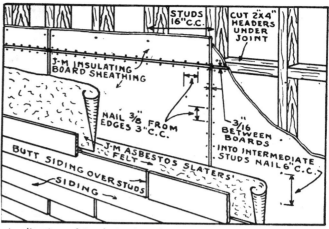

Application of insulating-board sheathing as exterior sheathing under clapboard siding.

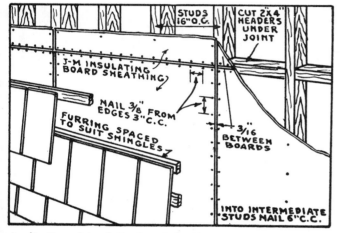

Application of insulating-board sheathing as exterior sheathing under shingles.

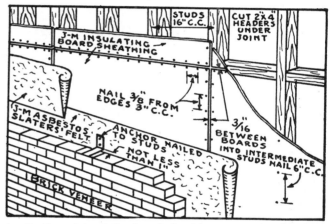

Application of insulating-board sheathing as exterior sheathing under brick veneer.

The following rules apply to diagonally placed sheathing for the several widths used.

For   6″ diagonal sheathing add 1/4 area.
  "   8″   "   "   " 1/6 "
  " 10″   "   "   " 1/8 "
  "   6″ horizontal   "   " 1/5 "
  "   8″   "   "   " 1/7 "
  " 10″   "   "   " 1/9 "

Estimate the quantity of sheathing required for the building in the accompanying set of house plans. Estimate in two or three different types of sheathing such as wood, manufactured wood, and synthetic boards.

In estimating diagonally placed sheathing find the area of the walls to be covered and add 1/6th of the area. Why?

In quantity estimating by the square method it has been found that about 125 board feet of 6″ sheathing will cover one square.

Insulating board sheathing.

Plywood sheathing.

Installation of vertical plywood panels against fir plywood under-battens. Sheathing is structural grade of fir plywood.

When diagonal sheathing extends down over the header joist and is nailed there, it ties the wall to the floor system. When the floor system is in turn bolted to the foundation wall, the total effect is high resistance to windstorms.

Horizontally sheathed houses should be diagonally braced unless they are of the low squat type with comparatively few openings. Otherwise, they will lack the rigidity desired in a good house, especially in the regions subject to high winds.

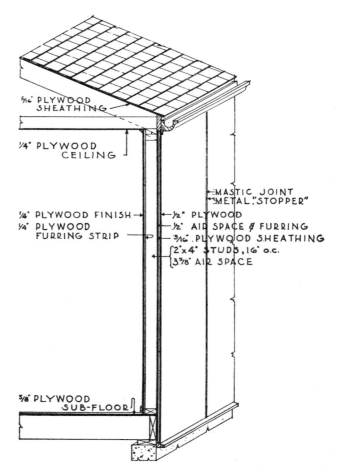

Plywood sheathing of walls; also of subfloor, ceiling, and roof.

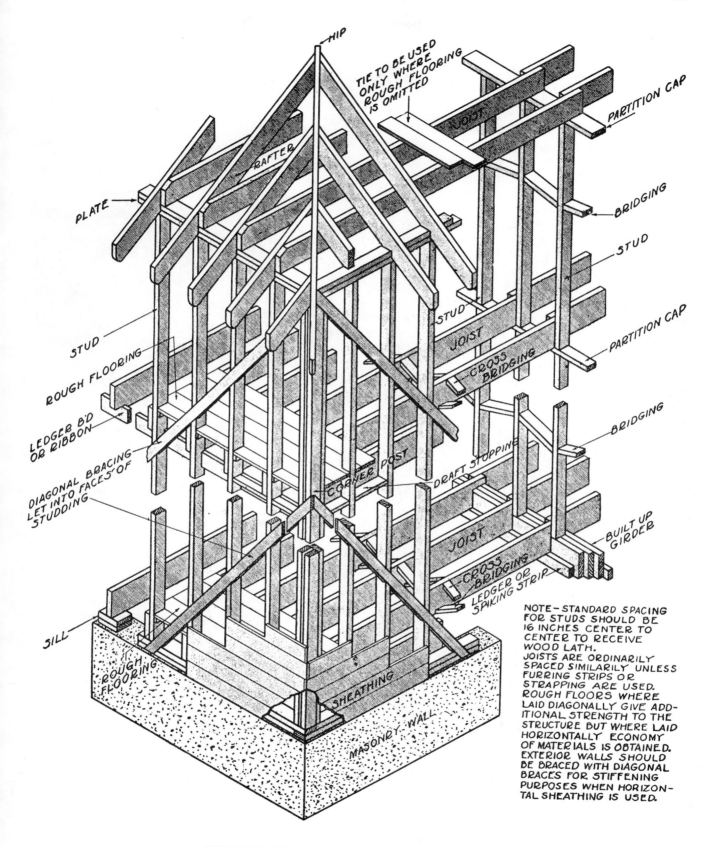

PLATE

HIP

TIE TO BE USED
ONLY WHERE
ROUGH FLOORING
IS OMITTED

JOIST

PARTITION CAP

RAFTER

BRIDGING

STUD

STUD

STUD

JOIST

PARTITION CAP

STUD

CROSS
BRIDGING

ROUGH FLOORING

LEDGER B'D
OR RIBBON

STUD

CORNER POST

DRAFT STOPPING

BRIDGING

DIAGONAL BRACING
LET INTO FACES OF
STUDDING

JOIST

BUILT UP
GIRDER

CROSS
BRIDGING

LEDGER OR
SPIKING STRIP

SILL

ROUGH
FLOORING

SHEATHING

MASONRY WALL

NOTE—STANDARD SPACING
FOR STUDS SHOULD BE
16 INCHES CENTER TO
CENTER TO RECEIVE
WOOD LATH.
JOISTS ARE ORDINARILY
SPACED SIMILARILY UNLESS
FURRING STRIPS OR
STRAPPING ARE USED.
ROUGH FLOORS WHERE
LAID DIAGONALLY GIVE ADD-
ITIONAL STRENGTH TO THE
STRUCTURE BUT WHERE LAID
HORIZONTALLY ECONOMY
OF MATERIALS IS OBTAINED.
EXTERIOR WALLS SHOULD
BE BRACED WITH DIAGONAL
BRACES FOR STIFFENING
PURPOSES WHEN HORIZON-
TAL SHEATHING IS USED.

SHEATHING IN BALLOON FRAME CONSTRUCTION.

16

Sheathing of Roof

After the outside walls have been sheathed with wide boards, tongue-and-groove boards, or manufactured boards, and the roof has been framed and braced, the next job is to sheathe up the gable ends of the house. If it is of simple gable construction, sheathe up to the rafters.

Gable studs are placed above each outside wall stud and run up to the bottom of the common rafter. A notch is cut in the top portion of the gable stud to house it under the rafter, bringing the gable stud flush with the outside edge of the end rafter and the outside wall studding.

All gable studs are set in place and nailed securely, allowance being made for any window openings, vent openings, etc., in the framing of the gable studs. Illustrations in Chapter 10 show gable studding as described above.

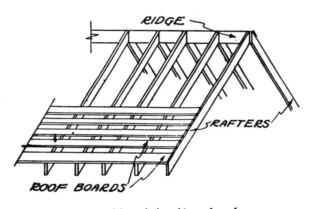

Spaced board sheathing of roof.

With the completion of the framing of the gable ends the sheathing is placed in the same manner as on outside walls. Run the sheathing up from the plate to the top edge of the common rafter and nail at each stud. Saw off any sheathing that projects over the top edge of the common rafter, as this will interfere with the laying of the sheathing on the roof.

In sheathing up the roof, start at the ends of the rafters and work up toward the ridge. Refer to the set of plans to determine the method of placing the boards, as some sheathing is placed solidly, some is spaced about 2 inches apart, and some, if in large pieces, may require special framing. Butt all joints

Close board sheathing of roof.

over the center of each rafter when sheathing material is joined.

Refer to the framing details for the length to allow for the overhang of the sheathing at the gable ends. Study the details for the methods of framing the cornice. Chapter 17 deals with the construction of cornices. Gable ends may be boxed, with trim; they may have little overhang or wide overhang, according to the style of the roof. Each detail must be studied and the sheathing erected accordingly.

To find the length of a common rafter by geometrical methods, first draw a horizontal line of indefinite length. On this line, which is called line XY, lay off a line AB equal to the run of the rafter. This line becomes line BC. AB and BC form a right-angle triangle ABC. Connect AC. This line AC is the length of a common rafter.

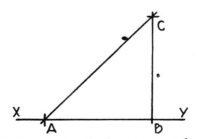

Finding the length of a common rafter.

To find the length of a hip rafter, proceed as below. Let EF equal the run of the hip rafter. Let FG equal the rise. EFG form a right-angled triangle. EG is the length of the hip rafter.

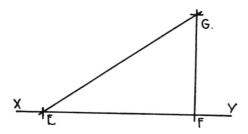

Finding the length of a hip rafter.

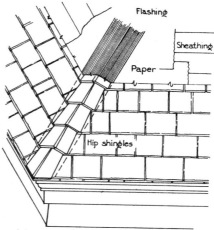

A shingle roof is as good as its valley flashing. The width of the flashing depends upon the slope of the roof, and high-grade zinc-coated iron or copper should be used for this purpose.

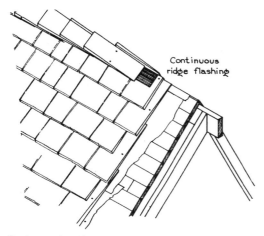

Where Boston style ridge is used, continuous flashing under the shingles is of importance because of the difficulty of maintaining a watertight joint at the peak. Notice in the illustration how the laced corner method is employed in this type of ridge.

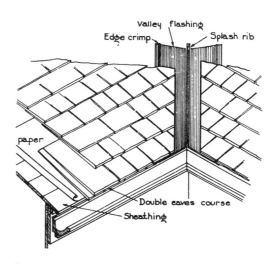

On small houses, it is good practice to use metal shingles as hip covering. Metal hip shingles are copper or galvanized-iron sheets 5 x 9 inches, the lower corner of which is crimped to slip under the shingles themselves. Application of metal hip shingles should be made after the shingles have been laid so that a straight line can be secured.

FLASHING
DETAILS

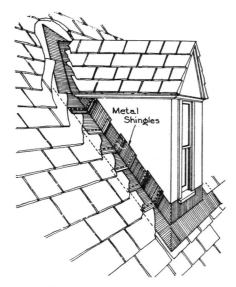

Dormers, which add much to the appearance of many houses, should give no construction problem if flashing at the roof and sides is done in accordance with the illustration. Galvanized-iron or copper flashing should be used for this purpose.

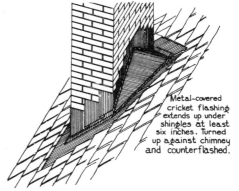

Metal-covered cricket flashing extends up under shingles at least six inches. Turned up against chimney and counterflashed.

Where a chimney extends through a continuous roof, a chimney cricket or chimney saddle should be used. This prevents moisture and snow from collecting behind the chimney.

17

Cornices and Gutters

After the outside walls have been enclosed with sheathing and the roof has been framed and covered with sheathing, attention is directed to forming the base for that portion of the exterior where the roof and walls meet.

Roofs are slanted or pitched, first to shed water and second for ornamentation or style. A simple gable roof meets the side walls at the gable ends and at the bottom of the slanted roof.

The construction of a base for the roof trim at the gable ends is relatively simple, as no water is carried off the roof along the gable side of the roof. The roofing boards are extended over the sheathed side walls just enough, in most instances, to house a wide board trim, placed vertically under the roof boards and resting flat against the gable sheathing. This wide board is known as a frieze and generally serves as a base for a molding known as crown molding, although a simple piece of

quarter-round can be used. The finished outside wall covering is placed directly under the frieze.

The following illustration shows the placing of the frieze, crown molding, and side-wall covering. This entire assembly is know also as a cornice, but not as an eave. Sometimes roofing boards are extended quite a distance from the side wall and boxed in with ceiling stock in the same plane as the roof. This ceiling stock is then known as a plancher and frieze on the side wall.

The following illustration shows the placing of the facia, plancher and frieze. A hip roof will not have this type of construction.

A gable roof and a hip roof, however, will have a cornice which houses a trough known as a gutter. The gutter hung onto the roofing boards is the simplest type to construct. It conducts the water from the lowest portion of the roof to the downspouts or conductors, which in turn conduct the water to the drains.

An assembly of a cornice constructed with a built-in gutter is known as a closed cornice and gutter and eaves.

There are so many ways of forming the base for the meeting of the roof and side walls that only general statements can be made, designating the names of the pieces used. Study of each case must be made and the details understood before work is begun.

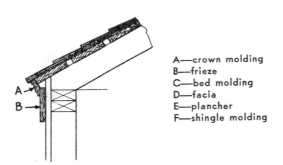

A—crown molding
B—frieze
C—bed molding
D—facia
E—plancher
F—shingle molding

Fig. 1. The frieze, crown molding, and side-wall covering.

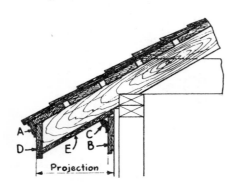

Fig. 2. The facia, plancher, and frieze.

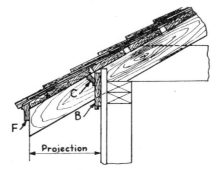

Fig. 3. An open cornice.

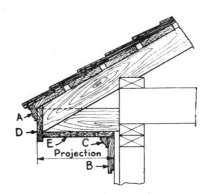

Fig. 4. A box cornice.

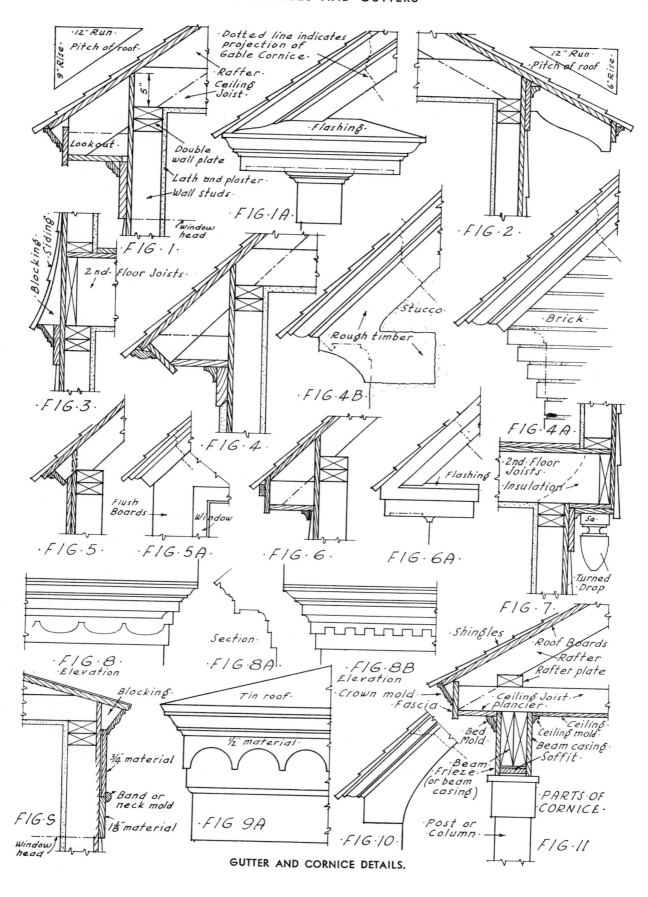

·12″ Run· Pitch of roof. 9″ Rise

Dotted line indicates projection of Gable Cornice.

Rafter Ceiling Joist.

Flashing.

·FIG·1A·

12″ Run Pitch of roof 6″ Rise

·FIG·2·

Lookout.

Double wall plate

Lath and plaster·

Wall studs.

Window head

·FIG·1·

Blocking Siding

2nd. Floor Joists.

·FIG·3·

Stucco

Rough timber

·FIG·4B·

Brick·

·FIG·4·

·FIG·4A·

Flush Boards

Window

·FIG·5· ·FIG·5A· ·FIG·6· ·FIG·6A·

Flashing

2nd· Floor Joists· Insulation

Sa.

Turned Drop

·FIG·7·

Section·

·FIG·8· Elevation

·FIG·8A· ·FIG·8B· Elevation

Shingles

Roof Boards Rafter Rafter plate

Crown mold· Fascia·

Ceiling Joist plancier·

Ceiling mold Beam casing Soffit

Bed Mold

Blocking·

¾ material

Band or neck mold

1⅛″ material

·FIG·S·

Tin roof.

½″ material

·FIG 9A·

Beam Frieze (or beam casing)

Post or Column·

·FIG·10·

PARTS OF CORNICE·

·FIG·11·

Window head

GUTTER AND CORNICE DETAILS.

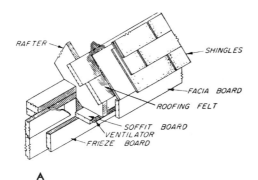

A

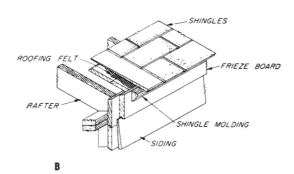

B

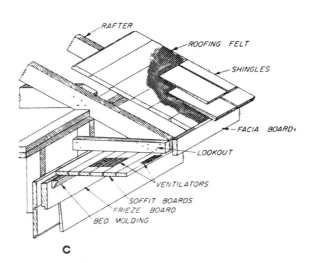

C

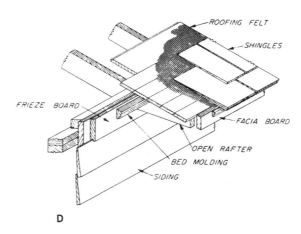

D

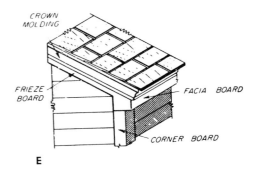

E

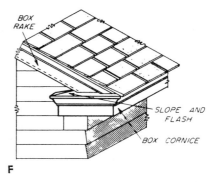

F

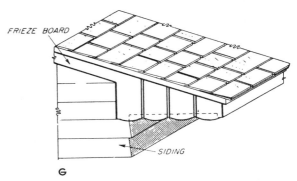

G

Cornice and Cornice-Return Construction

One of the easiest cornices to construct is the narrow box cornice, Figure *A*, which utilizes the projected ends of rafters for nailing surfaces of the facia and soffit members.

If rafters are not projected over the wall plates, a closed cornice, Figure *B*, consists of but a frieze board and a simple shingle molding. In this closed cornice the outside wall sheathing is carried above the plate members to the top face of the rafters.

A more elaborate cornice is made by projecting the rafters well beyond the plate, Figure *C*, and framing back, horizontally, with lookout members attached to the side of rafters and studding to serve as a nailing surface and support for the soffit assembly. In this type of cornice construction ample space is provided for ventilators, as shown, which are housed in the soffit trim.

In roof construction of one-third pitch, or less, an open cornice, Figure *D*, is constructed by extending the rafters beyond the plate members and attaching a facia board to the rafter ends. The frieze member can be housed between the sides of the rafters or notched out to fit up to the bottom of the roof sheathing.

In gable-roof construction the cornice return is the outside finish between the roof and wall running from the eaves to the topmost portion of the roof at the ridge. Figure *E* shows the trim construction or cornice return design for the small box cornice when the roof at the gable end is projected slightly.

If a wide box cornice is constructed, a box return may be built, as shown in Figure *E*, with the facia board and the bed molding carried around the return parallel to the siding.

In an open cornice construction having extended rafters, or in a wide cornice, a return, as shown in Figure *G*, may be constructed with an apron effect at the lower or eave portion.

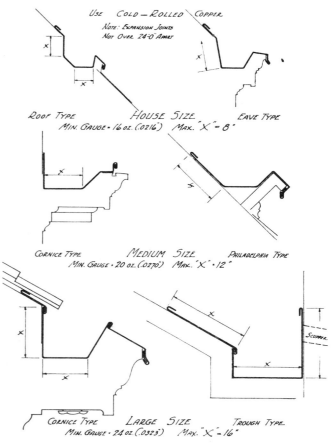

Cornices and built-in copper gutters.

Gutter and downspout.

Wide-overhang cornice and downspout arrangement.

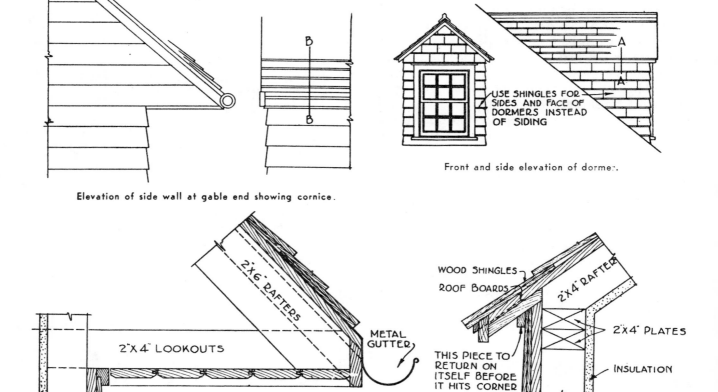

Elevation of side wall at gable end showing cornice.

Front and side elevation of dormer.

USE SHINGLES FOR SIDES AND FACE OF DORMERS INSTEAD OF SIDING

2"x6" RAFTERS

2"x4" LOOKOUTS

METAL GUTTER

Section B-B at cornice, showing overhang of rafters boxed up by lookouts and t and g ceiling trim.

WOOD SHINGLES
ROOF BOARDS
2"x4" RAFTER
2"x4" PLATES
THIS PIECE TO RETURN ON ITSELF BEFORE IT HITS CORNER
INSULATION

Section of dormer cornice at A-A.

CORNICE CONSTRUCTION DETAILS.

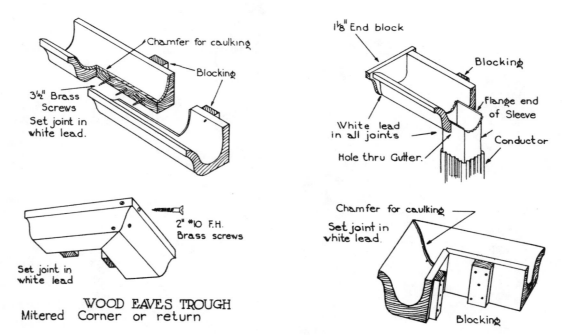

Chamfer for caulking
Blocking
3½" Brass Screws
Set joint in white lead.

1⅛" End block
Blocking
White lead in all joints
Flange end of Sleeve
Hole thru Gutter.
Conductor

2" #10 F.H. Brass screws
Set joint in white lead

WOOD EAVES TROUGH
Mitered Corner or return

Chamfer for caulking
Set joint in white lead.
Blocking

DETAILS OF WOODEN EAVES TROUGH.

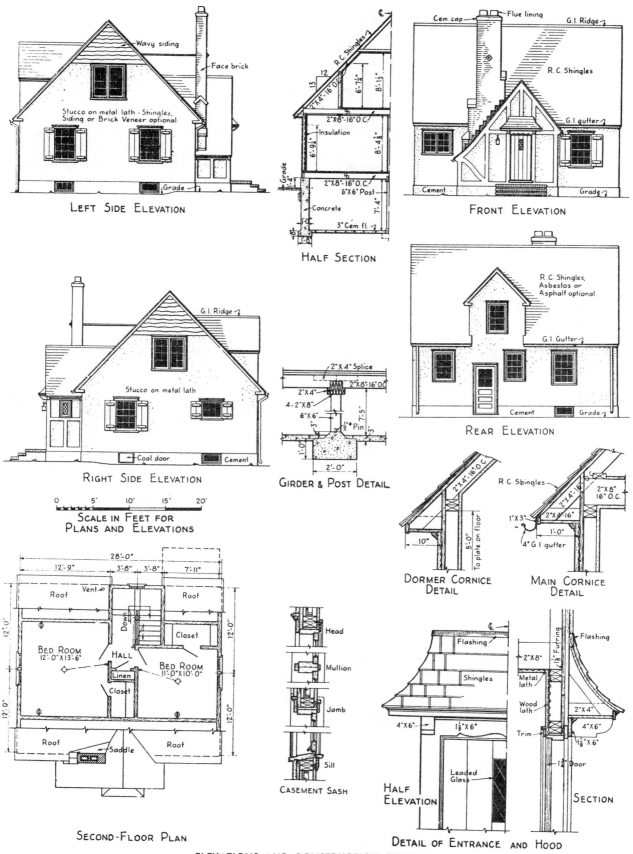

LEFT SIDE ELEVATION

Wavy siding

Face brick

Stucco on metal lath - Shingles,
Siding or Brick Veneer optional.

Grade

HALF SECTION

R.C. Shingles

12
13

6'-7½" 8'-1½"

2"X4"-16" O.C.

2"X8"-16" O.C.

Insulation

6'-9¼" 8'-4½"

Grade
1'-4"

2"X8"-16" O.C.
6"X6" Post   7'-4"

Concrete

3" Cem. fl.

FRONT ELEVATION

Cem. cap   Flue lining   G.I. Ridge

R.C. Shingles

G.I. gutter

Cement   Grade

RIGHT SIDE ELEVATION

G.I. Ridge

Stucco on metal lath

Coal door   Cement

GIRDER & POST DETAIL

2" X 4" Splice

2"X4"

2"X8"-16" O.C.

4 - 2"X8"

6"X6"

7'-5"

½" Pin   3"

1'-0"

2'-0"

SCALE IN FEET FOR
PLANS AND ELEVATIONS

0   5'   10'   15'   20'

REAR ELEVATION

R.C. Shingles,
Asbestos or
Asphalt optional.

G.I. Gutter

Cement   Grade

DORMER CORNICE
DETAIL

2"X4"-16" O.C.

10"

5'-0"
To plate on floor

MAIN CORNICE
DETAIL

R C Shingles

2"X4"-16"

2"X8"
16" O.C.

1"X3"

2"X8"-16"

1'-0"

4" G I gutter

SECOND-FLOOR PLAN

28'-0"

12'-9"   3'-8"   3'-8"   7'-11"

Roof   Vent   Roof

12'-0"

Down

Closet

BED ROOM
12'-0"X13'-6"

HALL

BED ROOM
11'-0"X10'-0"

Linen

Closet

12'-0"

12'-0"

Roof   Saddle   Roof

CASEMENT SASH

Head

Mullion

Jamb

Sill

DETAIL OF ENTRANCE AND HOOD

HALF
ELEVATION

Flashing

Shingles

4"X6"   1⅛"X6"

Leaded
Glass

SECTION

Flashing

2"X8"

Metal
lath

Wood
lath

Trim

1⅛" Furring

2"X4"

4"X6"

1⅛"X6"

1¾" Door

ELEVATIONS AND CONSTRUCTION DETAILS.

18

Roofing

The final weatherproof and ornamental covering applied to the sheathed roof may be of a number of materials, including wooden shingles, asbestos shingles, slate shingles, tile shingles, sheet tin or sheet copper, or roll roofing. All shingles are manufactured to certain sizes, colors, and shapes and are furnished in bundles ready to be applied. Sheet roofing, either tin, copper, or felt, must be applied from the roll, which requires a different method of attaching than does the cut shingle. Directions for applying shingles are furnished by the manufacturer and must be followed with care.

Roofing of asbestos or felt shingles are manufactured in large sheets in a wide variety of patterns and colors. These sheets are laid in much the same manner as shingles of wood, save at the ridge, which is crowned with a roll of the same material run clear along the length of the ridge and continued down several inches on either side.

In the illustrations in this chapter showing methods used in applying tile roofing and the creation of different styles in wooden shingles, attention is directed to the placing of flashing around the various meeting points of roof and side walls.

Wooden shingles are made of cypress, cedar, or redwood lumber. They are durable, warp very little, are easily applied, and are fire-resisting.

Slate shingles should be hard, tough, and free of soft ribbons. They should have a metallic appearance and a metallic ring when struck. They are inexpensive and are available in a variety of color schemes.

Ceramic shingles are not so serviceable but are attractive. They are available in a variety of patterns and colors. They are heavy and hard to handle.

Metal tile shingles are cheaper than clay tile shingles. They offer a cheap first cost but must be kept up.

Tin sheet roofing is inexpensive. It is easily laid and light in weight. It requires painting. It is very flexible.

Slag or gravel roofing is seldom used on a frame house or any type of residence. It is hard to apply though very durable. It is acid- and fume-resisting and is often guaranteed upward to twenty years.

Asphalt roofing has asphalt in it to take the place of tar. It does not last as long as tar roofs, but is quite attractive.

Steel and galvanized iron roofing is easy to apply. It is very heavy and requires paint.

Copper roofing is very durable and easy to apply. The first cost is the greatest.

Insurance rates offered by fire insurance companies on houses having various types of roofs is valuable information. According to a publication, cities and towns are divided into ten classes according to the type of fire protection offered. Buildings are divided into five classes: brick buildings, frame buildings, approved roof, unapproved roof, and mixed construction. These five classes are defined in an exact manner. Refer to a schedule of rates. Ascertain rates for different types of roofing.

Study the specifications and illustrations and become acquainted with the many types of roof covering. Observe roofing materials on dwellings in your neighborhood.

Roofing for framed houses may be obtained in the following materials:

    a. wood shingles
    b. slate shingles
    c. roofing tiles
    d. sheet metal tiles
    e. tin sheets
    f. slag or gravel roofing
    g. asphalt gravel roofing
    h. galvanized iron
    i. corrugated steel roofing
    j. copper roofing

The sizes of the different pieces of the above materials are as follows:

Material	Size of typical piece	Amount to weather	Lap
a.	4″ x 14″ or 16″ or 18″	4″–5″–6″	10″
b.	9″ x 18″	15″	3″
c.	5½″ x 9½″	4½″ x 8½″	1″
d.	8¾″ x 11⅝″	4½″ x 8½″	1″
e.	14″ x 20″	12½″ x 18½″	1½″
f.	36″ rolls 30′ long	10″	16″
g.	36″ rolls 30′ long	34″	2″
h.	36″ x 8′ No. 16	32″ x 7′ 8″	4″
i.	36″ x 8′ No. 14	35″ x 7′ 11″	1″
j.	2′ 6″ x 5′	2′ 5″ x 4′ 11″	1″

Find the area of each piece or unit of roofing. Find the area of the amount of material exposed to the weather. Which type offers the greater or lesser area?

Roofing material is estimated by the square. A square is 10′ x 10′, or 100 square feet. Any kind of roofing is ordered by the square. Find the amount of sheathing required for the roof of the house in the set of plans. Find the amount of roofing material needed.

Cornice trim is estimated by the actual lineal feet of measure. It is sold by the 100-foot measure and is designated by the pattern or stock number.

The following illustrations show the methods used in applying shingles of wood. Begin at the lowest part of the roof, working upward. Stretch a chalk line slightly lower than the lowest roofing board, from one side of the roof to the other, as a guide in making the slight overhang of the shingles in one straight line. This line and the first course of shingles is illustrated in the first diagram. The first course is applied all the way across the lowest edge and a second course is applied directly upon this first course, staggering the joints so that the second-course joints do not rest upon the first-course joints.

The second diagram shows the method used to continue the several courses up from the lowest point or the eave. A foothold is applied to protect the worker from slipping. It is nailed at the upper edge on the roofing boards.

Wood shingles should be moistened to some extent by having water thrown upon the opened bundles to allow some moisture to enter. If shingles are very dry upon application to the roof they will absorb moisture, and will swell and pull away from the nails. A 3d galvanized or copper nail must be used to hold shingles down. The nailing is done at the top end of the shingle, never at any place on that portion exposed to the weather, which usually overlaps the shingle below five or six inches.

Carry the rows of shingles up all the way to the ridge of the roof, checking on occasion for parallel rows. The top row should be made up of the butt end of the shingle, matching up carefully with the row on the other side of the ridge. A ridge roll of metal is applied, by the roofer, on the top or ridge.

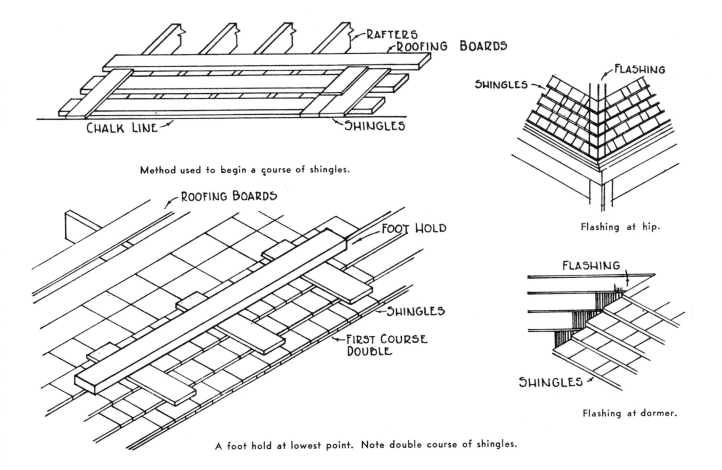

Method used to begin a course of shingles.

Flashing at hip.

Flashing at dormer.

A foot hold at lowest point. Note double course of shingles.

Photo 1.

Photo 2.

Photo 3.

Laying Asbestos Shingles on Tongue-and-Groove Roof Sheathing

Photo 1 shows a starter course of shingles applied to a gable roof of a dwelling. Note the use of asphalt-saturated sheathing felt applied over the wooden sheathing from one gable end to the other. The starter course overhangs the facia board at the cornice and the crown molding at the gable rake.

Photo 2 shows additional courses of shingles nailed in place. Note the completion of the starter course along the entire length of the roof; the first course applied directly above this starter course; and the cutting in half of the shingle at the gable. The device at the upper portion of the photo is a shingle cutter.

Photo 3 shows the first and second courses of shingles completed, and the method of matching each course, making true and even rows.

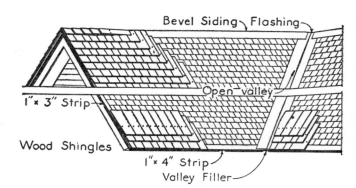

Method of reroofing a roof with wooden shingles.

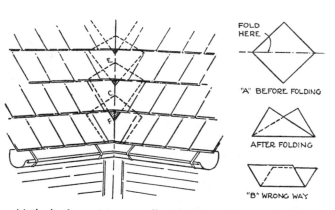

Method of repairing a valley flashing. Note methods in folding sheet metal.

Laying asbestos shingles over plywood sheathing.

Laying Asbestos Shingles on Plywood Roof Sheathing

In the photograph here two workmen are laying asbestos shingles over plywood sheathing which has been nailed to the rafters of the main roof. A 24-gauge galvanized drip edge, approximately 4″ wide, painted both sides, is nailed at the eaves, allowing an overhang of ½″ over the sheathing. For the starter course of shingles use the upper portion of the strip shingle, cut 7″ wide. This course is shown in the left-hand portion of the photograph. Lay a full starter course, 7″ x 36″, along the eave, placing the butts of the shingles flush with the lower edge of the metal drip edge, starting at the rake with a shingle piece, 7″ x 28″ in length. Continue laying the starter course across the roof with 7″ x 36″ pieces of shingle, having the edges just touching one another.

Each shingle is held by four 1¼″ 11-gauge, large-headed galvanized roofing nails. The nails should be driven down snugly with care taken not to countersink the nail heads.

The first course, or next layer of shingles, is applied directly over the starter course, with full-sized shingles.

The second course, or next layer of shingles, should be started with a shingle from which 4″ of the first tab has been cut off. Each course of shingles should be applied so that the lower edge of the butts is even with the top of the cutouts in the course below. Each succeeding course should be so placed that the cutouts are staggered.

As each piece of shingle is set in place, nail first at the center of the strip and then place additional nailing, four or six, outward from the center, not more than ½″ from the cutouts.

Each course is begun, as well as the galvanized strip, at the rake of the roof as shown by the lighter strip of wood in the extreme upper right portion of the photograph.

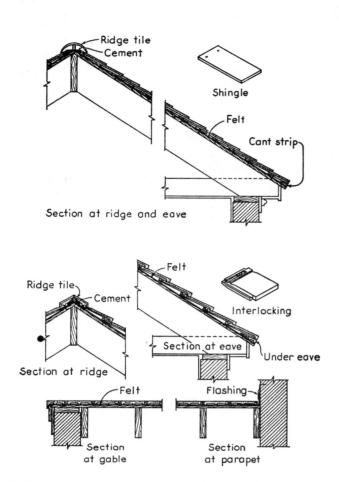

Sections and perspectives of typical tile roofs. The upper illustrates the flat, English shingle; the lower illustration represents the interlocking file.

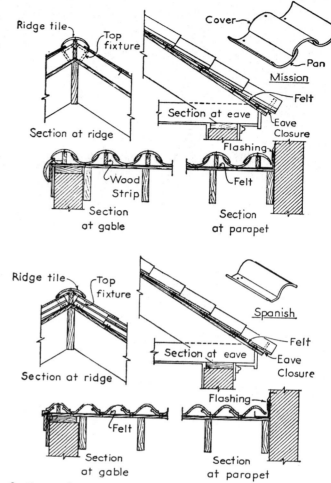

Sections and perspectives of two types of typical tile roofs. Both are of the two-piece, pan-and-cover construction, the upper being the Mission type and the lower the Spanish type.

Koroseal roofing membrane applied under Fenestra roof panels.

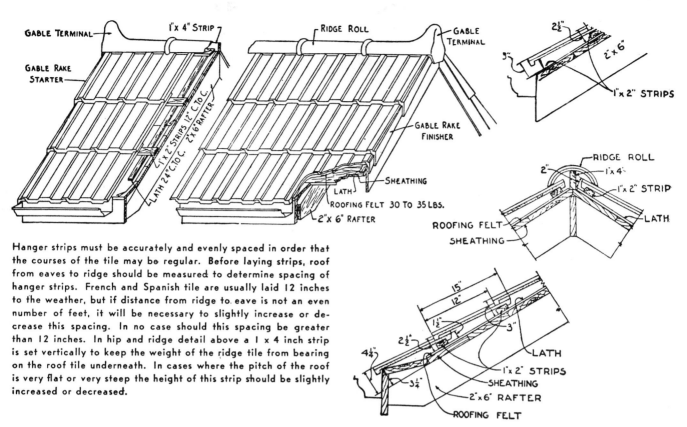

Hanger strips must be accurately and evenly spaced in order that the courses of the tile may be regular. Before laying strips, roof from eaves to ridge should be measured to determine spacing of hanger strips. French and Spanish tile are usually laid 12 inches to the weather, but if distance from ridge to eave is not an even number of feet, it will be necessary to slightly increase or decrease this spacing. In no case should this spacing be greater than 12 inches. In hip and ridge detail above a 1 x 4 inch strip is set vertically to keep the weight of the ridge tile from bearing on the roof tile underneath. In cases where the pitch of the roof is very flat or very steep the height of this strip should be slightly increased or decreased.

A METHOD OF LAYING TILE ROOFING OVER SHEATHING.

Gleaming white marble chip roof of 2-in-12 pitch has wide overhang (note shadow) and simple fascia. Texture 1-11 siding contrasts with roof expanse.

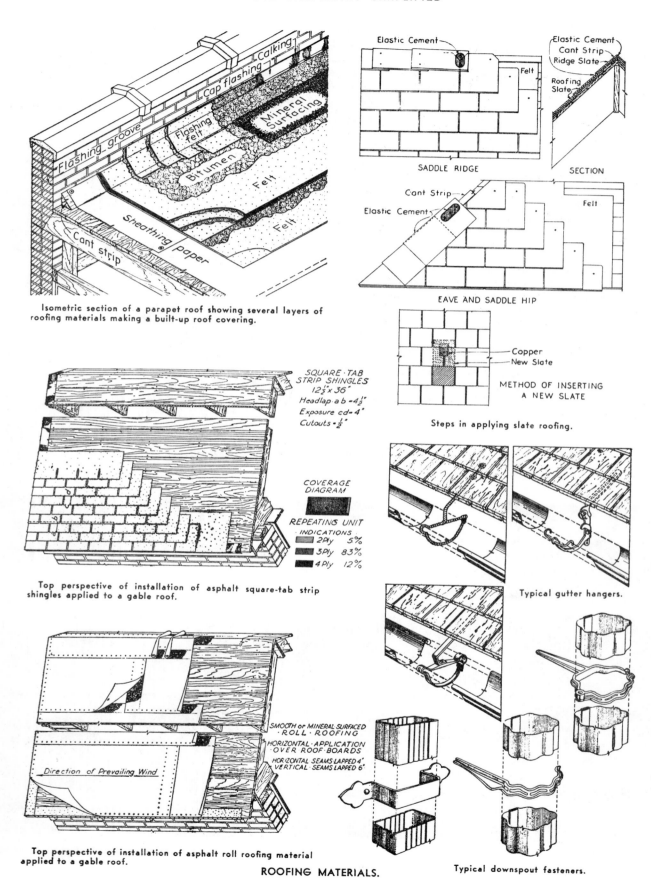

Isometric section of a parapet roof showing several layers of roofing materials making a built-up roof covering.

SADDLE RIDGE

SECTION

EAVE AND SADDLE HIP

METHOD OF INSERTING A NEW SLATE

Steps in applying slate roofing.

SQUARE·TAB STRIP SHINGLES
$12\frac{1}{2}" \times 36"$
Headlap a b = $4\frac{1}{2}"$
Exposure c d = 4"
Cutouts = $\frac{1}{2}"$

COVERAGE DIAGRAM

REPEATING UNIT
INDICATIONS
2 Ply   5%
3 Ply   83%
4 Ply   12%

Top perspective of installation of asphalt square-tab strip shingles applied to a gable roof.

Typical gutter hangers.

SMOOTH or MINERAL·SURFACED
ROLL·ROOFING
HORIZONTAL·APPLICATION
OVER·ROOF·BOARDS
HORIZONTAL·SEAMS·LAPPED 4"
VERTICAL·SEAMS·LAPPED 6"

Direction of Prevailing Wind

Top perspective of installation of asphalt roll roofing material applied to a gable roof.

ROOFING MATERIALS.

Typical downspout fasteners.

19

Porch and Bay Framing

A porch or bay window may be considered as another structure, even though attached to the house proper. Both have a foundation, sills, joists, flooring, roof rafters, sheathing, and roofing. Porches have posts or columns, railings, and steps. Bays have sashes and trim.

Concrete porches have footings, walls, and floors which are reinforced with steel rods. The cement finisher finishes off walls, steps, and floors with a smooth layer of fine cement. Since the carpenter builds the forms when poured concrete is used, he should have a general understanding of the cement contractor's work.

Since a concrete porch is much heavier than a wooden porch it must be securely attached to the main foundation wall with reinforcing bars. Otherwise it may settle and pull away from the building. Concrete steps also are built as an integral part of the foundation wall. Coal bins usually are housed below a porch, which necessitates the foundation walls being carried down to the same depth as the foundation walls of the main structure.

Read the sets of plans for the location of the porch and of the bay, if such are called for. If the porch is to be made entirely of wood, proper foundation walls or piers must be built by the mason. Sill stock for the porch floor is usually 2″ x 8″ in size and is placed on edge, flush with the outside wall of the foundation or pier. A sill plate may be used as well as a sill header. Porch joists are placed at right angles to the dwelling joists, or parallel, according to the specifications. Proper slant or fall must be made in the joists to allow for drainage of water from the porch floor.

The bay sills are framed like the dwelling sill, since the dwelling floor projects into the bay. The floor joists of the bay rest on the sill of the dwelling proper and on the sill of the bay. Sometimes a foundation contains a recess shaping up the same way as the bay-window wall. The side walls of the bay are framed like the side walls of the dwelling, with due allowances being made for window openings. The roof rafters of the bay rest upon a plate placed on top of the bay studding. They run up and rest on the sheathing placed on the house proper, and must be nailed securely.

Many variations of porch posts, railings, enclosed windows, etc., are utilized and their construction details must be studied. If porch columns are made on the job they are sometimes boxed around the studding running from the joists to the plate. Porch

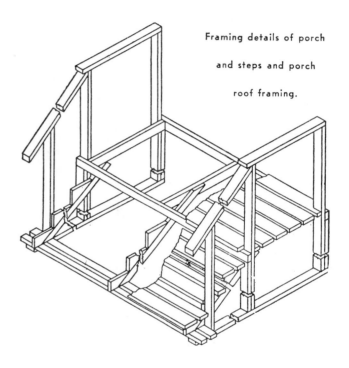

Framing details of porch and steps and porch roof framing.

roof rafters are framed up in much the same manner as are the rafters for the main structure.

Often a porch roof is ornamented with a superstructure around the roof and forming a part thereof. This entablature rests upon the columns and houses the gutter.

A stoop is not considered a porch, in a strict sense, since its construction is relatively simple. A stoop in most instances, is hung on to the outside wall and most generally without any column or projection downward to the floor of porch. *Veranda* is another term for a porch. It may be more elaborate if built from the second floor of the dwelling. A *portico* is more elaborate than a veranda and is generally supported by masonry pillars.

Sketch some details of simple porch construction. Learn each part's name and function.

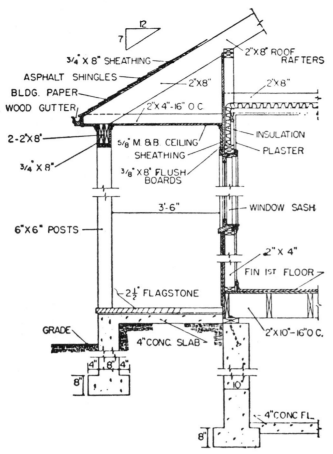

Section diagram of porch framing showing use of flagstone porch flooring.

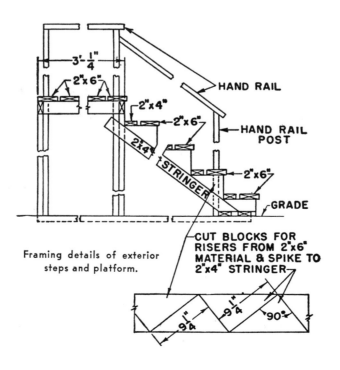

Framing details of exterior steps and platform.

Bays are generally placed in living rooms or dining rooms. Good design demands that only a certain portion of the floor area be used as bay-window space. A bay-window space could not be three-fourths of the main floor area, under any circum-

Balcony is protected by wide overhand, while glass window wall admits light for living room.

stances. If a living room measured 10' x 15' it would contain 150 square feet of floor area. If a bay-window floor space measured 3' x 5' it would contain 15 square feet of floor area.

To find the percentage of floor space of the living room proper, occupied by the bay-window floor space, one divides the area of the bay floor space by the living-room floor space (15 divided by 150), obtaining .10% as the answer. The fraction 15/150th is expressed in decimals as 10%. This is obtained by dividing the numerator (15) by the denominator (150) which gives a quotient of .1, which is read—one-tenth, or 10 per cent.

$$150 \quad 15.0 \quad\quad .1$$
$$150$$

In this example, the numerator is divided by the denominator and as many places are pointed off in the quotient as there are ciphers added in the dividend. Thus 15 is the dividend, 150 is the divisor and 1 is the quotient.

All-glass window wall is theme of California style, here used in a Scholz prefab. Design is adapted to sloping terrain and balcony added, with sliding glass doors to patio below.

Refer to a set of house plans having a bay window. Find the percentage of floor space of the living room or the dining room that is devoted to the bay window.

Study as many porch, veranda, and stoop details as possible since there is a very wide variation in taste and architectural expression.

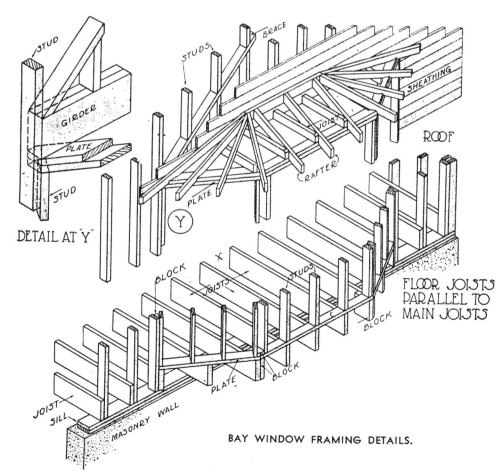

DETAIL AT "Y"

BAY WINDOW FRAMING DETAILS.

20

Exterior Wall Covering

Outside studded walls which have been sheathed with tongue-and-groove stock, plywood, or manufactured boards are given a final finish covering of either beveled siding, shingles, brick veneer, stucco, stone, or vertical battens. Refer to the set of plans and determine the kind of wall covering designated and the style of trim to be used around the windows and doors.

Before the exterior covering is placed on the outside walls, the door and window openings are prepared for their respective frames. Carry the window frames to the designated openings, by checking on the plans and the schedule of windows, making certain the correct size frame is at each opening. Carry the door frames to the openings.

Prepare the openings by squaring off any uneven pieces of sheathing, and wrap heavy building paper around the sides, top, and bottom of the window openings, from a point even with the inside portion of the stud to a point about six inches on the sheathed walls. Tack down the paper with small nails. Be careful not to tear the paper, as it acts as an insulation against drafts. Door openings are prepared in like manner, but since the sill must be worked into a portion of the rough flooring no paper is put on the floor.

Window frames are obtained from the lumber yard and delivered in one lot. Lift each frame into place. Check the plans carefully, seeing to it that the correct frame is at the designated opening. The frame should slide into the opening and must be held by wedges of wood after it is plumbed. Nail securely in several places. If metal windows are designated on the plans, the installation is essentially the same as for wooden frames. Outside trim around windows is nailed carefully in place after a slight bevel is placed on casings for wedging or squeezing the siding into place.

Door frames are set in place and plumbed. The sill stock is set in all outside door openings. Obtain the door sill stock and mark distance on rough floor equal to the length the sill will project back into the rough floor. The sill will have a ¾" or 1" overhang beyond the water table on the outside of the building. Allow for this overhang and mark on the rough floor. Saw away the portion of rough flooring in order that the rough flooring and sill will be on the same level. The sill must have a slight fall to the outside. The length of the sill is fixed by the width of the door opening plus the width of the outside casing. The sill juts beyond the far edge of the outside casing a trifle, 1" to 1½", so that the length of the sill will be a distance equal to the width of the rough door opening, plus twice the width of the outside casing, plus a slight extension.

Place the door frame in place over the sill and saw a light bevel on the bottom of the jambs to allow for the slight fall of the sill. Saw off any unnecessary extension of the jambs, beyond the head casing, in order to bring the entire frame within the correct height to allow for the true opening for the exterior door. Wedge the jamb into place and plumb and nail securely. Place the outside casing or trim into position and nail. Be certain that building paper is wrapped around the opening as described for window openings.

Any other trim coming in contact with the outside wall covering is placed and nailed into position. All porch trim coming in contact with outside wall covering is placed in position and nailed securely.

In applying beveled siding, or any other type of covering, the sheathed walls are covered, not too far in advance of the final covering, with a heavy building paper. This building paper serves as an insulator and must be applied with care. Hold the

Combination of types of wall covering in 2-story construction.

142

Overlaid plywood siding as exterior wall covering.

Panel system permits flexibility in placement and choice of materials in siding, fixed, and operable glass in Techbuilt prefab.

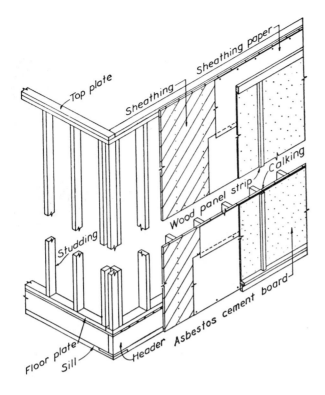

Asbestos cement wallboarding applied as exterior covering.

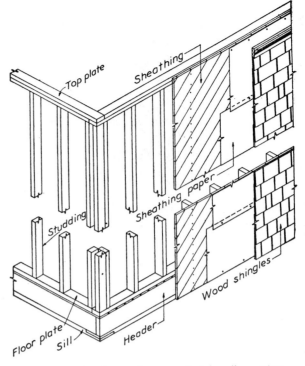

Wooden shingles used as an exterior wall covering.

paper on the sheated walls with scrap strips of stock until the siding is placed over it.

Place the drip cap or water table in place, allowing a slight overhang below the meeting of the sheathing and the concrete foundation. Place drip-cap molding above the water table, and nail the first course of beveled siding or other exterior covering. Check carefully with a level and plumb.

Since each piece of beveled siding must show the same, or nearly the same, lap, check the distances from drip cap to window, or drip cap to frieze board at the eave, spacing the pieces by using the divider. These spaces can be marked on a siding stick, which is a straight piece of stock long enough to run from the drip cap to a window or from a window to an eave. Equal spacing on the siding stick will save much trouble. A gauge for the equal spacing of siding is illustrated in Chapter 1. Nail each piece of siding in two places on the studding, with finish nails, and set the nails as the work is done. Join each piece of siding at the door or window trim and at the corner boards. If the siding is beveled at the corners, care must be taken to secure a perfect joint.

Other types of exterior wall covering are applied with equal care. The door and window frames are set in place by the carpenter.

Brick veneer is applied by the bricklayer. Consult details for the methods used. Note that metal bonds are nailed to the sheathing at regular intervals to secure bricks to the walls.

Shingles are applied by the carpenter in much the same manner as roof shingles. Wall shingles should be laid with not more than 6″ to the weather and for better protection a 5″ exposure is used. Courses of shingles must be perfectly level and evenly spaced.

Stucco is applied over metal lath after the lath has been securely nailed over building paper.

Vertical battens are applied in the same manner as beveled siding. Narrow strips are nailed over the joints of vertical siding to make them more weatherproof.

Study the types of exterior wall coverings used and designated in the plans in this book. Observe with great care the kinds of coverings placed on walls of building as you go past houses in your neighborhood. A great variety of coverings are used—in fact, as many perhaps as there are variations of porches. Covering the walls with an artistic cover is essential. Making the walls different from the walls of houses nearby is necessary to individualize their appearance. This entails the utilization of many varieties of patterns, ideas, and styles.

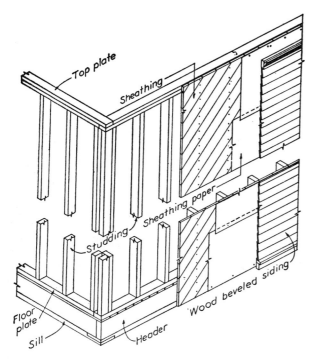

Beveled siding of wood used on exterior wall.

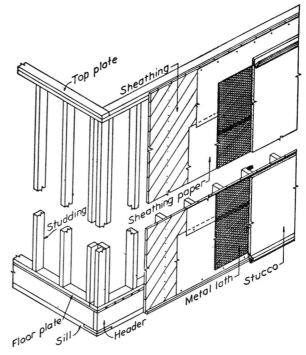

Portland cement stucco used on exterior wall.

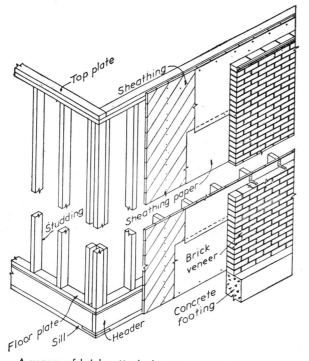

A veneer of bricks attached to exterior wall sheathing.

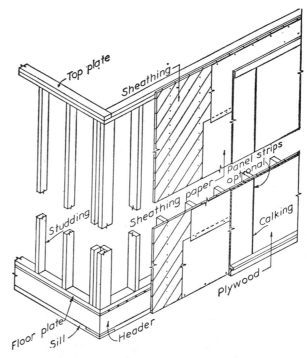

An exterior wall finished with plywood.

TYPICAL COVERINGS ON EXTERIOR WALLS.

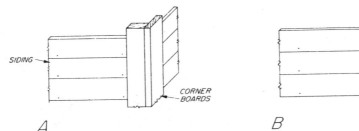

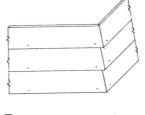

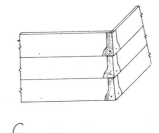

FINISHING THE WOOD SIDING AT EXTERIOR CORNERS

Corner boards may be applied vertically (Fig. A) against the sheathing with the beveled siding fitted tightly against the narrow edge of the corner boards.

Beveled siding, as an exterior wall covering (Fig. B) may be mitered at the corner without the use of corner boards and must fit tightly and smoothly for the full depth of the miter. The mitered ends should be given a coating of white lead when the siding is applied, and the exposed faces should be primed with paint after nailing siding in place.

Metal corners (Fig. C) are often used at corners when the beveled siding is mitered. Before the metal corners are nailed in place each must be given a coat of white lead paint to protect the mitered joints of the siding.

These asbestos-cement siding shingles have a rib-textured pattern that helps to conceal nail heads and vertical joints between shingles. They are made in a range of pastels.

Striated siding has nailing strip at top for added protection.

Asbestos-cement board used as exterior siding is primed with a masonry paint with a Pliolite S-5 base, applied with a roller, to make the boards ready to take any kind of house paint.

Combination of varied-sized stone siding, wood shingles, and vertical wood siding at entrance gives variety to elevation of Thyer prefabricated house.

Fir plywood is being applied here right over old siding where possible. 4 x 8-foot plywood is rip-sawed to 18-inch widths and lapped 1 inch, providing for an exposure of 16 inches. Nailing points are backed with shingle wedges.

Applying pre-cut striated fir plywood.

Stucco exterior: first course—building paper and wire mesh application.

Second course: foundation stucco application.

Third course: second, or smoothed-surface, stucco application.

Fourth course: paint finishing of stucco exterior.

21

Interior Wall and Ceiling Covering

The outside walls of a dwelling usually form two of the four walls of each room in the house. The area inside the four outside walls is broken up into rooms by partition walls which may or may not be weight-bearing walls. In a framed house both the partition walls and the inside of the outside walls are studded. The covering for these walls will be laths of wood or metal or a manufactured board. If an interior of wood is desired in one room the studding can be covered with heavy plywood.

To insulate the dwelling as the interior walls are covered, the carpenter places the bulk or batten insulation between the studding as the base for the plaster is built up. Heavy manufactured board takes the place of bulk or batten insulation and forms the base for the finish coat of plaster.

Brick houses generally have an inside backing of cinder or concrete blocks as a base for the plaster. The partitions in a house of brick are made up of studded walls similar to the walls in a framed house.

In preparing studded walls for the plaster work, the first job is to visualize the places of the interior trim, such as the baseboard and door and window trim and to provide a nailing base known as plaster grounds. These grounds not only form a base for the trim but also act as a guide for the plasterer to work to. Plaster-ground stock is generally 3/4" x 2" in size. Nail this stock around the inside walls at the floor level and at a position above the floor level to form a nailing base for the baseboard. The window and door frames will extend into the walls a slight distance into which the plaster is worked evenly. The trim around the windows and doors utilizes the rough frame of studding as a nailing base. If this does not serve the purpose, a plaster ground must be placed at window and door openings to form a nailing base for the trim.

Lathing is done by either a lather, plasterer, or carpenter, according to agreements. The work of each must be understood by one another. Consult the plans and specifications to determine just where to place grounds, nailing blocks, etc., as a base for trim.

Lathing, whether of wooden strips or of metal, must be applied with care. Joints must be made over the framework. Corners must be solid and secure. External corners, at entrance ways, etc., are prepared by the use of metal corners, even if wooden lath is used. This metal corner acts as a ground or working guide for the plaster.

The illustrations in this chapter should be carefully studied. They will help the apprentice see the many places needed for solid backing for the plaster, manufactured board, or plywood.

Plywood paneling at left and panels and battens at right.

Large panels with grooved surface.

The spacious living room shown in the upper photograph accents the use of wood as a covering for interior walls. The wall in the back is made up as a permanent wall and an 8' sliding wall of plywood panel. Two large panels are doweled and glued together to form the wall which when pulled aside separates the living room from the combination extra room. Note the panels and battens forming the wall at the right.

In the lower photograph the wall at the right is finished in plywood paneling, and the wall at the left is in a natural wood siding that combines large panels with a striking grooved surface. A large storage unit, at the left, is made of plywood and is finished in striking contrasting color.

Plaster Reinforcing

Some drying may take place in framing members after the house is completed, resulting in shrinkage which may cause plaster cracks to develop around openings and corners. Plaster cracking may be minimized by the use of expanded metal lath placed over window and door openings as shown in these four details. Detail A, shows the placing of small pieces of metal lath over a door opening.

Junctures of walls and ceiling may be reinforced by the use of cornerites or wire fabric, detail B.

Corner beads, detail C, should be installed on all exterior corners. This bead also acts as a leveling edge for the plastered wall.

Metal lath, detail D, can be used in ceiling plastering, extending well beyond the edges of the beam.

Check the house plans or floor plan for the building code requirements relative to lighting, ventilating, room size, room height, alcoves, and alcove rooms. Check the code requirements for inside wall coverings and see if the plans meet these requirements. Check specifications also, if they are available, for the plaster requirements.

Estimate the amount of covering for the inside walls. Manufactured board is estimated by the square foot and is sold in various sizes. Care must be taken to make the maximum use of standard manufactured sizes. Wire lath is estimated by the square 10 x 10, or 100 square feet, and is made in various rectangular shapes. Wooden lath is likewise estimated by the square. It takes about 1,500 pieces to make up one square. About 9½ pounds of 3d nails are used on a square of lath. Plaster is estimated by the square according to the specifications.

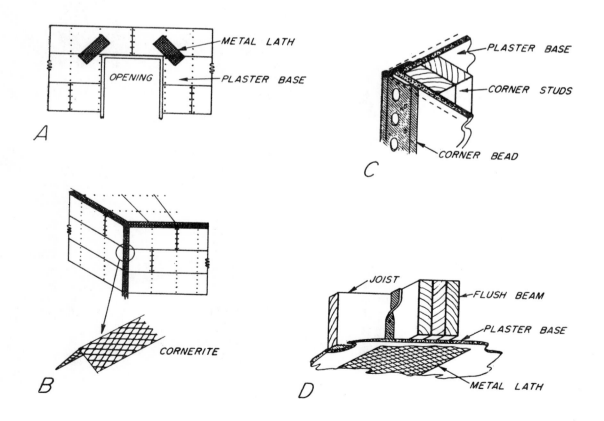

Lath stock must be of well-seasoned spruce, hemlock, or white pine. The stock must be sap free, bark free, and dead knot free. Pine containing much pitch is not good for lath stock.

Plaster is applied in three coats, known as the scratch, brown, and finish coats. The scratch coat usually consists of 1 part lime paste, 2 parts sand and 2 parts of hair. The brown coat may consist of 2½ bushels of lime, 7 barrels of screened sand and 1 bushel of hair. The finish coat consists of 1 part lime and 1 part white sand. Lime plaster is a product of lime powder and water. Lime is sold as quick lime, hydrated or slack lime, and alca lime.

Wallboard

In the making of a certain manufactured board the sawmill edgings, slabs, and short lengths are reduced to chips about the size of a dime. These chips are then exploded under terrific steam pressure into a moss-like mass of long fibers. The fibers, without any artificial binder, are then thoroughly felted to gether into thick heavy blankets. These while steam-heated are put under hydraulic pressure to form boards 7/16" thick. These boards honeycombed with millions of dead air cells, the most effective type of insulation. Additional pressure on these boards makes the product extremely dense, strong, and moisture resistant.

NOTE—Window walls are discussed in Chapter 24—Windows and Window Walls.

For heating and air-conditioning details refer to Chapter 14.

Acoustic tile, random pattern, is combined with textured plywood to make attractive playroom ceiling.

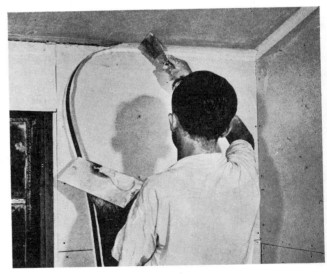

Application of steel corner tape.

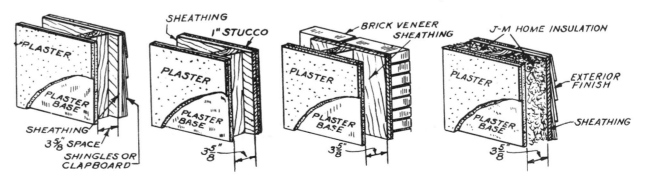

Gypsum plaster board on interior walls.

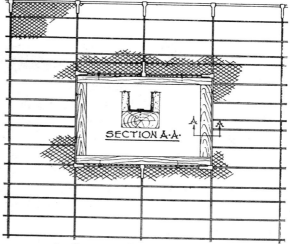

Small opening framed in metal lath.

Mosaic tile.

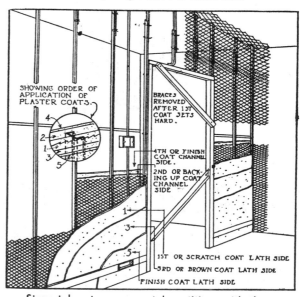

Steps taken to cover metal partitions with three coats of plaster.

Knotty pine walls.

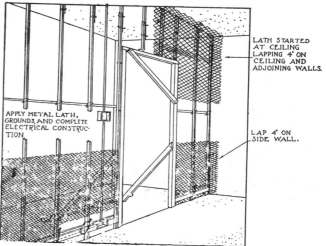

Steps taken to install plastered partition wall on metal lath and studs.

Wood fiber ceiling tiles interlock and can be blind-nailed.

Insulite acoustic squares.

Acoustic tiles are featured in sloped ceiling of Modern Homes prefab. Note hopper panels under fixed glass windows, sliding by-pass closet doors.

Random width knotty board paneling carries out theme of exposed rafters, extended through sidewall for overhang. Ceiling is of combination roof-deck panels.

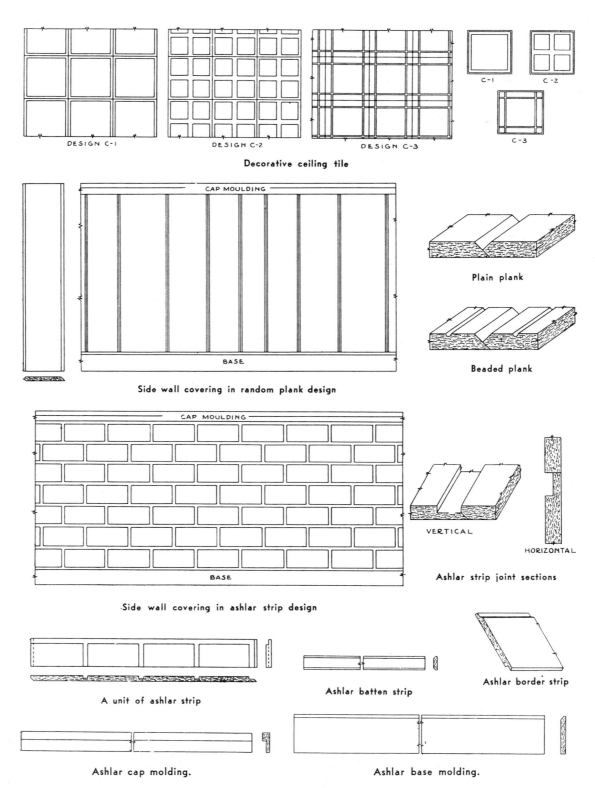

DESIGN C-1   DESIGN C-2   DESIGN C-3   C-1   C-2

C-3

Decorative ceiling tile

CAP MOULDING

BASE

Side wall covering in random plank design

Plain plank

Beaded plank

CAP MOULDING

BASE

Side wall covering in ashlar strip design

VERTICAL   HORIZONTAL

Ashlar strip joint sections

A unit of ashlar strip

Ashlar batten strip

Ashlar border strip

Ashlar cap molding.

Ashlar base molding.

SEVERAL DESIGNS OF INTERIOR WALL COVERING OF MANUFACTURED BOARD.

Plastic Tile Standards

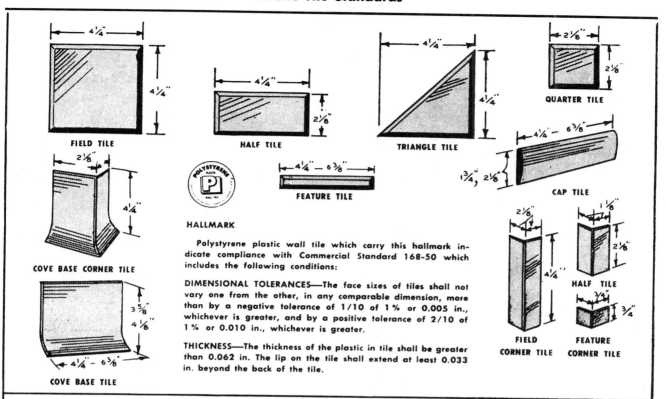

FIELD TILE

HALF TILE

TRIANGLE TILE

QUARTER TILE

COVE BASE CORNER TILE

FEATURE TILE

CAP TILE

COVE BASE TILE

FIELD CORNER TILE

HALF TILE

FEATURE CORNER TILE

HALLMARK

Polystyrene plastic wall tile which carry this hallmark indicate compliance with Commercial Standard 168-50 which includes the following conditions:

DIMENSIONAL TOLERANCES—The face sizes of tiles shall not vary one from the other, in any comparable dimension, more than by a negative tolerance of 1/10 of 1% or 0.005 in., whichever is greater, and by a positive tolerance of 2/10 of 1% or 0.010 in., whichever is greater.

THICKNESS—The thickness of the plastic in tile shall be greater than 0.062 in. The lip on the tile shall extend at least 0.033 in. beyond the back of the tile.

ESTIMATING AND DESIGNING FACTORS
(Based on 4¼ x 4¼ Tile)

LENGTH	NO. OF TILE	LENGTH	NO. OF TILE	LENGTH	NO. OF TILE	LENGTH	NO. OF TILE	LENGTH	NO. OF TILE	LENGTH	NO. OF TILE	LENGTH	NO. OF TILE
4¼″	1	3′-10¾″	11	7′- 5¼″	21	10′-11¾″	31	14′- 6¼″	41	18′- 0¾″	51		
8½″	2	4′- 3 ″	12	7′- 9½″	22	11′- 4 ″	32	14′-10½″	42	18′- 5 ″	52		
1′- 0¾″	3	4′- 7¼″	13	8′- 1¾″	23	11′- 8¼″	33	15′- 2¾″	43	18′- 9¼″	53		
1′- 5 ″	4	4′-11½″	14	8′- 6 ″	24	12′- 0½″	34	15′- 7 ″	44	19′- 1½″	54		
1′- 9¼″	5	5′- 3¾″	15	8′-10¼″	25	12′- 4¾″	35	15′-11¼″	45	19′- 5¾″	55		
2′- 1½″	6	5′- 8 ″	16	9′- 2½″	26	12′- 9 ″	36	16′- 3½″	46	19′-10 ″	56		
2′- 5¾″	7	6′- 0¼″	17	9′- 6¾″	27	13′- 1¼″	37	16′- 7¾″	47	20′- 2¼″	57		
2′-10 ″	8	6′- 4½″	18	9′-11 ″	28	13′- 5½″	38	17′- 0 ″	48	20′- 6½″	58		
3′- 2¼″	9	6′- 8¾″	19	10′- 3¼″	29	13′- 9¾″	39	17′- 4½″	49	20′-10¾″	59		
3′- 6½″	10	7′- 1 ″	20	10′- 7½″	30	14′- 2 ″	40	17′- 8½″	50	21′- 3 ″	60		

HOW TO USE THIS TABLE

This table can be valuable to the designer and estimator in several ways.

1. In designing or layout, the number of courses of tile can be ascertained, for any required height or length of wall.

Example: Assume that a wainscot height of 4′-6″ is desired and it is required to know the number of tiles necessary to approach this dimension. Checking the table it will be found that 13 tiles give a course height of 4′-7¼″. If desirable to hold close to the 54″ dimension 12 full tiles may be finished with a half tile or cap of 2⅛″ giving a total height of 4′-5⅛″.

2. Estimating tile quantities for a given area.

Example: Length of wall in lineal feet—17′-0″
Height of wall—5′-8″
Number of tile in 17′-0″=48
Number of tile in 5′-8″=16
48 x 16=768 tiles required.

3. Estimating the number of pieces of 4¼″ cap, base or feature strip required for lineal feet of wall.

Example: Assume total lineal feet of wall to be tiled to be 48 feet.
Consulting the table it will be found that 34 pieces are needed for 12 feet. Therefore: 34 x 3=102 the total number of pieces required.

Courtesy The Society of Plastics Industry, Inc.

22

Stairs

The floor joists must be properly framed around the stair well, or wellhole, in order to have sufficient space for the erection of the stair framing and finish trim of the entire staircase. Refer to a set of plans and study all items and details relative to the construction of stair work. Stairs leading from the first floor to the basement are relatively easy to build.

Stair work is made up of the framing on the sides, known as *stringers,* and the steps, known as *treads.* Sometimes pieces are framed into the stairs at the back of the treads, these pieces are known as *risers.* Usually basement stairs have only stringers, treads, and risers. These are framed up from framing stock, 2" x 10", and tread and riser stock. Refer to the drawing which shows many points of stair construction.

To frame simple, straight-string stairs, take a narrow piece of straight stock, called a story pole, and mark on it the distance from the basement floor to the first-floor level. This is the basement room height, plus the thickness of the first-floor joists, and the rough and the finish flooring. It is also the total rise of the stairs. If it is kept in mind that a flight of stairs forms a right-angled triangle, with the rise being the height of the triangle, the run being the base of the triangle, and the length of the stringers being the hypotenuse of the triangle, it will help in laying out the stair distances.

On a divider set the distance of 7", the average distance from one step to another, and step off this distance on the story pole. If this distance will not divide into the length of the story pole evenly, adjust the divider span slightly and again step off this distance on the story pole. Continue this adjusting and stepping off until the story pole is marked off evenly. The distance on the divider must be near 7" and represents the rise of each step. Count the number of spaces stepped off evenly by the divider, on the story pole. This will be the total number of risers in the stairs.

Measure the length of the wellhole for the length of the run of the stairs. This length may be obtained also from the details on the plans. The stair well length forms the base of a right-angled triangle. The height of the triangle and the base of the triangle have now been obtained.

To obtain the width of each tread, divide the number of risers, less one—since there is always one more riser than tread—into the run of the stairs.

The numbers thus obtained are to be used on the steel square in laying off the run and rise of each tread and riser on the stringer stock. These figures will be about 7" and 10", respectively, since the ideal run and rise totals 17". Lay off the run and rise of each step on the stringer stock equal to the number of risers previously obtained by dividing the story pole into equal spaces. The distances of the height, base, and hypotenuse of a right-angled triangle are thus obtained.

The apprentice will see the problems involved in stair construction if a diagram is made of the right-angled triangle, placing the distances, to scale, as previously explained.

After the stringer has been marked off there are several ways to build up a stairway. One way is to cut out the run and rise of each step and nail this notched piece to the side of a 2" x 12" piece, completely boxing in the cut-out stringer. Two members will be required in this type of construction, one for each side of the staircase. Another way is to take the cut-out stringers and place them in place, using two or three as a backbone for the treads and risers. Porch stringers and basement stringers are generally built up this way.

The specific details of each set of plans must be studied and the stair framing done as specified. The carpenter is responsible for the framing of stringers, platforms, etc., so that the stair builder can build on the trim as furnished by the mill.

Illustrations in Chapter 10 show many details of stair construction. Carpenters must follow details carefully from as early in construction as the framing of floor joists for the stair well.

Stairs in dwellings may be open, closed, winding, or platform types. Open stairs, such as are placed in basement, are free of walls. Closed stairs, which may extend from the first floor to the second floor, are closed in by one or two walls. Winding stairs may be free of walls or closed in by walls and involve more elaborate and complicated construction. Platform stairs have a short or a long landing in the staircase, at which point the direction is changed, usually at a right angle.

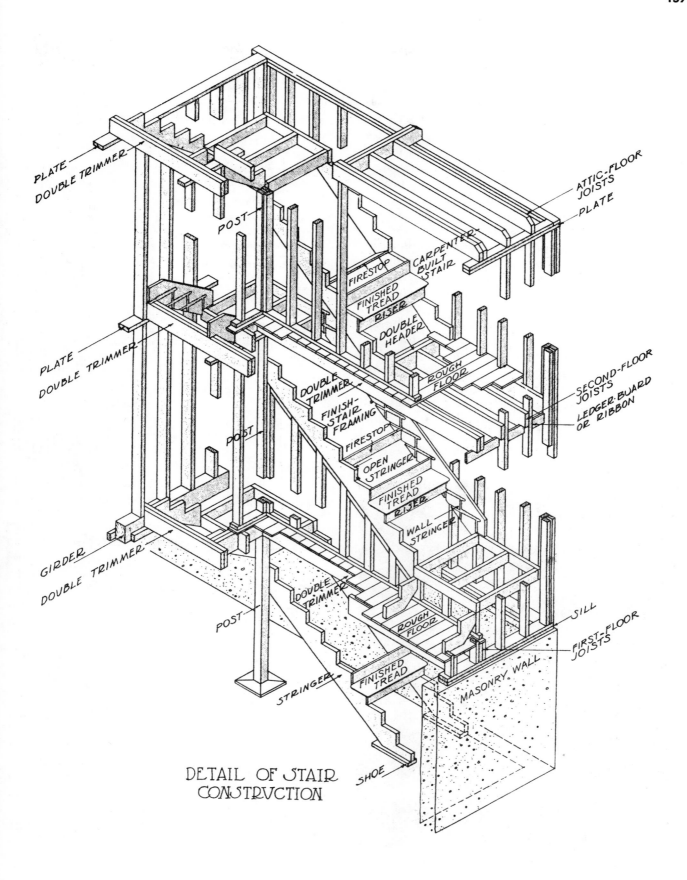

PLATE
DOUBLE TRIMMER
POST
ATTIC-FLOOR JOISTS
PLATE
FIRESTOP
CARPENTER BUILT STAIR
FINISHED TREAD
RISER
DOUBLE HEADER
PLATE
DOUBLE TRIMMER
DOUBLE TRIMMER
FINISH-STAIR FRAMING
FIRESTOP
OPEN STRINGER
ROUGH FLOOR
SECOND-FLOOR JOISTS
LEDGER-BOARD OR RIBBON
POST
FINISHED TREAD
RISER
WALL STRINGER
GIRDER
DOUBLE TRIMMER
POST
DOUBLE TRIMMER
ROUGH FLOOR
SILL
FIRST-FLOOR JOISTS
STRINGER
FINISHED TREAD
MASONRY WALL
SHOE

DETAIL OF STAIR
CONSTRUCTION

The combined widths of a tread and riser generally equal 17″, the tread width being 10″ and the riser height 7″. The head room should be not less than 7′.

In estimating the quantity of material for stairs each piece must be listed separately. The rough framing will take at least three lengths of 2″ x 10″ stock, plus the 2″ x 4″ or 2″ x 6″ framing stock for platforms. Finished material from the mill is sold in sets and ordered by the size of stairs at hand.

The illustrations at the right show the typical parts of stairs as milled at a wood mill.

The word *stair* means 'any one of a set of steps connecting different levels' and is usually used in the plural as in the word *stairs*. The word *staircase* means 'a flight of steps with handrails, balusters, etc.' This term implies the whole unit of stair work done by a staircase builder. The term *stairway* carries the same meaning as the term *stair* or *stairs*.

The rise of a stair step is measured from the top of one tread to the top of the next. The total rise of the stairs is the height from one floor level to another. In dwelling construction no stairs should have more than 15 steps in a flight.

Stair work is generally milled at a planing mill or in a millwork factory and assembled on the job. The work of assembling, fitting, and joining of finished stair work is done by an expert known as a stair builder.

Turn at landing accommodates limited space.

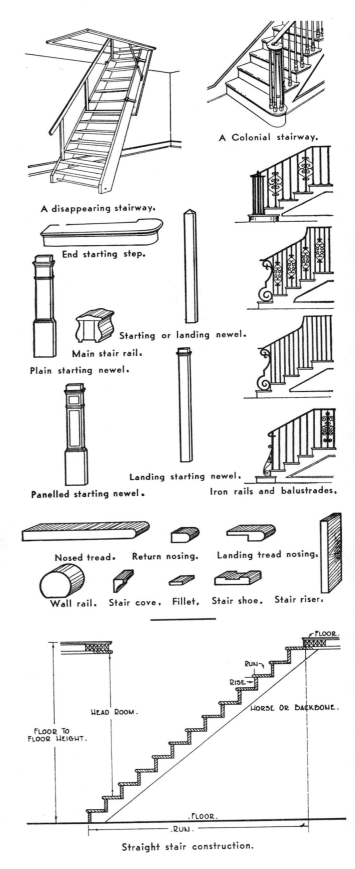

A disappearing stairway.

A Colonial stairway.

End starting step.

Starting or landing newel.

Main stair rail.

Plain starting newel.

Landing starting newel.

Panelled starting newel.

Iron rails and balustrades.

Nosed tread.   Return nosing.   Landing tread nosing.

Wall rail.   Stair cove.   Fillet.   Stair shoe.   Stair riser.

Straight stair construction.

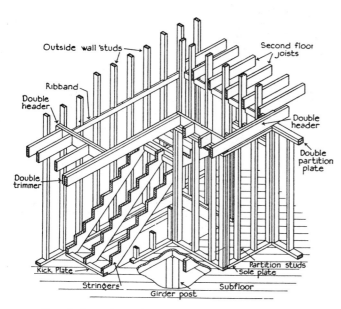

Rough framed members of isometric cutaway view.

Labels on isometric view: Outside wall studs; Second floor joists; Ribband; Double header; Double header; Double partition plate; Double trimmer; Kick Plate; Partition studs; Sole plate; Stringers; Girder post; Subfloor

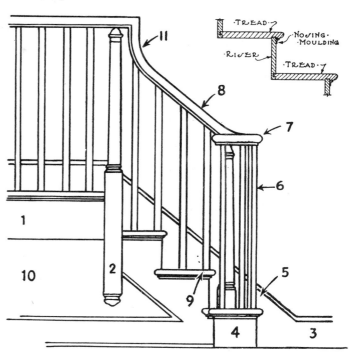

TREAD; NOSING; MOULDING; RISER; TREAD

Stair components: 1, fascia board; 2, newel; 3, base board; 4, bullnose step; 5, skirt board; 6, balusters; 7, volute; 8, hand rail; 9, return nosing; 10, spandrel; 11, goose neck.

Stairs built in the garage as access to storage space in attic.

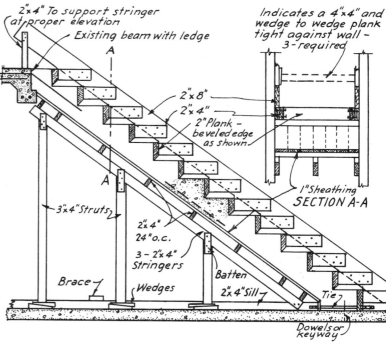

Labels: 2"x4" To support stringer at proper elevation; Existing beam with ledge; Indicates a 4"x4" and wedge to wedge plank tight against wall — 3-required; A; 2"x8"; 2"x4"; 2"Plank — beveled edge as shown; A; 3"x4" Struts; 2"x4" 24"o.c.; 3 – 2"x4" Stringers; 1"Sheathing SECTION A-A; Brace; Wedges; Batten; 2"x4"Sill; Tie; Dowels or keyway

Elevation and section of wooden frame construction of a substantial form for a poured re-enforced concrete stairs. Note the sturdy construction and proper bracing at all points.

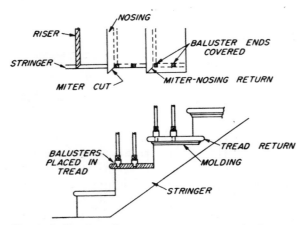

Plan and elevation of open stringer cut out to fit the risers and treads.

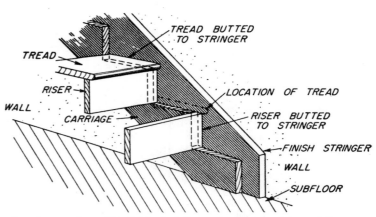

A cutaway view of a finished stair construction having a stringer as a support for a carriage which in turn supports the butted tread and riser members. A carriage is known also as a stair horse or stair backbone.

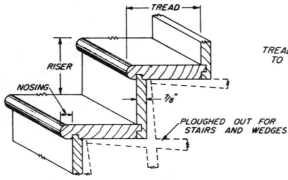

A sectional view showing the top of a stair riser tongued into the front of a stair tread and the back of the tread tongued into the bottom of the next riser.

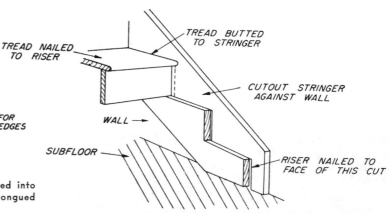

A cut-out wall stringer superimposed over treads and risers.

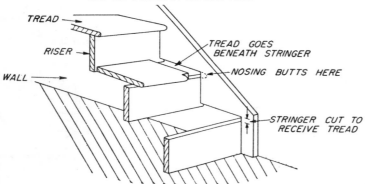

A cut-out stringer having the same rise and run as the stair carriage but cut out in reverse, allowing the stair treads and risers to run underneath the tread and riser cuts on the cut-out stringer.

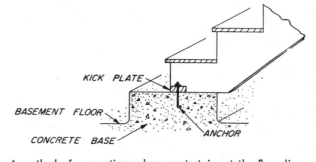

A method of supporting a basement stairs at the floor line.

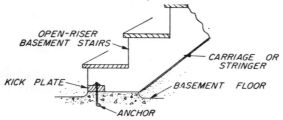

A method of terminating a basement stairs at a height of one riser above the floor level. No riser members are used in this construction.

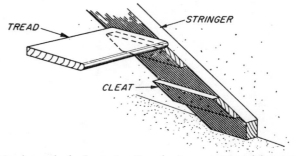

A simple method of constructing short-run stairs and basement stairs. The treads are supported by cleats nailed securely to the inside faces of the stringers.

23

Trim

Woodwork in a dwelling may be divided roughly into framing and interior or exterior trim work. Carpenters may specialize in framing up the framing stock or in placing on the finished millwork, either on the exterior or interior of a house. The mill supplies practically all pieces of interior and exterior trim cut to shape, and the finish carpenter is concerned with cutting pieces to length and making accurate joints. The exterior trim around porches, stoops, verandas, and on side walls, if of wood, is a painstaking job and requires just as much skill as the placing of interior trim.

Interior trim work consists of baseboards, plate rails, picture moldings, door casings, door hanging, window casings, window hanging and fitting—in fact, all fine wood or metal work which is exposed to view.

places. In some cases the cutting of lengths must be done and joints made. In many cases trim comes from the mill in wrapped packages and requires only the careful fitting and hanging or attaching to make a good job.

In working up trim around a door opening the carpenter should place the lower pieces on first, if a base block is designated, allowing for the thickness of the finished flooring. If the side pieces or casings are not cut, the proper butt or mitered joint must be made with a high degree of accuracy. Finishing nails must be used in all cases and set below the surface level so that the painter can putty the holes and apply paint or varnish to make an even surface.

In most all cases the window frame is set in place before the plastering is done. This allows the plas-

WALL TRIM.

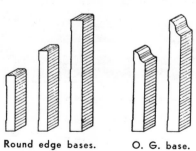

Wall strip.

Closet pole.

Ceiling coves.

Picture mold.

Shelf cleat.   Base mold.   Quarter-round.   R-E base shoe.

Clove-leaf shoe.

Round edge bases.   O. G. base.   Molded base.

The bill of materials, specifications, and plans designate the style and location of all trim. A wide variety of trim is made available in order to give individual style and character to a dwelling.

All trim must be attached to the designated

DOOR OR WINDOW TRIM.

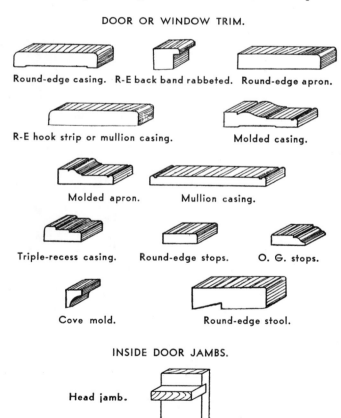

Round-edge casing.   R-E back band rabbeted.   Round-edge apron.

R-E hook strip or mullion casing.   Molded casing.

Molded apron.   Mullion casing.

Triple-recess casing.   Round-edge stops.   O. G. stops.

Cove mold.   Round-edge stool.

INSIDE DOOR JAMBS.

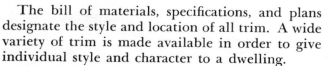

Head jamb.

Side jamb.

Round-edge stop.   Threshold.   O. G. stop.

terer to bring the plaster up tight against the frame, on all sides, top, and bottom. The trim is placed around the casing in much the same manner as door trim is placed around the door header and jambs. The fitting of the stool on the sill must be done with care so that the sash slides down properly. The apron trim must be tight against the stool stock.

Study the details of window construction and door construction in order to be well acquainted with the many parts involved since trim is applied

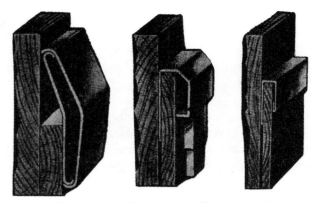

Snap-on and slip-in base moldings of steel.

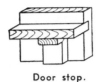

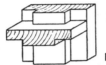

Door stop.

Rabbeted side jamb.   Rabbeted head jamb.

Rabbeted side jamb (both sides)

Rabbeted head jamb (both sides)

WINDOW TRIM.

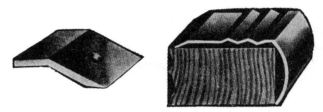

Carpet trim and stair tread nosing of aluminum.

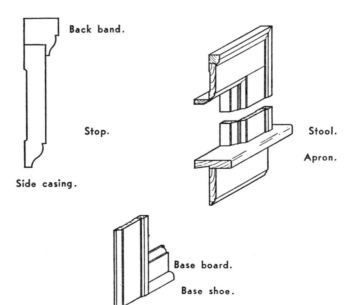

Back band.

Stop.

Stool.

Apron.

Side casing.

Base board.

Base shoe.

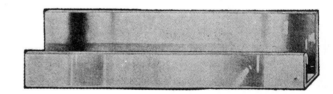

Three styles of snap-on moldings of steel.

in connection with these operations. Window fitting is discussed in Chapter 24, door hanging is discussed in Chapter 25. Finish floor laying is considered in Chapter 28.

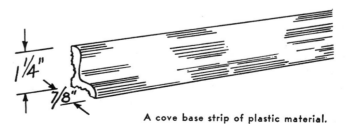

1/4"   7/8"

A cove base strip of plastic material.

Trim members meeting on inside corners are open coped—that is, the shape of the joint takes the special shape of the member to be fitted by marking thereon. Trim members on outside joints are mitered at the required angle and this must be done with hairline joints.

Metal sash placed in a framed wall may require no trim whatsoever. A window stool of marble may be specified, and, if so, is set placed by the mason.

Of the several wood stock items used in finish carpentry probably the most widely used mill products are plywoods and pines. Of all of the wood species manufactured into lumber, ponderosa pine is an outstanding material. Ponderosa pine is soft textured, with typically straight, close and uniform grain. It is unexcelled for smoothness and fine appearance when surfaced and easy to work with both hand tools and machine tools. It is used extensively in the manufacture of sash, doors, blinds, moldings, paneling, mantels, trim, and built-in cases and cabinets. Knotty ponderosa pine is used extensively for interior finish and the intermediate grades are used for sheathing, subflooring, and roof boards.

The wood of ponderosa pine is light in color, varying from creamy white to straw, a distinctly light wood, and, after surfacing and sanding, presents a delicately figured grain. For its weight, this pine ranks high in strength properties for all of its uses. It equals the average of the white pines in bending strength, compressive strength and shock resistance, but is somewhat harder and slightly less stiff than soft-textured pines.

All woods shrink as they dry and swell as they absorb moisture. The heavier woods, as a group, shrink and swell more than the lighter species with any given change in moisture content. The shrinkage of ponderosa pine, a light wood, is about equal to the average for the soft-textured pines, which when compared to all softwoods, is very little. Wood, however, unlike metal, does not appreciably expand or contract with changes in temperature. The normal season changes on moisture content of interior finishes are not enough to cause serious dimensional change is the stock is properly seasoned and the woodwork is carefully designed and assembled. Large members of interior trim, such as ornamental beams, cornices, newel posts, stair stringers, and hand rails should be built up from comparatively small pieces of stock. Wide, plain surfaces, such as table tops, counter tops, and panels should be crossbanded. Door and window

trim and baseboards should be hollow-backed. Backband trim, if mitered at the corners, should be glued and splined before erection; otherwise butt joints should be used for the wide faces.

Large solid pieces, such as knotty pine panels, should be stained and finished as much as possible before erection and should be so designed and installed that the panels are free to move across the grain.

The low shrinkage and swelling of pine makes it an outstanding wood material for the manufacture of sash and doors and many other types of trim work as well as for use in light construction requiring close-fitting joints and high dimensional stability.

Grain is often used in reference to the annual rings, as in fine grain and coarse grain. It is also employed to indicate the direction of the fibers, as in straight grain, spiral grain, and curly grain. Texture is often used synonymously with grain, but usually it refers to the finer structure of the wood rather than to the annual rings. Raised grain, which develops from uneven shrinkage is flat-grained pieces of some of the heavier woods, is not found in pine because of its slight shrinkage.

The ability to stay in place is synonymous with dimensional stability and depends upon the amount of shrinkage and swelling, either sectionally or throughout the whole board, that the wood will undergo in actual service. Because of its low shrinkage and swelling, pine stock is classed as one of the premier woods in dimensional stability.

Well known for their resistance to splitting, the soft-textured pines are woodworkers' favorites for their ability to take nails without extra care in fastener selection. Ponderosa pine, because of its low density, soft texture, and uniform grain, nails more easily and has less tendency to split than harder, denser softwoods. In general, relative resistance to nail withdrawal is dependent upon specific gravity; the higher the wood's specific gravity, the greater the resistance. Under actual service conditions, lower withdrawal resistance in the light density softwoods is more than offset by the increased split resistance, for proportionately larger nails may be used without fear of splitting to accomplish withdrawal resistance comparable with heavier woods. Nails driven into lead holes with a diameter slightly smaller than the nail have somewhat higher withdrawal resistance than nails driven without lead holes. Lead holes also prevent or reduce splitting of the wood.

Grain texture is important in nailing. Hard, easily separated fibers cause deflection of nails. Even-textured pine allows nails to be driven straight and true. Always important is the relative dryness of lumber when nailed. Improperly seasoned lumber, shrinking after installation, allows wood fibers to pull away from fasteners, which is not true in dry lumber. A nail with a long, sharp point will usually have a higher withdrawal resistance, particularly in the softer woods, than the common wire nails, which usually has a diamond point. A nail tapered at the end and terminating in a blunt point will cause less splitting than the common nail.

Pine is widely known for its high degree of workability with either hand tools or machine tools and is universally respected by woodworkers for the ease with which it is fashioned into fine moldings and other intricate detail work. Pine produces a lustrous finish requiring only the slightest amount of sanding to remove surface inequalities. The ability of a wood to take and hold a protective coating, an important factor in its use, rests upon the wood's natural characteristics. Soft texture, uniform cell structure, and low resin content are essential.

Another outstanding wood stock used in finish carpentry is the Douglas fir. This wood is straight-grained, moderately heavy, and normally dense. It is classed as a resinous wood, although the amount of resin is limited. It machines to a smooth, even surface. The sapwood ring in Douglas fir is almost pure white in color and very narrow. The heartwood is orange red in color, making the color contrast between springwood and summerwood quite distinct.

Douglas fir is used for many glued-up products such as furniture, shelving, and cabinets, as well as in the manufacture of framing lumber, window frames, door frames, and interior trim. Pound for pound, it is one of the strongest softwoods being used in many instances where strength is the primary requirement.

Douglas fir ranks approximately midway among all commercial softwoods in nail-holding ability. It is a good practice to drive nails or turn screws into lumber after it has been brought to a moisture content consistent with atmospheric conditions at point of use. This is true because wood fibers shrink slightly around the nail shank as moisture content decreases. Care must be exercised when using sharp-pointed nails to avoid splitting. Douglas fir, of relatively high specific gravity, tends to split more readily than softer textured woods. Average handling care and the use of proper fasteners will prevent most splitting problems. Blunt-pointed or ordinary common nails will cause very little trouble. Douglas fir works very readily by machine or hand tools and glues satisfactorily with different glues with moderate care in the gluing operations.

A third outstanding material used for interior work is plywood or crossbanded wood panels. Plywood is a term generally used to designate glued wood panels that are made up of layers, or plies, with the grain of one or more layers at an angle, usually 90 degrees, with the grain of the others. The outside plies are called faces or face and back, the center ply or plies are called the core. The plies immediately below the face and back, laid at right angles to them are called the crossbands.

The essential features of plywood are embodied in other glued constructions with many variations of details. The core may be veneer, lumber, or various combinations of veneer and lumber; the total thickness may be less than $\frac{1}{16}''$ or more than $3''$; the different plies may vary as to lumber, thickness, and kinds of wood; and the shape of the members also may vary.

The crossbands and their arrangement largely govern the properties, particularly the warping characteristics, and the uses of all such constructions. When compared with solid wood, the chief advantages of plywood are its approach to equalization of strength properties along the length and width of the panel, greater resistance to checking and splitting, and less change in dimensions with changes in moisture content. The greater the number of plies for a given thickness, the more nearly equal are the strength and shrinkage properties along and across the panel and the greater the resistance to splitting.

The tendency of crossbanded products to warp as the result of stresses caused by shrinkage and swelling is largely eliminated by balanced construction. This construction consists of arranging the plies in pairs about the core, so that for each ply there is an opposite, similar, and parallel ply. The use of an odd number of plies permits an arrangement that gives a substantially balanced effect; that is, when three plies are glued together with the grain of the outer two piles at right angles to the grain of the center ply, the stresses are balanced and the panel tends to remain flat with the moisture content changes. Broadly speaking, two classes of plywod are available: hardwood and softwood. Most softwood playwood is made of Douglas fir; but western hemlock, white fir, ponderosa pine, redwood, and other species are used. Hardwood plywood is made of many species.

Having considered a few of the characteristics of some of the materials used by the finish carpenter it is well to point out ways of handling tools and equipment. In laying out work on stock care must be taken to avoid waste and to simplify the tool operations. When many pieces are to be cut from a large piece of stock it is easiest to sketch the arrangement on a piece of paper, then transfer for exact cutting. Be sure to allow for saw cuts between adjacent pieces. Try to work out the markings on the larger pieces of stock so that the first one or two saw cuts will reduce the larger pieces by halves for easier handling. One of the most important points to watch in planning the sequence of operations is to cut all mating or matching parts with the same saw setting. In cutting plywood always watch the direction of the face grain when sawing.

In using a hand saw, place the stock on the horse or support with the good or finish face up. Use a crosscut saw for sawing across the grain and a rip saw for sawing with the grain of the wood. In sawing thin pieces, splitting can be eliminated by placing a scrap of lumber under the stock, which also helps to hold the saw at a low angle. Most important of all is to use a good, sharp saw.

In using a powered saw, such as a band saw or a radial saw, always place the good face of the stock up. When a radial saw is used in cutting plywood use a sharp combination blade or a fine-tooth blade without much set. Let the blade of the saw protrude above the stock just the height of the teeth. In sawing large panels of plywood an easier job can be done if an extension support, with rollers, is built on the same level with a saw table. In sawing long lengths with a portable hand saw the good face of the stock should be kept down. A support can be placed below the stock to avoid sagging and striking the saw on the horse.

If edges of stock are exposed in the finish work, use a block or bench plane working from the ends of the stock toward the center to avoid tearing off small slivers from the length nearest the ends.

Practically all finish stock comes to the job milled to proper thicknesses, there being need of but cutting lengths and widths to fit into particular places.

After the needed sawing operations, rough edges, if any, can be taken off by a block plane or a smooth plane. Ofttimes sandpaper on a sanding block is used to touch up rough spots. The sanding of the face of plywood is unnecessary since the sheets are already sanded.

NOTE—For installation of baseboard heating systems, see Chapter 14—Heating Installations and Air Conditioning.

Louvered closet doors are a standard in interior trim in the warmer climates.

Shutters are a traditional form of exterior trim. Their functionalism has never diminished.

24

Windows and Window Walls

Framing of the openings for windows and doors is described in Chapters 10, 11, and 12. The window frame itself is made up of the several members as illustrated in the details on the opposite page. Different types of outside walls and inside walls require slight changes in the kind of frames used. These different frames are shown in various illustrations throughout this book.

The term *sash* is used loosely to designate not only the several members in a dwelling which hold the glass in place but also the frames in which these members are placed. A correct designation of a sash is but one unit of a window set holding one or several pieces of glass in a window frame. *Sashes* are the entire lot of sashes used in a building.

The mill furnishes many items already cut and ready to install. Several types, styles, and special sashes and windows are shown in the following illustrations.

Each sash is fitted after all plastering has been done. Reference must be made to the door and window schedule on the set of plans to determine exactly where each sash is used. Sashes come from the mill already glazed, primed with paint, and ready to be fittted into the frame.

Select the proper sash for the respective opening and try in the frame. In almost all cases the side members of each sash, or stile, will have to be hand-planed a bit to form a good sliding fit in the frame. Plane off equal amounts from each stile and round off the corners a bit to insure easy installation.

Place the upper sash in position and trim off a slight portion of the top rail of the sash to insure a good fit, then tack the upper sash in position. Fit the lower sash in position by trimming off the stiles. Place the lower sash in position and trim off, from the bottom rail, a sufficient amount to permit the meeting rails (lower rail of upper sash and top rail of bottom sash) to meet on the level. Study of the details will show need of a slight bevel on the meeting rails, to provide a tight fit and to provide a proper position for the latch.

If sash weights are used, remove each sash after it has been properly fitted and weigh each one. Select sash weights equal to half the weight of each sash and place in position in the weight pocket. Measure proper length of sash cord for lower sash

and attach the stile and weight on both sides. Adjust length of cord so that sash moves up and down easily and the weight does not strike the pulley or rest on the frame. Install the cord and weights for the upper sash and adjust the cord and weight so that each cord and weight runs smoothly. Close the pockets in the frame and put in blind stop, parting stop, and bead stop, and the installation is completed.

Sash balances may be used instead of cord and weights and are easy to install. In heavy sash, chains or steel ropes may be used instead of sash cord and are attached to weights as shown on page 170, lower left.

A casement type of sash is hinged by the use of surface hinges or butt hinges and must be fitted accurately. Transom sashes are fitted with a variety of transom sash hardware which must be fitted according to manufacturer's directions given with the respective sets of hardware.

Installation of steel sash is illustrated on page 172. Manufacturers' literature usually provides adequate instructions for installation of the particular type of steel sash they supply.

Several patented complete window sets are on the market and have various merits. A study of trade magazines will give one many ideas.

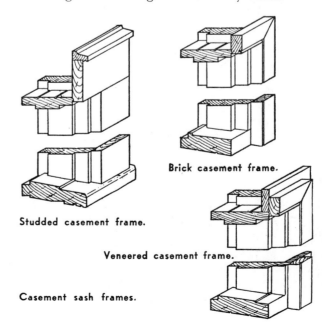

Brick casement frame.

Studded casement frame.

Veneered casement frame.

Casement sash frames.

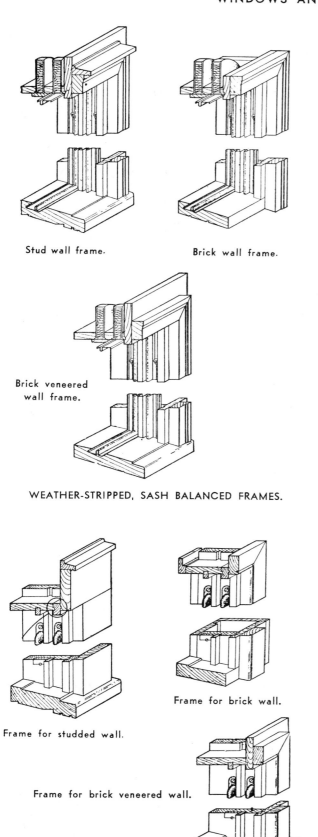

Stud wall frame.

Brick wall frame.

Brick veneered
wall frame.

WEATHER-STRIPPED, SASH BALANCED FRAMES.

Frame for studded wall.

Frame for brick wall.

Frame for brick veneered wall.

REGULAR WINDOW FRAMES.

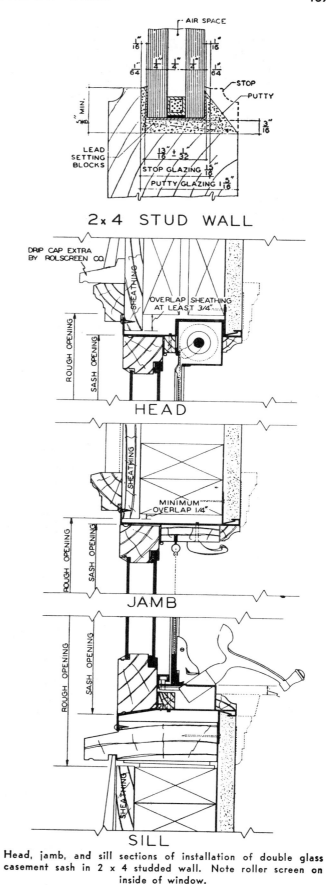

2 x 4 STUD WALL

HEAD

JAMB

SILL

Head, jamb, and sill sections of installation of double glass casement sash in 2 x 4 studded wall. Note roller screen on inside of window.

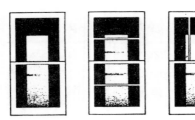
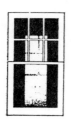
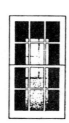

Regular two-light, not divided.
Top and bottom divided, 2 lights high.
Two-light top divided, 3 lights wide.

Two-light top divided, 6 lights.
Top and bottom divided, 6 lights.

FIVE STYLES OF SASHES.

Sash lock.   Hook sash lift.   Bar sash lift.

Braided sash cord.   Sash weight.   Sash chain.

Muntin bars for divided lights in all 2-light windows
are ⅜-inch between glass or ¾-inch overall.

Sash pulleys.   Sash stop.   Spring bolt.

Jamb type sash balance.

SASH HARDWARE.

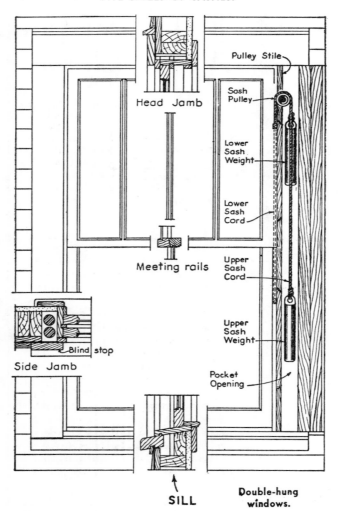

Head Jamb
Pulley Stile
Sash Pulley
Lower Sash Weight
Lower Sash Cord
Meeting rails
Upper Sash Cord
Upper Sash Weight
Blind stop
Side Jamb
Pocket Opening

SILL   Double-hung windows.

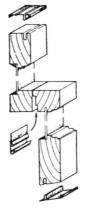
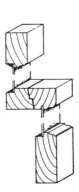

Weather-stripped sashes.   Regular window sashes.

Metal louver section.

Wooden ventilators or louvers.

Window Planning Principles

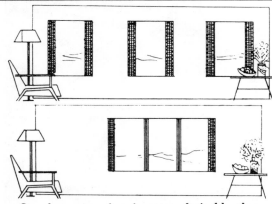

One large opening is more desirable than several small windows. Not only does the former provide a better distribution of light but dark areas between smaller openings are eliminated as well as undesirable contrasts in brightness.

Windows in more than one wall give more effective light distribution throughout the room. Strip or clerestory windows furnish light and ventilation with maximum privacy.

Consideration should be given in the placing of windows so that sills and horizontal muntins or rails do not interfere with vision either seated or standing. The sketches show the eye-level range for persons sitting and standing. Avoid horizontal window divisions within these levels. Dimensions are based on persons from 5'-0" to 6'-4" tall as well as the usual window head and sill heights as determined by furniture.

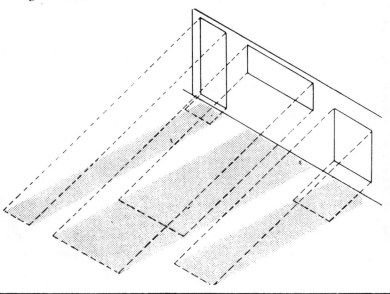

Window shapes may be selected to give any desired distribution of light within the room. This diagram shows graphically how the sun's rays entering a room at a 45° angle give various patterns of light depending upon the shape of the opening. The closer the head of the window is to the ceiling, the greater the depth of penetration, as shown in openings 1 and 2. Opening 3, placed lower in the wall creates a much shorter light pattern. Strip windows, opening 2, are desirable where it is preferable to have the area beneath in shadow such as a bedroom. This diagram also illustrates why it is desirable to use windows in more than one wall for better distribution of daylight.

Steel Sashes

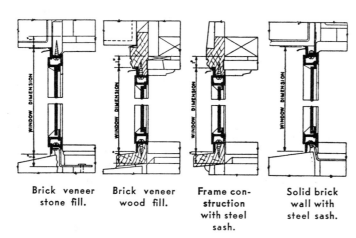

Brick veneer stone fill.   Brick veneer wood fill.   Frame construction with steel sash.   Solid brick wall with steel sash.

DETAILS OF INSTALLATION OF STEEL SASH
IN FOUR TYPES OF WALLS.

Steel top and bottom divided sash.

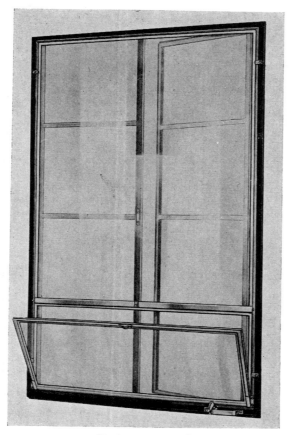

Steel casement sash.

Installation of Etling In-Swinging Window

A double-hung, in-swinging window unit is installed in the same manner as the conventional double-hung window. Fig. 1 shows the frame and upper and lower sashes partially opened to show the in-swing of each member. The sashes slide up and down, in an open or closed position, and hang suspended at any desired height.

Fig. 2, the cross-section detail, cut horizontally at the jambs, shows the method of placing the window unit in a rough stud opening. The wall studs must be doubled and framed to a rough opening 7″ greater than the width of the glass. This unit is held in place by nailing through the blind stop to the framed stud. For twin units of windows 13″ is added to the total glass width, and for triple units of windows 19″ is added to the total glass width to determine the rough opening of the studding at the respective openings.

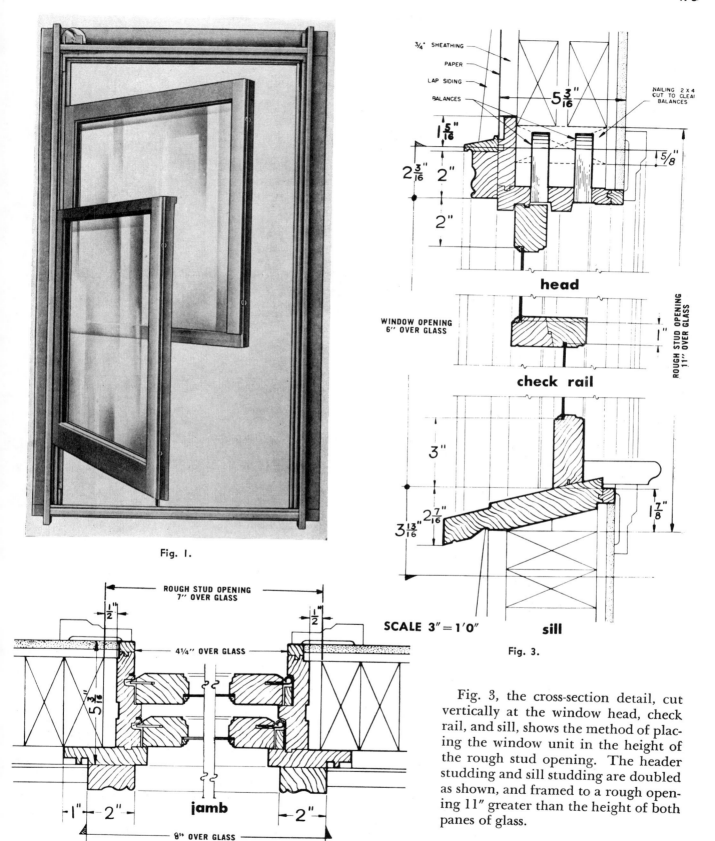

Fig. 1.

head

check rail

SCALE 3" = 1'0"

sill

Fig. 3.

Fig. 2.

jamb

Fig. 3, the cross-section detail, cut vertically at the window head, check rail, and sill, shows the method of placing the window unit in the height of the rough stud opening. The header studding and sill studding are doubled as shown, and framed to a rough opening 11" greater than the height of both panes of glass.

Glass Block

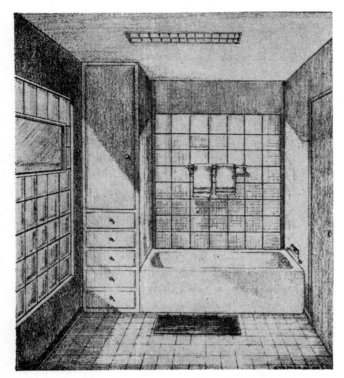

Penciled perspective of two paneled walls of glass blocks.

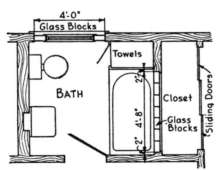

Plan of bathroom.

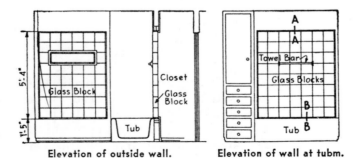

Elevation of outside wall.   Elevation of wall at tubm.

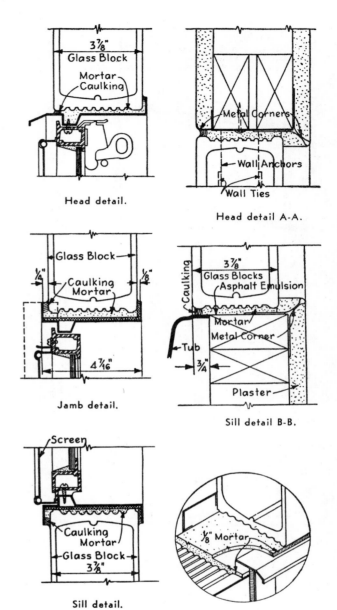

Head detail.

Head detail A-A.

Jamb detail.

Sill detail B-B.

Sill detail.

Method of bedding drip flange in mortar joint.

Glass block is universal in its appeal and widespread use in house construction. The use of glass block in the bathroom permits a sturdiness and variation in design which makes for beauty and cleanliness. The desire for an abundance of outside light without a sacrifice of a privacy which is an essential part of all bathrooms has been obtained by providing a large panel of glass block on the exterior wall as shown in the penciled perspective

sketch. A steel frame with hinged steel sash is installed in the upper part of the panel for ventilation.

The floor plan and elevations illustrate the possibilities and extent to which glass block can be used. When placed on rear wall of tub recess, the glass wall serves a twofold purpose: one of providing a clean, splashproof back panel that can be cleaned in a jiffy; and another of permitting an infiltration of light through the glass into the adjoining closet. Towel bars of structural glass can be securely fastened to glass block, providing uniformity of appearance. Details A-A and B-B indicate the ease with which glass units can be applied to the flange of a tub and to adjoining wall materials.

Sectional views of the window head, jamb, and sill are shown and indicate the methods of construction. Note that a special steel frame with flanges on jam and sill and drip cap at the head provides an enclosure for the standard type of sash to be used. All glass blocks are tied together with galvanized wall ties every third course.

Glass block as light aid to plants.

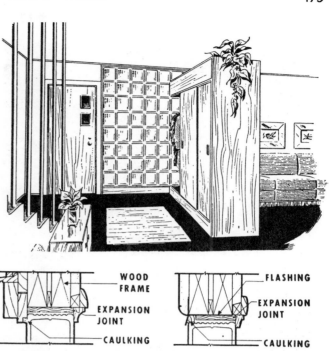

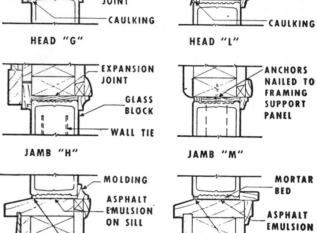

HEAD "G"
WOOD FRAME
EXPANSION JOINT
CAULKING

HEAD "L"
FLASHING
EXPANSION JOINT
CAULKING

JAMB "H"
EXPANSION JOINT
GLASS BLOCK
WALL TIE

JAMB "M"
ANCHORS NAILED TO FRAMING SUPPORT PANEL

MOLDING
ASPHALT EMULSION ON SILL
RAKE AND CAULK

MORTAR BED
ASPHALT EMULSION
CAULKING

Sectional details of glass block installation in framed and stucco walls.

Glass block below high windows.

The framing of a window over a kitchen sink is made attractive by the use of glass blocks.

Window Walls

Large-area window wall panels.

The method of framing at the right can be applied to all openings in the house regardless of their location. The units to be used, ranging in groups from two to nine both horizontally and vertically, are of a size to meet all conditions. This standardization is of particular value in window wall construction where a maximum of nine units, three high and three wide, are integrated into one large frame.

Picture window units make window wall.

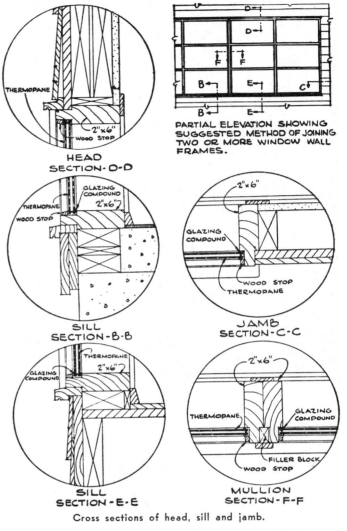

PARTIAL ELEVATION SHOWING SUGGESTED METHOD OF JOINING TWO OR MORE WINDOW WALL FRAMES.

Cross sections of head, sill and jamb.

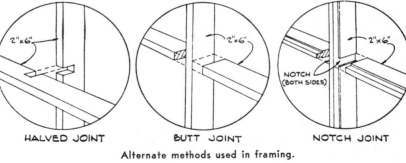

Alternate methods used in framing.

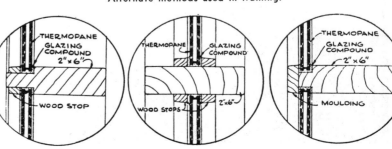

Alternate position of glass and stops.

The Manufacture of Glass

The manufacture of glass dates back to the days of the Egyptians, although it was the Venetians who first made small plates of glass for windows.

Through the Middle Ages little progress was made, nor was glass employed extensively in architecture. It was not until the coming of the Machine Age with the corresponding advance in house building, that glass became an important building material. Strangely enough, no machinery was designed for the actual manufacture of glass until the last century. Prior to then glass was hand-blown by men (glass blowers, they were called) through tubes dipped in molten glass, into cylinders which were cut apart and flattened into sheets before being cooled.

Glass is made from silicates or sand, together with lime and other chemicals, which are melted in glass tank furnaces at extremely high temperatures.

Glass tank furnace.

A small amount of broken glass or *cullet* is always included as, strangely enough, this lowers the melting point. The furnaces are seldom allowed to cool, since, when once shut down, several weeks are required to get them into operation again.

Ladling out glass.

The molten glass is ladled out of the furnace and the ladle is conveyed by overhead track to the casting table where the glass is poured out and rolled into a large sheet. This makes what is known as flat-drawn glass, in comparison with the old cylin-

drical or hand-blown product, and the waves and imperfections can thus be eliminated mechanically to secure glass which will be stronger and clearer. The flat-drawn process was invented by a Belgian, Fourcault, and most of the machines and improvements to them are still covered by patents.

Processing of glass.

Rolled sheet and wired glass is further processed at this point to retard direct vision, improve daylight illumination, or provide glass which will withstand a breakdown test of 1800° F. as required by the Underwriters' Laboratories for fireproof work. The wide variety of opaque, translucent, and decorative glass available today at small cost is indeed a tribute to the progressiveness of the industry.

The sheets of glass, after being rolled, pass through cooling chambers, or lehrs, where the temperature is gradually reduced so that the difference between internal and external stress will not cause the glass to shatter when handled. When cool, the

Cooling chamber.

glass is taken from the lehr to the cutting tables and cut into stock-sized sheets. Plate glass then goes to the polishing plant where the surfaces are rubbed uniformly until they have the required luster. Plate-glass mirrors are first given chemical baths to

Cutting table.

clean the surface of all impurities before they are coated with silver.

The silver coating in turn is protected by an electrolytic copper backing on the more expensive mirrors and varnish on cheaper products.

Boxing glass.

Window glass is uniformly boxed, the insides of the boxes being lined with straw so that glass can be shipped and transported with a negligible amount of breakage. Huge stocks are of necessity maintained, as the manufacturing process cannot be speeded up nor slowed down to suit the fluctuation in demand for building products.

How Wooden Sashes Are Made

The manufacture of window sashes is carried on simultaneously with the production of doors for the reason that the sashes use up the shorter and smaller cuttings which would otherwise be a waste product in a door factory. This does not mean, however, that the grade of lumber used to make sashes is inferior to that required for doors. On the contrary, sash stock has to be very carefully selected for texture and grain so that it will machine smoothly and fit together snugly. The kiln-dried western pine lumber from which practically all sashes are made is surfaced ripped, cut, and stored. Cut stock is

later taken from the storage bins to be put through the factory in large runs—so that the machines can be set up several days on a single size.

The first operation is to work the various parts to pattern, which includes cutting the glass rabbet and putty lock grooves as well as the ogee molding.

Chain mortiser.

This is done on a *sticker* or *molder*. Sashes are all made mortise-and-tenon construction, and one of the important machines in the process of manufacture is the multiple chain mortiser. Storm sash stiles are loaded in a hopper and automatically

Hand assembly.

fed through the machine, coming out at the bottom mortised at both ends and in the center, at one operation. Double-end tenoners work the tenons on both ends of the rails simultaneously, and after several other operations, including ploughing and boring for sash cord, etc., the parts are ready to be keyed up.

The various sash parts are selected by bench men who stick them together by hand and get each sash into its approximate shape. The sashes then go to the clamps where they are drawn up to the exact size and are squared up. Care must be taken to see that the muntins are all in proper alignment and the sashes are then pinned at each joint with metal dowels, after which they are removed from the clamps and sent to the sanders. The sashes are fed through triple-drum sanders and the check-rail sides of windows are sanded on disc sanders.

Clamps.

At this point, modern science has injected a new operation consisting of immersing the completed sash in a tank containing a chemical solution which destroys all fungus growth in the wood. The solution does not harm the sash in any way but simply permeates the cell structure of the wood and poisons any living organism that may be there or that may attempt to work in later. The sash thus treated

Chemical baths.

are *rot-proofed* as well as *termite-proofed* and as the solution is a water repellent they are also *moisture-proofed* and will positively not absorb moisture later on to cause swelling and sticking.

The glass is filled-in, being first cut to proper size if necessary, and is held in place with diamond-shaped glazers' points. The putty is spread or run by experts who know how to keep the putty at just the right consistency and who work with lightning speed. The faster they work, the smoother and

Glazing.

more even is the finished job. A few minutes spent in the glazing room will convince anyone that factory glazing has many advantages both in cost and in finished appearance over glazing done on the job where the temperature and other conditions cannot be controlled.

After being glazed, the sashes are stacked, putty side up, for several days until the putty sets and hardens, and they are then put in stock, from which the orders can be filled promptly as they come in.

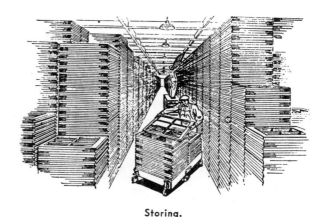

Storing.

For shipment, all windows and sashes are carefully and securely crated, with 200-lb. test corrugated board over all exposed glass surfaces. Breakage in transit is really no more serious than the breakage which usually occurs when glazing is done on the job, but where desired the sashes can be shipped open with the glass and putty boxed separately.

How Steel Sashes Are Made

Iron windows, as they were first called, were for many years looked upon with disfavor by the building industry in general and all lumbermen in particular. Thousands of reasons were advanced why they should be confined to fireproof buildings, but in spite of this resistance, they have come into general use for practically all types of buildings, largely due to the fact that, being metal, they can be completely fabricated with precision so that labor on the job is largely eliminated.

Flat steel, containing copper and other special alloys, is cut into strips and fed through rolling machines which form it into the various standard shapes. The smaller forms are cold-rolled while the heavier ones must be rolled hot, and of course the rollers are in reality dies working under tremendous pressure.

The rolled sections are cut to proper lengths and

then pass through a series of fabricating operations consisting of cutting the miters at the corners, punching the frame members for hardware and the sash members for muntins, and punching and

Rolling machine.

notching the muntins so they will interlock. The muntins are also punched for the wire glazing clips which later are used to secure the glass before the putty is applied.

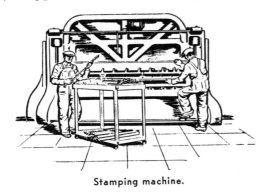

Stamping machine.

Then the various members are assembled, sashes and frames separately, and are then squared up and driven together by hand, securely enough to be

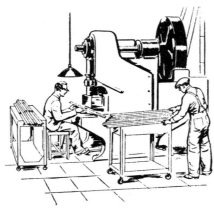

Punching machine.

welded. Electric welding is done in a heavy, powerful machine. The sash or frame is held square and in perfect alignment while the four corners are

welded from both sides and then ground off until they are smooth. After careful inspection and testing for alignment, the sashes go to the spot welder where the muntins are welded together so as to

Welder.

stiffen the sashes and make them leak-proof where the muntins intersect.

The sashes are now ready for installation in the frames, in the case of hinged sash, and both the

Spot welder.

hinges are riveted and then welded. After this the units are given final inspection to make sure they are still in alignment and close tightly. Among other tests, a piece of paper is inserted between the sash and frame members and must be held too tightly to move when the sash is closed.

From the inspector's bench, the sashes move on to the dipping tanks, where a series of baths remove all foreign matter and impurities, and coat every exposed part with heavy lead oxide primer. After passing on an overhead carrier through drying temperatures, the completed window units are placed in stock.

Metal screens and storm sashes are fabricated in much the same way as the sash, although of course the process is much simpler. The finish, however, is baked-on so that no further painting is ever required. The screen wire is rolled-in with splines and the glass is set in cork and felt bedding. Either iron or bronze hardware is available, and is shipped separately, boxed complete with proper machine screws for installation.

25

Doors

Framing for the openings for doors is described in Chapters 10 and 11.

The vertical members of a door frame are known as side jambs and the horizontal member is known as a door-frame head jamb. (See illustrations on page 182.)

All doors are fitted after all plastering, or other interior wall covering, is completed, since it is one of the final jobs of placing on the finish woodwork. Study the set of plans and determine the kinds of doors to be hung at outside openings, inside openings, closets, and cupboards. If sliding doors are designated, determine types and details of installation.

Select the doors and carry to the proper openings. Determine from the plans the hand of the door, that is, determine which way the door is to swing. Mark this swing on the floor, in chalk, in order to see that the door swing encounters no obstructions.

Hold the door up and sight along both edges to determine if there is wind or bow in the length. Any slight bow must be placed toward the sweep or swing of the door so that the wind can be drawn up somewhat by the center hinge.

Cut off the stile extensions, if any, and place the door in the opening. Plane the edges of the stiles until the door fits tightly against the hinge side and clears the lock side of the jamb about 1/16". Be certain the top fits squarely into the rabbeted recess and that the bottom swings free of the finish floor about ½". The lock stile of the door must be beveled slightly so that the arris of the stile will not strike the arris of the jamb. A sash must have a snug sliding fit, while a door must have a free-swinging fit in the frame. Hinges and a lock are to be attached to the door and the frame and due allowances must be made for these.

After proper clearances have been made, tack the door in position in the frames and wedge at the bottom. Obtain the set of butt hinges, generally three in number, and with a sharp-pointed knife mark positions of hinges on the stile and on the jamb. The lower hinge must be placed slightly above the lower rail of the door and the upper hinge of the door must be placed slightly below the top rail of the door in order to avoid cutting out a portion of the tenons of the door rails which are housed into the stile. The position of the hinges may be laid off by using a butt gauge. The use of this tool is described below and on the opposite page.

Using a butt chisel, cut out the wood and house the hinges snugly in place. The hinges must sink slightly below the surface of the wood. These mortised recesses for the hinges must be cleanly and squarely made, for any blemish will show up. Fasten the hinge leaves in place with the screws coming with the set and hang the door in position on the hinges. Swing the door gently, testing for accuracy of work. There must be no binding or catching of any kind.

After placing hinges in position, mark off on the lock stile the position of the lock set. The lock is placed about 36" from the floor level. Hold the case of the mortise lock on the face of the lock stile and mark off with a sharp knife the area to remove from the edge of the stile to house the entire case. Mark off position of door knob hub and position of key. Mark off position of strike on the jamb and everything is ready for the removal of the wood to house the lock and strike. Bore out and chisel cleanly the mortises and fit lock set in perfectly. Check over the job for any adjustments, seeing that hinges and lock work perfectly.

There are many different styles of lock sets, cylinder locks, door guards, etc., to attach to doors, and manufacturers supply detailed instructions for installation with each particular set. Refer to the illustrations of builders' hardware in Chapter 26.

Using a Butt Gauge in Hanging a Door

In hanging doors there are three measurements to be marked: the location of the butt on the casing, the location of the butt on the door, and the thickness of butt on both casing and door. A butt gauge has three separate cutters arranged with the necessary clearances so that no change of setting is necessary when hanging a number of doors. It serves also as a rabbet gauge, marking gauge, and mortise gauge and has a scope sufficient for all door trim including lock plates, strike plates, etc.

The illustrations show the method of using butt

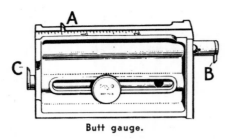

Butt gauge.

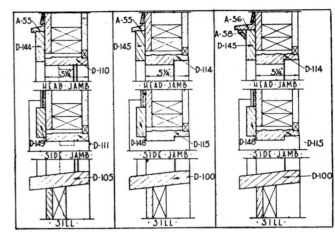

Doors placed in frame in studded wall.

gauges on doors having rabbeted jambs or nailed-on strikes.

For Gauging Casings with Rabbeted Jambs

Set cutter A to gauge from back of rabbeted jamb (Fig. 1); cutter B is then in correct position for gauging from edge of door (Fig. 2) which engages in closing. These cutters are made so as to allow sufficient clearance to enable the door to close properly, without catching or binding. (See dotted line Fig. 1.)

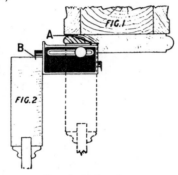

Gauging of casings.

For Gauging Jambs to Which Strike Is Nailed After Door Is Hung

Reverse the bar to which cutter B is attached, place flange against edge of casing, and mark with cutter B (Fig. 3). Use same setting of cutter B for marking door, placing flange against the outer edge (Fig. 4.)

To Gauge for Thickness of Butt

Set cutter C to depth required; gauge from depth of jamb (Fig. 5) and from edge of door (Fig. 6).

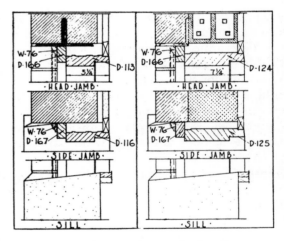

Doors placed in frame in brick wall.

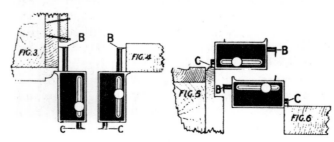

Gauging of jambs.

Interior panel doors.

French doors.

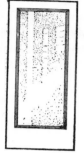

Mirror door.

Braced door.

Accordian or pleated door.

Basement door.

Dutch door.

Exterior door with intercom, mail drop, and one-way view aperture.

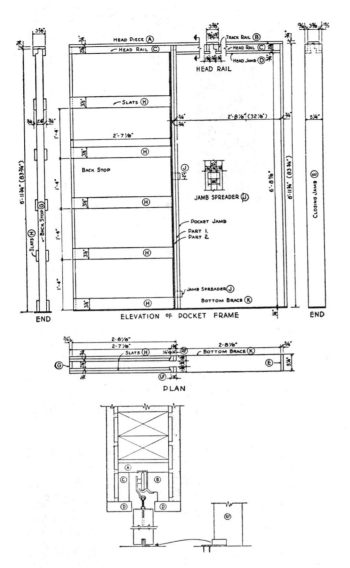

ELEVATION AND PLANS OF A SLIDING INTERIOR DOOR
FRAME UNIT INSERTED INTO A NORMAL 2 x 4 FRAMED
PARTITION WALL.

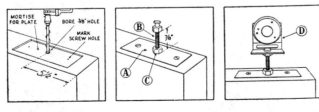

Method of fastening roller hanger on the top of the door.
Two hangers are required for each door.

The Manufacture of Wooden Doors

Fine hardwood and softwood doors require heavy and intricate machinery, competent machine hands, and exacting supervision during the entire process of manufacture, which accounts for the fact that their production is concentrated in a relatively small number of large and old-established factories. Pine doors, like sashes, are largely made from Western pine, and fir doors come from the same forests of the Northwest from which we get fir plywood. Both kinds of doors are made with solid stiles and rails, and the initial stages of manufacture are the same

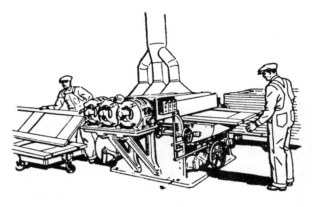

Sanding machine.

as described for frames and sashes—the shop lumber is reduced to cut stock and placed in storage bins to await further production.

Hardwood doors are invariably made with veneered stiles and rails for the reason that hardwood lumber can never be dried out enough so that solid doors will not warp or twist. However, thin veneers, which are either sliced, sawn, or rotary cut, can be thoroughly dried, and these are then *bonded* on cores in the hydraulic *hot-plate* press. Synthetic resin is used instead of glue, and under tremendous heat and pressure a union or *bond* is formed which is many times as strong as the wood itself and thus will not allow the door to twist or warp. The synthetic resin bond is also waterproof, so hardwood doors made in this manner are impervious to moisture.

Doors of course must be put through the factory in sizeable run, as it is quite expensive to set up the various machines for only a few doors of each size at a time and for this reason special doors are much more expensive than stock doors even though the actual manufacture is exactly the same. The cut stock for pine or fir doors, and the glued-up stiles and rails for hardwood doors, are first fed through a sticker, or molder, where the sticking or molding on either side of the panels is worked-

sides up at the same time, making sure that the various joints go together properly and that the door is absolutely square before it is squeezed or given the final thrust which closes all the joints

Hydraulic press.

Mortiser.

on. The rails go through a double-end tenoner where the reverse of the sticking is cut in each end, and then through three-in-one machines where they

tightly. The glue used in the dowel joints sets quickly and the doors are then ready for the sander.

Careful sanding, particularly in the case of hardwood doors, is essential. The panels of course are all sanded before the doors are put together, and the final operation therefore is merely to remove any unevenness between the surfaces of the stiles and rails and to clean up the doors ready for the painters. The doors now go into stock and must

Clamping machine.

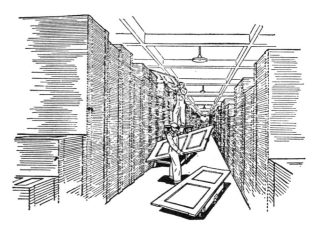

Storage stacks.

are bored for dowels, and the hardwood dowels, after being thoroughly covered with hot glue, are inserted.

The stiles are likewise bored for the dowels and sent along to the door clamps. The panels, having been manufactured and cut to proper size in a process which must parallel the fabrication of the stiles and rails, come up to the door clamps at the same time, and the stiles, rails, and panels are then stuck together. Each door is placed in a power clamp where the operator gently brings all four

be kept in a clean, dustless warehouse, from which daylight is excluded so that the wood does not discolor in the event it is to be given only a light stain or varnish finish. For shipment in less than full carloads, all doors are packed in heavy corrugated cartons, bound with iron strapping. This is superior to crating, as no nails need to be driven into the stiles to mar them, and the doors arrive on the job clean and ready to be finished.

26

Builders' Hardware and Fasteners

Builders' hardware is divided into two groups: the rough hardware used to hold the building members together, such as nails, bolts, screws, etc., and the finish hardware used to secure movable members. This consists of door sets, window sets, door pulls, plates, ornamental hinges, etc.

There are several kinds of nails used by the carpenter, the most common being what is known as the common nail which is used in all rough framing or on work which is covered with another covering of building material. Common nails are not set or sunk below the wood's surface, hence the full use is made of the relatively large round head.

Experience in the driving of nails is needed by apprentices as there is far more to the use of a hammer and a nail than appears. Study the driving of nails from three points; namely, the correct use of the hammer, the correct nail and holding, and the wood and structure that is to be nailed.

Bolts and connectors are used in house construction in several places and a study of the plans will show specific uses. Sills must always be bolted to foundation walls. These are designed in the plans. Timber connectors are used in larger structures and a study of these connectors is an interesting one.

Screws used in wood are made in three shapes: flat-headed, round-headed, and oval-headed. All locks, hinges, bolts, etc., are held in place by screws. Starting a screw is an important operation that must be studied and certain tricks must be learned. The correct screw, the correct way of starting it and the kind of wood it is placed in must be studied.

No work on carpentry could ever attempt to describe the many important features and kinds of builders' hardware. This is a study in itself.

Listing hardware used in a dwelling is a very important part of estimating quantities of building materials. A very thorough job of drafting by an architectural draftsman or architect will include the listing of many items of hardware on a set of house plans. A thorough job of specification writing will designate the quality, quantity, and trade names of hardware to use on a particular set of house plans.

It must be kept in mind that hardware is manufactured in various grades of quality in much the same manner as other building materials.

Various forms listing dwelling hardware are on the market. These forms list the several items used in various rooms (finish hardware) together with the items of general hardware (rough hardware). These forms are intended as time savers for the estimator and also serve to eliminate overlooking many smaller items.

The apprentice will do well to take a set of house plans and study the items of hardware needed, room by room. Visualize the various hardware items needed in each room, and list item by item.

A book dealing with trade operations in dwelling construction would be rendered too voluminous if an attempt were made to give all the rules of estimating, especially estimating hardware. Not alone does the factor of quantity estimating come in, but the factor of estimating the craftsman's time to hang a door, set a lock set, hang a window, apply cupboard hardware, etc., becomes very important in a field of competitive bidding.

One must become acquainted with many items of hardware. Obtain lock sets and familiarize yourself with the names and functions of each part. Obtain trade catalogs and study the hardware shown. Secure as many hinges as possible and designate the several uses.

Simplified Carpentry Estimating, by Wilson and Rogers, published by Simmons-Boardman, includes instructions on both rough hardware and finish hardware estimating.

Use of anchors in place of double stud.

Hangers for screens or storm sash.

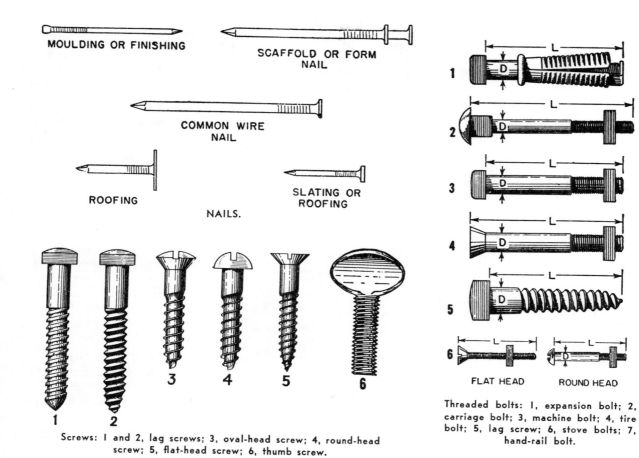

MOULDING OR FINISHING

SCAFFOLD OR FORM NAIL

COMMON WIRE NAIL

ROOFING

SLATING OR ROOFING

NAILS.

Screws: 1 and 2, lag screws; 3, oval-head screw; 4, round-head screw; 5, flat-head screw; 6, thumb screw.

FLAT HEAD   ROUND HEAD

Threaded bolts: 1, expansion bolt; 2, carriage bolt; 3, machine bolt; 4, tire bolt; 5, lag screw; 6, stove bolts; 7, hand-rail bolt.

Turnbuckle.

Drawer pull.

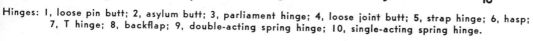

Hinges: 1, loose pin butt; 2, asylum butt; 3, parliament hinge; 4, loose joint butt; 5, strap hinge; 6, hasp; 7, T hinge; 8, backflap; 9, double-acting spring hinge; 10, single-acting spring hinge.

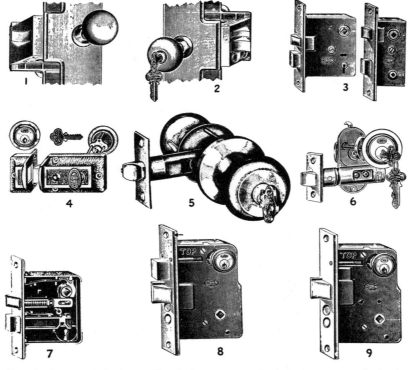

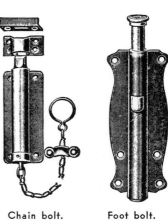

Chain bolt.   Foot bolt.

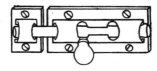

Barrel bolt.

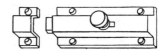

Cupboard bolt.

Door locks: 1, unit lock; 2, office lock; 3, mortise knob lock; 4, rim night latch;
5, cylinder lock; 6, tubular lock; 7, butted key lock; 8, mortise front door lock;
9, mortise vestibule lock

Flush bolt.

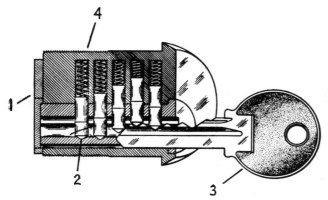

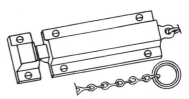

Cupboard catch.

Transom catch.

Cylinder lock: 1, cylinder; 2, pins; 3, key; 4, springs.

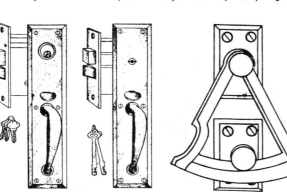

Store door lock sets.   Dutch door quadrant.   Escutcheon plates.

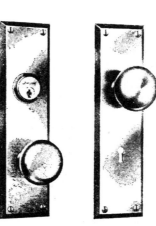

Door knocker.

Drawer knob.

27

Closets, Shelving, and Built-ins

A set of house plans may have a sheet, or portion, devoted to details of built-in equipment. Built-in equipment consists of mill-made china closets, bookcases, linen closets, ironing boards, telephone cabinets, kitchen cabinets, etc. If stock items of built-in equipment are used there is very little need of devoting time to the making of details, the mere listing of the same and designating the place for the device being sufficient. If stock items are not used, then details must be drawn and such are to be included in the set of plans.

Shelving is generally placed in closets off hallways, bathrooms, or bedrooms and must be fitted accurately. Open bookcases are in the nature of shelving, although generally made of more expensive woods than shelving hidden by solid doors.

Kitchen cabinets are seldom built on the job, since the home owner is able to visit display rooms and see several cabinets on display and make a choice of the type to fit into the space allowed in the kitchen. These cabinets are delivered to the job ready to install in the specified space. Such must be securely fastened, squared, and leveled up. Sometimes a cabinet is delivered knocked-down and is assembled in the house. In this case adequate directions are sent with each item of equipment, together with the required hardware.

Fine china cases or closets are usually milled and assembled at the mill and put in place in the dwelling. The carpenter may or may not assemble a case, depending upon it being shipped knocked down or not. If he is to assemble the case he must be careful to do an excellent job.

In any instance of putting in, building up, or assembling shelving, closets, or built-in equipment the carpenter must see that no heel marks of the

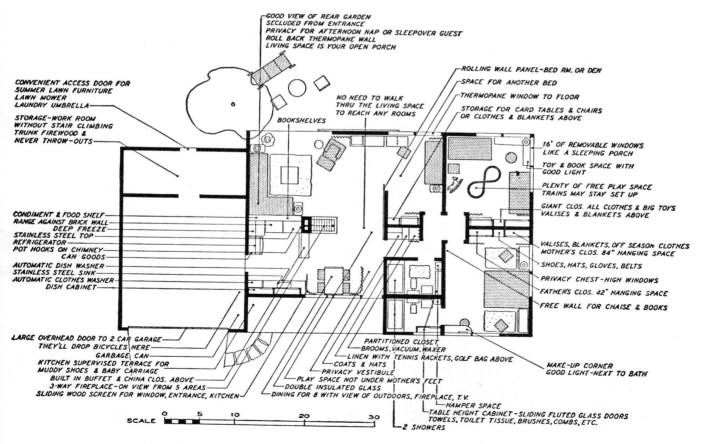

Plan of house detailing features of modern construction and built-in equipment.

189

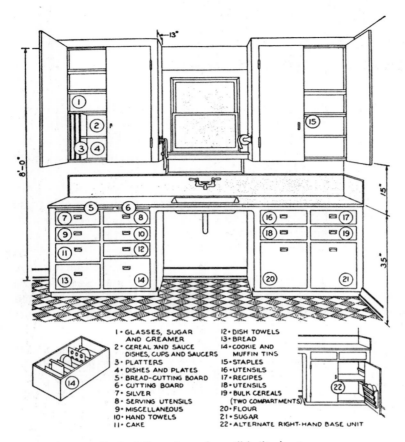

1 · GLASSES, SUGAR AND CREAMER
2 · CEREAL AND SAUCE DISHES, CUPS AND SAUCERS
3 · PLATTERS
4 · DISHES AND PLATES
5 · BREAD-CUTTING BOARD
6 · CUTTING BOARD
7 · SILVER
8 · SERVING UTENSILS
9 · MISCELLANEOUS
10 · HAND TOWELS
11 · CAKE
12 · DISH TOWELS
13 · BREAD
14 · COOKIE AND MUFFIN TINS
15 · STAPLES
16 · UTENSILS
17 · RECIPES
18 · UTENSILS
19 · BULK CEREALS (TWO COMPARTMENTS)
20 · FLOUR
21 · SUGAR
22 · ALTERNATE RIGHT-HAND BASE UNIT

Typical dimensions of a mill-built closet.

The following illustrations show typical shelf arrangements found in linen closets and in bathroom slosets. Closets off bedrooms are arranged with one or two shelves and a rail on which to hang suits and dresses.

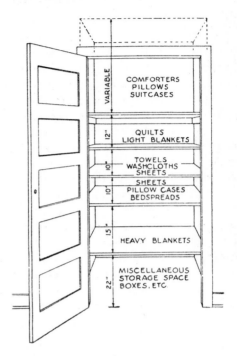

COMFORTERS
PILLOWS
SUITCASES

QUILTS
LIGHT BLANKETS

TOWELS
WASHCLOTHS
SHEETS

SHEETS
PILLOW CASES
BEDSPREADS

HEAVY BLANKETS

MISCELLANEOUS
STORAGE SPACE
BOXES, ETC.

Typical dimensions of a linen closet.

Built-in kitchen installation.

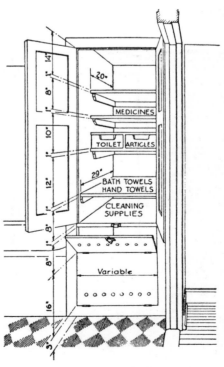

MEDICINES

TOILET ARTICLES

BATH TOWELS
HAND TOWELS

CLEANING
SUPPLIES

Variable

Typical dimensions of a bathroom closet.

Combination storage unit with accordian doors.

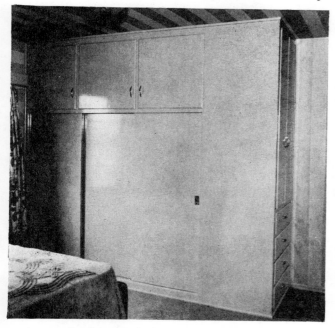

Combination wardrobe and storage unit.

hammer are made on exposed surfaces; he must see that edges are true and square, that no planer marks exist in exposed surfaces, and that all exposed surfaces are sanded smoothly for finishing by the painter.

Too much emphasis cannot be laid upon learning to make a good, readable, freehand sketch. The carpenter is always "talking" or expressing himself in terms of lines of projection or views of different members used in the dwelling. Good copies of built-in equipment can be made and much can be learned from these copies. Decide upon some item to copy and make the required views. Is the original sufficiently clear to permit a craftsman to build it? What details would you add in order to make the construction or installation clearer or more accurate? From an illustration in this book make different views of an article.

Select an item of equipment in this chapter and make a stock bill of parts. List each piece, the thickness, width, and length, and the number of

"Rotacloset."

each piece required. List hardware. Figure the board feet of lumber used and compute the cost. Is the cost you figured in harmony with the cost as listed in a supply catalog? Could you make it at a lower cost by buying the stock at the mill and doing the work yourself?

Most of these mill-built cabinets are furnished completely set up, square and true, with hardware applied, and completely finished inside and out. The cabinets come in units and are screwed to the wall and bolted together. A work space of 16" is generally left above the counter, but this varies according to the height of the ceiling since the upper unit must fit tightly to the ceiling. Top sections are generally made in 18", 24", 30", and

36" heights and two sections can be used one above the other when ceiling heights permit.

If corner units are used, these are installed first and trim strips are used to cover joints. Trim strips are also used to hide uneven ceiling lines and uneven floor lines.

If edges of plywood shelving or table or counter tops are to be matched up with the finished face, thin strips of wood edge banding, coated with pressure-sensitive adhesive may be applied. Peel off the backing paper from the strips and apply the edges with pressure. To fill end grain on plywood edges that are to be painted, several varieties of wood putty are available: either powdered, to be mixed with water, or prepared, ready for use.

Garbage disposal. Built-in disposal bin is easily emptied from outside. (Designed by Dorothy Paul.)

Plaster spackling also works well in filling end grain, which must be sanded smooth, when dry, then painted.

Finish woodwork and built-in features require the use of various joints in final assembly. The more common joints used are the butt joint, butt joint with frame construction placed on the inside of drawers, dado joint, and the rabbet joint. The butt joint is the simplest and easiest to make and assemble. All cuts must be square and true. A reinforcing block is used at inside corners where thin stock is butted. Butt joints should be glued, then nailed or held together with flat-head wood screws. When long pieces of thin stock, either solid or plywood, are butted together a glued frame or reinforcing piece is run along the inside edges to add additional strength.

In shelving work, dado joints are used successfully by power-sawing dado grooves in the supporting pieces of stock to house the edges of the shelves. Shelves can then be glued, nailed, or screwed in place or left not fastened to allow for removal and adjustment.

For drawers, chests, or cupboards a good, strong joint can be made at corners by rabbeting one edge of the larger piece, generally the front member, then housing the side member into the front piece. Other but more difficult joints to make in finish work are the miter, slip, dovetail, doweled-butt, and mortise-and-tenon joints.

In gluing joints, before applying metal fasteners, see that all cuts are true, uniform, and at the correct angle. Set up the C clamps or cabinet clamps and try the pieces in position. For lasting strength, all surfaces to be joined must make contact at all points. Remove the pieces after trial clamping and apply glue with a brush or small glue paddle. End grain absorbs glue so quickly that it is best to apply a preliminary coat which is allowed to become tacky before the second and final coat is of glue is applied. After the surfaces to be joined are glued, clamp the joints tightly with clamps, then nail or

Sectional hinged folding doors.

Accordian door made of wood strips joined by adhesive fabric.

screw the joints or apply metal fasteners as an added security to hold the joined pieces of stock. Use blocks of wood under the jaws of the clamps to avoid marring any finished face of the assembly. Wipe off excess glue, since some glue will stain wood and make it more difficult to achieve a good finish. Test the members again for correct position or squareness, then allow the glue to act.

Choose a glue for the particular job at hand. Hide glue can be used satisfactorily for furniture and cabinet work. This glue is not waterproof, hence should not be used for joints exposed to dampness or in contact with weather. Hide glue should be applied in a warm place, then allowed to become tacky before joining and clamping. Hide glue sets rather rapidly and should be held in clamps for about three hours.

Urea resin glue is a good general-purpose glue. It is almost waterproof, holding well on work exposed to some extent to dampness. Urea glue requires well-fittted joints, tight clamping, in a room having a 70-degree temperature, or even warmer Urea-glued joints require at least 16 hours to set and dry when clamped.

Liquid resin glue is an all-purpose adhesive usable at most any temperature but preferably above 60 degrees. It sets rapidly, taking but $1\frac{1}{2}$ hours before clamps can be removed. This glue can be used for small jobs where tight clamping or a good fit may be difficult.

Resorcinol waterproof glue should be used for stock or finish exposed to extreme dampness but requires application in temperatures above 70 degrees. This glue is applied in thin coats, taking some 16 hours to dry before removing the clamps.

Metal fasteners, such as nails, screws, and corrugated fasteners are other means of holding together members of finish woodwork and built-in items of equipment in the dwelling.

Nails are the most common mechanical fasteners used in construction. There are many types, sizes, and forms of standard nails, and, in addition, many special-purpose nails. A few of the more common nails for wood are the bright, smooth wire nail; the cement-coated nail; the zinc-coated nail; the chemically etched nail; the annular-grooved nail; and the barbed nail. Nail sizes are stated in "penny," a suffix designating the length, such as 6d (penny) nail, originally indicating the price as so many pence per 100 nails. The size, length, and number of nails per pound are: 2-d, 1-in., 875; 3d, $1\frac{1}{4}$-in., 568; 4d, $1\frac{1}{2}$-in., 317, etc.

The proper nail size to use is determined primarily by the thickness of the stock, either solid

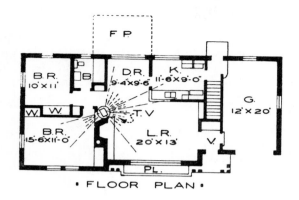

· FLOOR PLAN ·

A built-in television receiver will add much to the enjoyment of programs and entertainment for the family, especially if the programs can be viewed from more than one room.

The floor plan layout shows but a slight modification of standard dwelling construction needed to have the television visible from four rooms.

The television receiver must of course be mounted on a platform which can be rotated to make the screen visible from various angles.

or plywood, to be joined. For the joining of ¾″ stock, either glued or not, 6d casing or 6d finish nails will hold the stock in place. To join stock ⅝″ thick, use 6d or 8d finish nails. To join stock ½″ thick, use 4d or 6d nails. To join stock ¼″ thick, use 1″ brads or 3d finish nails. In joining any pieces of stock with glue and nails a much neater and safer job can be done if the nails are inserted in holes drilled through the first member of the joint. A drill bit, slightly smaller than the diameter of the nail, should be used to insure a good tight fit and avoid splitting of ends of stock; especially if nailing is to be done close to edges. Do not place nails much closer than 6″ except in joining thin solid stock or plywood stock. All nails should be countersunk below the surface, to be later covered with filler for a more satisfactory finish. Corrugated metal fasteners are also used in joining pieces of wood stock, especially to reinforce corners.

When more holding power is needed than provided by nails or corrugated fasteners the wood screw is used. Common types of wood screws have either flat, oval, or round heads. The flat-head screw is used most generally, especially if a flush surface is desired. Oval-head or round-head screws are used for appearance or when countersinking is objectionable. Screws should be turned in, never started or driven with a hammer, as this practice tears the wooden fibers and injures the screw threads, thus seriously reducing the load-carrying capacity of the screw.

To join solid or plywood stock, ¾″ thick, use a No. 8, 1½″ wood screw, drilling a ⁵⁄₃₂″ hole to receive the screw practically the length of the screw. To join ½″ stock, use a No. 6, 1¼″ wood screw, drilling a ⅛″ hole to receive the screw.

Built-in equipment is held together by glued joints reinforced with nails or screws. The placing of drawer pulls, handles, catches, hinges, and rollers are important items of hardware used in assembling and holding members in place.

Drawer pulls may be fastened to the front member of the drawer by screws or held in place by the threaded portions of the pulls which are inserted through holes bored in the wood to which nuts are attached on the inside face of the front.

Small doors take handles or knobs fastened to the stiles. The door catch is of either the friction, magnetic, or roller type, installed on the inside of the door, generally the lower rail, and the receiving member of the catch is placed on a shelf or directly under the catch on a rail of the main portion or stationary portion of the cabinet.

In addition to the mounting or handles and catches for doors, surface hinges are mounted on the opposite stile or stiles. Surface hinges require no mortising. They add an ornamental touch and are available in many styles and shapes. Two surface hinges, H or H-L style hinges, will suffice for small and average size doors in cabinet work. Overlapping or lipped doors are hung neatly with semi-concealed hinges. Concealed pin hinges give a neat appearance to flush doors since mounting is done directly on the door edges and sides of cabinet. Sliding doors for closets and large storage units often have rollers and track mounted at either the top or bottom of the door.

Care and skill must be taken by the finish carpenter while working with any of the materials used in finish woodwork. The attaching of hardware requires the careful reading of instructions furnished with each item before actual work is begun. Suggestions have been given for work in ponderosa pine, Douglas fir, and plywood. Other woods used in finish woodwork, such as maple, oak, walnut, cherry, gum, and many others, require care and skill in finishing and joining and the attaching of hardware.

The final finishing job of decorating and preserving surfaces is done by the painter in applying paints or varnishes.

Following are two designs of cabinets by Douglas Fir Plywood Association, who have worked up many fine cabinet designs. A great variety of built-ins also are delineated in the book *How to Build Cabinets for the Modern Kitchen*, by R. P. Stevenson, published by Simmons-Boardman.

Utility Closet and Cleaning Cart

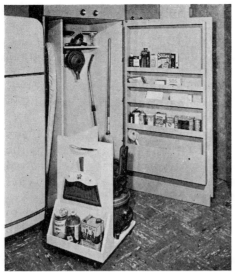

Establish the variable dimensions according to the equipment and supplies you wish to provide for and the space you have.

Cut all panels and frames to size, sand edges, and check fit.

Attach sides and partition to top, bottom, and intermediate shelves; then attach back. Glue all joints and nail with 6d or 8d finishing nails.

The closet may be assembled flat on the floor or erect. If you assemble on floor, be sure the diagonal dimension of the sides does not exceed your ceiling height. Level base if necessary to compensate for an uneven floor.

Attach frame around door, then install shelves and shelf rails and hang door, making certain all door edges are carefully primed and both faces finished alike.

Cut parts for the cart, sand edges and check fit. Glue and nail divider panels together, then attach bottom.

Finish complete units as recommended and attach fittings.

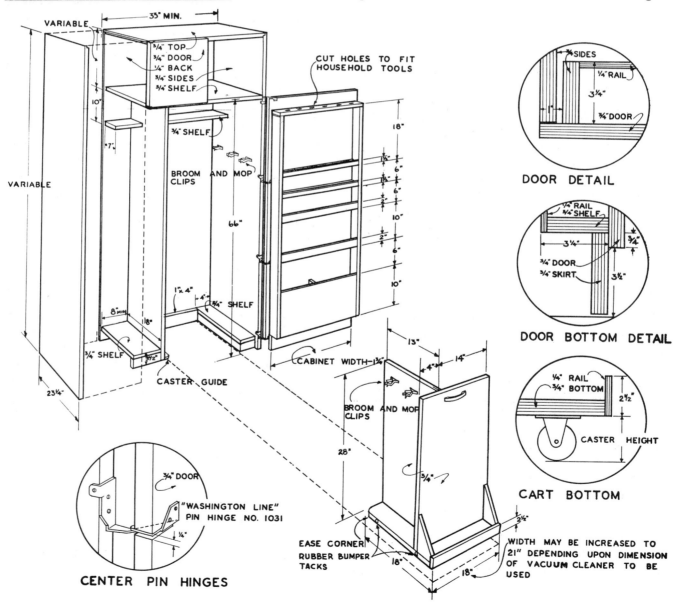

Mixing Center Cabinet

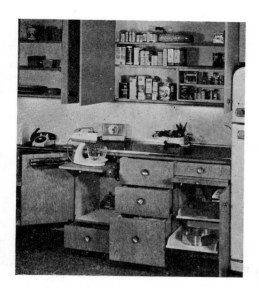

Individual sections or details of this base cabinet may be constructed easily with plywood if you do not have space for the entire unit. With its companion overhead cabinet, this plan centralizes in one area food preparation for oven, range or table.

Determine final dimensions according to the space you have. Cut structural parts and framing members to size, sand edges and fit in place.

Assemble frames, ends, back, intermediate standards, fixed shelves and bottom, starting at the base. Glue all joints and nail with 6d or 8d finishing nails. Level cabinet if necessary to compensate for an uneven floor.

Attach top and apply counter surfacing material. Cut drawer fronts and doors, fit in place and install. Finish plywood as recommended . . . making certain all door edges are carefully primed and both faces finished alike. Install fitting and accessories.

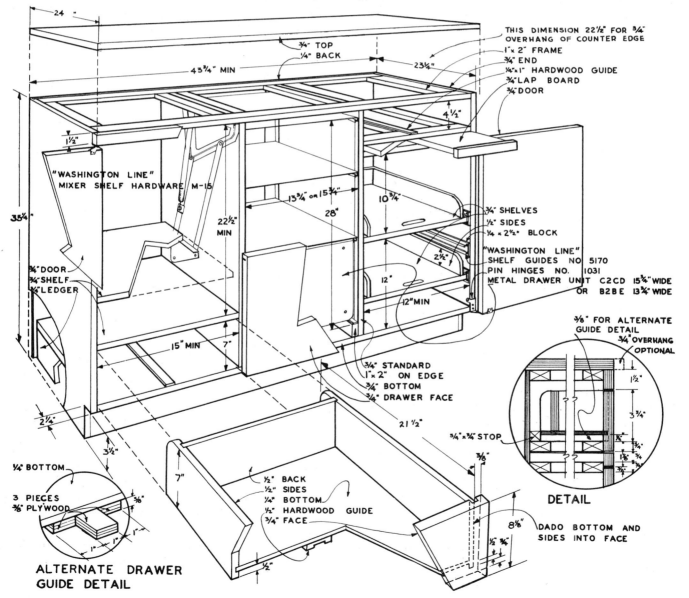

28

Finish Flooring

Most modern dwellings have a finish flooring of thin oak in the living room, dining room, and bedrooms, a linoleum covering on the kitchen floor, and a tile covering on the bathroom floor. The tile covering on the bathroom floor is applied by the tile setter but the rough flooring must be sound and free of rough spots, which is the responsibility of the carpenter. A tile wainscoting is generally applied to the bathroom walls, fixtures permitting, by the tile setter. The covering of inside bathroom walls vary a great deal and the individual preferences of the owner must be considered. These preferences are written carefully into the specifications, listing the make of tile or wall covering and the color schemes desired.

Specialists in laying linoleum do a quick job of placing linoleum on kitchen floors. This covering is attached to the rough floor by a specially prepared adhesive. Read the article, "How to Lay Linoleum Flooring" in this chapter.

The woodworker lays the hardwood flooring and is often a specialist in this work. The rough flooring must be cleared of all scrap stock, nails, plaster, and any dirt that may have been tracked in. The hardwood floor is practically the final job of woodwork in the house, except, of course, any cabinet work which may have to rest upon this flooring.

Flooring is finished by the mill, in wrapped packages, tongued and grooved on sides and ends, which makes for a perfect fit. Refer to the plans and note the design or pattern called for. If a border is required, such must be laid all the way around the room as the first portion of the job in order to get it even and balanced. A heavy strip of felt paper is laid on top of the rough flooring, acting as a cushion for the finish flooring and as insulation too. All flooring joints are butted (seldom, if ever, mitered) and secret-nailed so that no nails work loose and extend above the surface of the flooring. All flooring is worked squarely, one piece to another, without regard to the possible out-of-squareness of the room walls.

Parquetry work is used in floor laying and is simply an inlaying or mosaic pattern for floors, sometimes of different hardwoods.

Hardwood flooring may be laid over a concrete floor or over a rough floor of wood. If laid over concrete, a mastic preparation is placed under the flooring in order to secure it to the concrete. Parquetry block flooring comes from the mill in blocks of flooring pieces, generally three in number, and is often held by metal splined clamps in order to hold the blocks together. Often the edges of each block of flooring are slightly beveled in order to make each more noticeable and to hide any possible crack that may develop later.

Hardwood flooring is furnished by the mill also in strips, generally less than 24″ in length, finished and waxed. This strip flooring is laid in the same manner as rough flooring, with greater care of course, secret-nailed, except the last piece laid, which must be face-nailed. Following illustrations show the setting of parquetry flooring in mastic on concrete, and the nailing of flooring on rough flooring. Shown also are the end views of hardwood flooring tongued and grooved on the edges and ends.

Heavy plank flooring is used to some extent in dwelling work. The installation of plank flooring is discussed in this chapter. The manufacturing of hardwood flooring is discussed, too, in an article in this chapter.

Hardwood flooring, linoleum covering, cork covering, or rubber covering is estimated by the square, 10′ x 10′ in size. Estimate the number of squares in the flooring job the plans in the accompanying drawings. Find the cost of flooring in your locality. About 250 to 300 square feet of flooring can be laid in an hour. A certain percentage must be allowed for waste in cutting stock.

Laying Strip Flooring on Wood Subfloor

Fig. 1 shows a workman laying plain-sawed strip flooring. Each piece of flooring is milled with a tongue on one side and end and a groove on the other side and end. This side-and-end matching allows each piece to join the other more snugly, giving greater solidity and strength to the entire floor. Note the flooring nail and the method of secret-nailing to the subflooring.

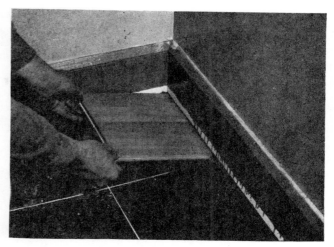

Fig. 2

Laying Flooring in Mastic

Fig. 2 shows a workman laying the initial or key block of a finish flooring of unit wooden block squares. Working lines are established which allow an expansion between the baseboard trim and allow the block and the tongue to protrude over the lines. This block is being laid in mastic which has been spread and allowed to set overnight. Blocks will slip into place easier if mastic sets several hours.

Fig. 3 shows block flooring pieces laid along the working lines leaving tongues exposed for nailing. The pieces laid along the working lines or at the wall line are face-nailed along the edges nearest the walls, using 4d casing nails about ⅜" from the edges so that the nail heads will be concealed by the baseshoe nailing. Subsequent nailing of tongue is done by secret or blind nailing; then as each row of blocks are laid each is blind-nailed through the exposed tongue. The workman is laying blocks on

Fig. 1

Fig. 3

mastic which has been allowed to set for several hours.

The Construction of a Plank Floor

Although the architectural and construction details of plank-and-beam floors are simpler than those for joist construction because there are fewer members mutually attached, it is important that they are designed and constructed adequately. General architectural and construction considerations which are somewhat different from those of joist construction are discussed below.

Properly designed plank spans up to 7 feet are entirely practical.

Finish Flooring—The finish flooring should be laid at right angles with the plan of the subfloor. When a 25/32 in. thickness of flooring is used and the under side of the plank serves as the exposed finish ceiling, the finish floor nails should not be longer than 1¾ in. to avoid the splitting out of the fibers on the under side of the plank.

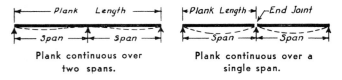

Plank continuous over two spans.   Plank continuous over a single span.

Ceiling Finish—Since practically any species of lumber may be used and consequently the choice is largely a matter of personal preference, the exposed plank-and-beam ceiling lends itself to many attractive finishes. It may be painted in various colors; it may be stained in natural finish or given an antique or weathered finish by a filler of white lead or other color wiped off before dry. The joints in the plank make an attractive pattern in the ceiling. If an applied finish is desired, the plank will serve also as an excellent solid over-all nailing base.

Plank—Since the 2-inch plank floor frequently serves the dual function of a subfloor and a finish ceiling for the room below, the appearance as well as the structural requirements of the plank should be considered. From a structural viewpoint, stock dimension lumber with the finish floor laid at right angles to the plank to provide load distribution [see (1)] or interlocking patterned lumber such as splined or tongue-and-groove material may be used. Where the appearance of the exposed plank ceiling is important, the use of patterned material to provide the desired treatment of the joints on the ceiling side of the plank is recommended. A large

number of pleasing decorative effects is possible. Various suggested plank patterns which are illustrated include (2) grooved and splined with a V-joint, (3) tongued and grooved with a V-joint, (4) grooved and splined with exposed spline.

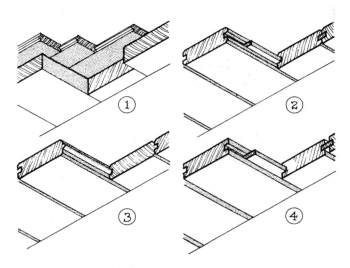

End view of plank flooring.

Ordinarily 2 x 6 or 2 x 8 well-seasoned plank with moisture content close to that which it would reach in service should be used. When the under side of the plank is to serve as the exposed ceiling of living quarters below, No. 1 (common) or other tight-knotted material with a suitable appearance is used. It should be sound material, selected at the yard and on the job for good appearance. When the plank does not serve as the exposed ceiling of living quarters below, e.g., in the ceiling over living quarters when covered with other material, in first-floor construction, or in roofs over attics, No. 2 (common) or other material having the appropriate required minimum structural properties may be used. To avoid undue contraction of plank after laying, the seasoned plank should be protected from the elements during storage and construction.

In laying the plank floor there are certain economies and additional advantages of maximum rigidity and strength which may be obtained from the continuity of the plank when laid in accordance with certain schemes over the longer spans.

Using plank extending over two or more spans takes advantage of the added stiffness and strength obtained through continuity. For example, when the span and the uniformly distributed load per foot of span are identical in both cases, plank that is continuous over two spans, i.e., supported at the middle and two ends, is nearly two and one-half times as stiff as a plank that extends over a single span, i.e., supported at its two ends.

In general, with plank continuous over two spans the type B arrangement for an even number of equal spans and the type D arrangement for an odd number of equal spans give the stiffest floors. However, when an odd number of spans are used and one of the end spans is less than 92 percent of the other spans, the type E arrangement proves more advantageous than that of type D.

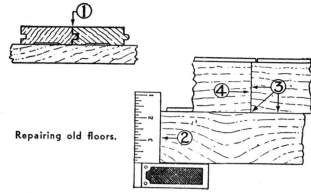

Repairing old floors.

(1) Face edge even, (2) Square butt joints, (3) Clean sharp edges, (4) Hairline joints.

Blind nailing.

Square-edge oak flooring.

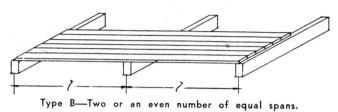

Type B—Two or an even number of equal spans.

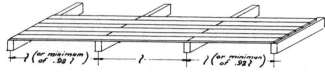

Type D—Three or an odd number of equal spans or when end span is 92% or more of interior span.

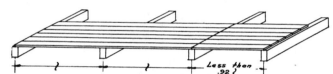

Type E—Three or an odd number of spans when one end span is less than 92% of interior span.

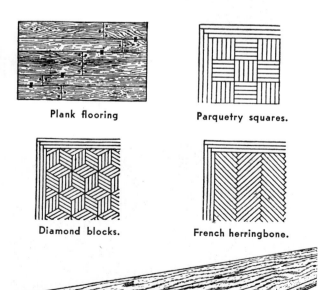

Plank flooring

Parquetry squares.

Diamond blocks.

French herringbone.

Strip flooring.

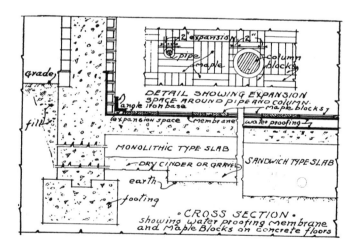

DETAIL SHOWING EXPANSION SPACE AROUND PIPE AND COLUMN.

CROSS SECTION
showing water proofing membrane and Maple Blocks on concrete floors

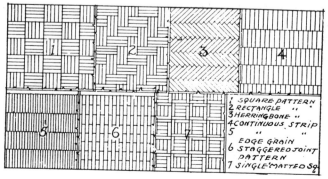

Maple blocks laid in mastic.

Preparing Old Subfloors for Resilient Flooring

A resilient floor is no better than the subfloor-over which it is installed, and satisfactory results depend on correct preparatory work.

The installation of resilient floors in an existing structure usually involves the conversion of what was once a wearing floor into a subfloor.

Two main conditions must be met before such a floor forms a satisfactory base for a resilient finish floor. First, it is necessary to have a relatively smooth-surface subfloor, free from serious irregularities which would mar the appearance of the finish floor. Second, since nearly all resilient floorings are applied with adhesives, the old floor must be prepared to provide a satisfactory bonding surface for the adhesive.

Single wooden floors, not tongue-and-groove, should be covered with $^{25}/_{32}$" flooring or $5/8$" or heavier plywood. Single wooden floors, of tongue-and-groove stock, should be covered with hardboard or plywood not less than $3/8$" thick.

Double wooden floors having a subfloor of stock over 3" in width should be covered with a hardboard or plywood of not less than $3/8$" thick. If the subfloor is less than 3" in width, loose boards should be renailed and badly worn boards should be replaced. All holes and cracks should be filled with plastic wood or snugly fitted with a dutchman. All surface irregularities should be removed by planing or sanding. Fig. 1 shows a workman performing some of these operations of conditioning a floor for a resilient covering.

All traces of oil or paint must be removed by sanding, scraping, or scrubbing with chemical solvents. Paint is often speedily removed by the use of an acetylene paint burner as shown in Fig. 2.

The problem of securing proper adhesion to concrete subfloors usually arises from dusty, chalky, or flaky concrete surfaces and previous treatments with oils or other solutions. This can usually be overcome by thorough sweeping with a wire brush to remove all loose particles and the complete removal of oils, paint, varnish, or wax. A strong grease-cutting solution of tri-sodium phosphate or an alkaline type cleaner can be used with a powered brush as shown in Fig. 3.

Although resilient flooring adhesives will fill minor cracks and crevices in concrete subfloors, it is best that all holes, cracks, and crevices be cleaned, dusted, and moistened, and then filled with a reliable cement crack filler before installation is

Fig. 1

Fig. 2

Fig. 3

Fig. 4

started. This operation is shown in Fig. 4. It is important that all repairing and cleaning work done on concrete floors or newly poured concrete floors be allowed adequate time to dry thoroughly before installing flooring.

Complete resurfacing of worn or damaged areas of concrete subfloors may be avoided by troweling a thin layer of latex underlayment cement as shown in Fig. 5.

Floors of single wooden members are covered with a hardboard or plywood underlayment, as shown in Fig. 6, and firmly nailed with coated or ring-grooved nails. Nails should be placed not over 6″ on center in all directions and at all edges, and straight-nailed but not countersunk.

Wooden floors which cannot readily be corrected by sanding may be given an underlayment of 4′ x 4′ hardboard or plywood sheets carefully fitted and nailed as shown in Fig. 7.

Joint spacing of approximately 1/16″ is left between sheets of hardboard or plywood underlayment, as shown in Fig. 8, to allow for slight expansion and contraction with varying moisture

Fig. 5

Fig. 7

Fig. 6

Fig. 8

conditions. The sheets should be laid with joints staggered, ashlar fashion.

Another method of resurfacing damaged wooden or concrete subflooring is to resurface with a cold mastic floor fill. Wooden screeds and a straight-edge, as shown in Fig. 9, may be used to maintain the required thickness for leveling. This mastic

Fig. 9

can be laid directly over old floor but will not adhere to subfloors treated with oil.

An asphalt type of underlayment is used in resurfacing wooden subflooring as shown in Fig. 10. To retard any damage by expansion or contraction of the asphalt fill, galvanized wire or expanded metal lath is used, held in place by wooden

Fig. 10

screeds, which allow the workman to maintain a uniform level of the underlayment.

When burlap-backed linoleum is used as resilient flooring over wooden subflooring, lining felt is used as an underlay. After the felt is scribed and cut, it should be fitted, unpasted as shown in Fig. 11, in order to check position at vertical surfaces. If the fit is satisfactory, the material is tubed back, pasted, replaced in position, and rolled to smooth seams and uneven places.

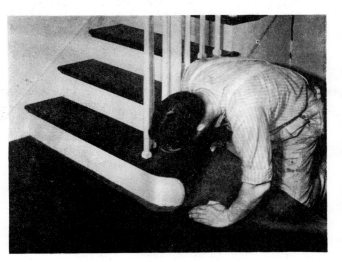

Fig. 11

The life and serviceability of any resilient flooring installation depend greatly upon the proper application of the correct adhesive which will meet its specific installation requirements. Frequently, the selection of the proper adhesive is as important as the selection of the floor itself. To bond properly, the adhesive must hold the flooring material to the subfloor by surface attachment. This surface attachment, or bonding strength, must be great enough to prevent the separation of the flooring material from the subfloor under stresses slightly greater than those encountered in normal use. At the same time, the bond must not be so strong that it will be too difficult to remove the resilient flooring at a later date if necessary.

Shown in Fig. 12 is paste adhesive spread on the exposed part of the lining felt with a notched spreader. The linoleum is cut to size to fit the space to be covered, and placed in position or lapped by folding back the material the short dimension. Folding the linoleum the long dimension is called "tubing" the material. After the adhesive is applied to the prepared subfloor the linoleum is put in place, adjusted, or cut if necessary, and rolled for proper bonding.

Fig. 12

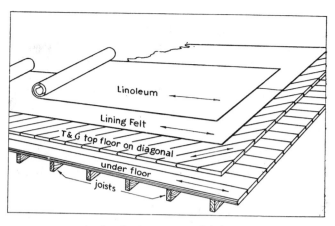

Laying linoleum over a felt base.

How to Lay Linoleum Flooring

A double wood subfloor provides one of the best surfaces for linoleum installation. Although a large amount of linoleum is laid over a single wood subfloor, it is not recommended generally because the floor boards may show through. Lining felt is desirable but not mandatory for monolithic subfloors (concrete, terrazzo, etc.), but it is essential for laying linoleum over wood subfloors.

The most satisfactory type of wood subfloor for linoleum is a bottom layer of $\frac{7}{8}$-inch kiln-dried tongue-and-groove boards, not over 8 inches wide, face-nailed at each end and at every bearing with two 8-penny nails. This should be covered with building paper and $\frac{25}{32}$-inch kiln-dried tongue-and-groove boards not over 3 inches in face width. These boards should be laid at an angle of 45 degrees to the boards in the first layer. This assures that none of the seams in the linoleum will run in the same direction as the boards of the top layer. and prevents the seams from opening because of expansion or constraction. A less expensive installation is laying the top boards at an angle of 90 degrees to the under floor. However, if this method is employed, the lining felt and linoleum should be laid so that the seams run across—and not parallel with—the boards in the top layer. A seam protector is recommended if the laying of the linoelum brings a seam parallel to the direction of the floor boards.

If the floor is an old double floor with a tongue-and-groove top layer, the surface should be examined carefully and all defective boards should be

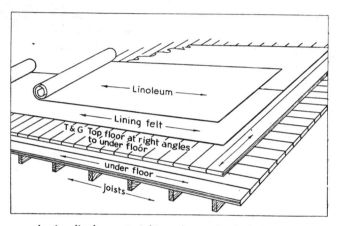

Laying linoleum at right angles to finished flooring.

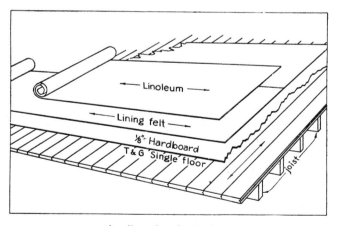

A hardboard under linoleum.

replaced, loose boards renailed, all nails countersunk, and uneven joints planed or sanded smooth. Cracks wider than $\frac{1}{8}$-inch or holes larger than $\frac{1}{4}$-inch diameter should be carefully filled with wood or plastic wood.

The least expensive way to convert a single

tongue-and-groove subfloor into one of double proportions is to cover it with a layer of building paper and hard-pressed wallboard or plywood. Exact specifications should be secured and followed in this installation. If the single subfloor consists of square-edged boards, it should be covered with a layer of building paper and a single layer of $\frac{25}{32}$-inch kiln-dried tongue-and-groove.

It might be well to point out that numerous modern builders are recommending permanent linoleum installations in rooms other than kitchen and bath because the linoleum is easy for the house-wife to clean and wax, and is resilient and quiet.

Linoleum makes a very satisfactory installation over supported concrete subfloors, but care should be taken that there is no moisture lurking in the concrete. Where this condition exists, asphalt tile, which is moisture resistant, is recommended for the flooring. Even though a concrete floor is well ventilated on the under side, moisture in the concrete will eventually ruin an excellent linoleum installation.

Recently poured cement should be allowed to dry for several months before linoleum is installed. While most concrete floors are stone-filled concrete, the builder occasionally is called upon to install linoleum on concrete floors which are poured over cinders. Cinder-fill concrete presents a particular dampness problem, and careful tests should be made to determine its dryness.

Smooth, trowel-finished concrete is preferable for linoleum installations. Float-finished concrete is undesirable because it may be rough, dusty, or unsound. All concrete floors should be carefully inspected to determine whether the finish coat has a good bond to the under layer and is free from scales or cracks caused by the concrete freezing.

Imperfect concrete can easily be conditioned. Expansion cracks can be filled with a mixture of portland cement and plaster of paris. Fillers may be used to level off rough spots or hollow places. If the cement is dusty, it should be swept with a size or filler.

The alkali on all concrete floors should be neutralized by applying an inexpensive mixture of $\frac{3}{4}$ pound of zinc sulphate in 10 quarts of water. This at the same time will settle the dust. If the concrete is covered with a good single coat of paint, it should be scored with a wire brush. Varnish, oil, wax, and grease should be removed by scrubbing with a strong solution of tri-sodium phosphate or, if necessary, by scraping and sanding until it is thoroughly clean.

The same recommendations should be followed in working with terrazzo, marble, and ceramic tile subfloors. In addition, these materials must be thoroughly machine-scrubbed with soapy water and clean, sharp sand.

Magnesite floors are slow drying and quite often old ones are structurally weak. Before laying linoleum over magnesite, it is advisable to send a complete description of the condition to the floor-covering manufacturer for job recommendation.

In general, linoleum makes an extremely satisfactory flooring for homes or commercial establishments, and complete satisfaction is virtually assured if conditions governing the subfloors are followed according to exact specifications.

The Manufacture of Flooring

The production of oak flooring is concentrated largely in Tennessee, where the soft-textured Appalachian Mountain oak is most plentiful, and in Arkansas where the lumber comes from the Ozarks. Southern maple and beach grow interspersed with red and white oak, while Northern maple flooring comes principally from the upper peninsular of Michigan and from northern Wisconsin. The lumber is cut and manufactured much the same as is yellow pine lumber except that the best oak grows in mountainous territory which makes it much more difficult to get the logs from the stump to the mill.

After a carefully checked period of air and kiln drying, the lumber is brought to the flooring mill

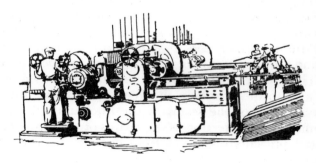

Double surfacer.

where it first goes through heavy-duty double surfacers, to bring it to an even thickness. From this point on the stock moves swiftly on endless chain belts from one operation to another, beginning with the gang rip saws. These reduce the wide boards to narrow strips of uniform size which then travel right along to the flooring machines.

The criterion by which any flooring mill is judged is the character of work that its flooring

Flooring machine.

From the graders, the stock moves again on endless belts to the first end matcher where at a single operation the clear portion of each strip is cut off exactly at right angles and a tongue is worked on the end to match the tongue on the side of each board. Coming out of this machine, the boards are sped in the opposite direction to a similar machine,

machines turn out. These are massively built for long years of heavy duty, and great care is taken to eliminate any possible vibration which would result in an imperfect product. The four cutting

End matcher.

Graders.

heads on each machine are accurately set by a standard template to make sure the flooring is absolutely uniform at all times, and the matching, or tongue-and-groove joints, are frequently checked by the operator. Although the flooring moves through the machines at the rate of about 150 lineal feet per minute, the heads revolve at such tremendous speeds that the flooring not only is worked to pattern but has a shine or polish as it comes out.

Behind the flooring machines stand the key men in the plant—the graders. They pick up and carefully inspect every piece, marking on each the grade and kind of wood and indicating the defects which must be eliminated. Constant vigilance at the grading table is the price of a high-class, dependable, uniform grade of flooring. The rules of the Oak Flooring Manufacturers Association are of course the uniform standard of the industry.

reversely situated, where the other end of each board is cut off square and grooved, so that it makes the same tight and perfect joint at the end as it does on the sides.

The flooring is now ready to sort and bundle, and for this large racks or series of bins are needed where the flooring can be separated by size, grade, and kind of wood. As soon as a bin contains enough pieces for a bundle, it is emptied and the flooring is securely bound with wire to insure its getting through to the job in first-class condition.

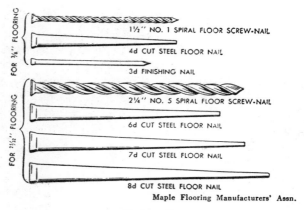

FOR ⅜″ FLOORING

1½″ NO. 1 SPIRAL FLOOR SCREW-NAIL

4d CUT STEEL FLOOR NAIL

3d FINISHING NAIL

FOR 25/32″ FLOORING

2¼″ NO. 5 SPIRAL FLOOR SCREW-NAIL

6d CUT STEEL FLOOR NAIL

7d CUT STEEL FLOOR NAIL

8d CUT STEEL FLOOR NAIL

Maple Flooring Manufacturers' Assn.

Floor nails.

29

Garages

Garage doors are usually made at the mill, brought to the dwelling, and installed by the carpenter or service men employed by the manufacturer. If a separate garage is built away from the dwelling proper, construction is essentially the same as the framed, or brick, or prefabricated dwelling. Swinging doors for a garage may be made of standard framing stock. Building of doors may be done on the job when construction is relatively simple. Details in the plans must be followed, with all members of the doors held in place with screws.

Other than the simple hung and swinging garage door there are several other types of doors, some of which are hung on tracks and trolleys, and are pushed from the closed position along the inside sides of the garage. Other types fold from the closed position to the left-hand and right-hand sides in an accordion fashion. Other types raise from the closed position in a vertical manner, disappearing overhead inside the garage.

All special styles, other than the simple hung doors, require sets of special hardware, pulleys, tracks, springs, etc. Illustrated are several popular styles of garage doors. Some of the installation details are shown, but no attempt is made to describe in full the steps of installing, since each manufacturer supplies this information in printed form with each set of garage doors or else the doors are installed by service men.

Three-door trolley garage set.

Semi-attached double garage having overhead doors.

Two-door trolley garage set.

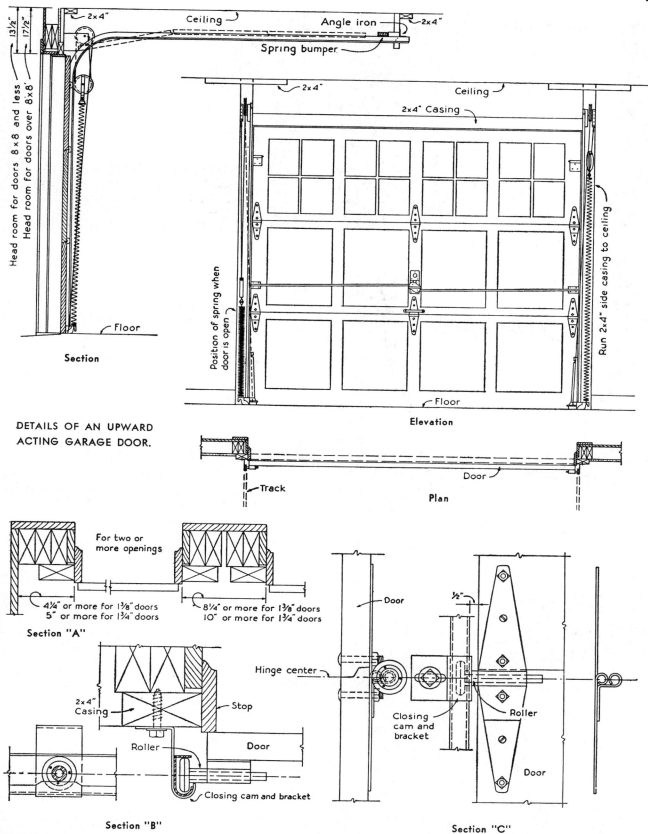

Head room for doors 8 x 8 and less
Head room for doors over 8 x 8'
13½"
17½"

2 x 4"
Ceiling
Angle iron
2 x 4"
Spring bumper
Floor

Section

2 x 4"
Ceiling
2 x 4" Casing
Position of spring when door is open
Run 2 x 4" side casing to ceiling
Floor

Elevation

DETAILS OF AN UPWARD ACTING GARAGE DOOR.

Track
Door

Plan

For two or more openings
4¼" or more for 1⅜" doors
5" or more for 1¾" doors
8¼" or more for 1⅜" doors
10" or more for 1¾" doors

Section "A"

2 x 4" Casing
Stop
Roller
Door
Closing cam and bracket

Section "B"

Door
½"
Hinge center
Closing cam and bracket
Roller
Door

Section "C"

SECTION "A"—Showing side jamb and center post arrangement for two or more openings for doors 1 ¾ inches in thickness.
SECTION "B"—Plan of cam action closing device that provides positive closure.
SECTION "C"—Section and elevation of cam action closing device showing track and roller arrangement at hinge center.

Taylor overhead garage door.

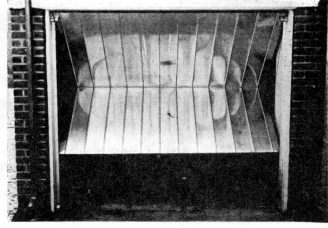

Taylor door half open.

National overhead garage door.

Strand all-steel garage door.

Garage, on right, helps frame yard.

Driveway Design

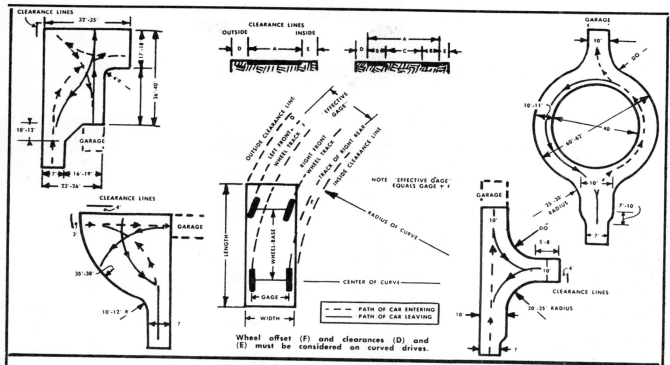

Wheel offset (F) and clearances (D) and (E) must be considered on curved drives.

RECOMMENDED DRIVEWAY WIDTHS
Widths of curved and straight drives of both ribbon and slab types.

WHEELBASE	PROBABLE FRONT OVERHANG	RADIUS OF CURVE	MINIMUM OUTSIDE CLEARANCE (D)	OFFSET DISTANCE (F)	MINIMUM RIBBON WIDTH (B)	MINIMUM RIBBON SPACING (C)	MINIMUM OVERALL WIDTH (A)	ADEQUATE RIBBON WIDTH (B)	ADEQUATE RIBBON SPACING (C)	ADEQUATE OVERALL WIDTH (A)	AMPLE RIBBON WIDTH (B)	AMPLE RIBBON SPACING (C)	AMPLE OVERALL WIDTH (A)
Inches	Inches	Feet	Inches	Inches	Inches	Inches	Inches	Inches	Inches	Inches	Inches	Inches	Inches
112	29	20	17	20	44	14	102			108			114
		30	14	15	39	19	97	45	13	103			109
		40	12	12	36	22	94	42	16	100			106
		50	11	9	33	25	91	39	19	97	45	13	103
		60	11	8	32	26	90	38	20	96	44	14	102
120	29	20	17	23			105			111			117
		30	15	17	41	17	99			105			111
		40	13	13	37	21	95	43	15	101			107
		50	12	11	35	23	93	41	17	99			105
		60	11	9	33	25	91	39	19	97	45	13	103
132	29	20	18	28			110			116			122
		30	15	20	44	14	102			108			114
		40	13	16	40	18	98	46	12	104			110
		50	12	13	37	21	95	43	15	101 ₂			107
		60	11	11	35	23	93	41	17	99			105
144	32	20	33	33			115			121			127
		30	24	24			106			112			118
		40	19	19	43	15	101			107			113
		50	16	16	40	18	98	46	12	104			110
		60	13	13	37	21	95	43	15	101			107
154	33	20	37	37			119			125			131
		30	28	28			110			116			122
		40	22	22			104			110			116
		50	18	18	42	16	100			106			112
		60	15	15	39	19	97	45	13	103			109

The above table is for drives curving left. For drives curving right, add 6 in. to obtain widths and over-all surface widths

FOR STRAIGHT DRIVES
Dimensions of straight drives are the same for all lengths of wheelbase.

					MINIMUM B	MINIMUM C	MINIMUM A	ADEQUATE B	ADEQUATE C	ADEQUATE A	AMPLE B	AMPLE C	AMPLE A
					18	40	76	24	34	82	30	28	88

Ribbon widths of 46 in. are considered to be the maximum that it is practical to build; therefore, no larger widths are shown.

30

Thermal Insulation and Moisture Barriers

Temperature Control

Thermal insulation of dwellings as discussed here is concerned mainly with the problem of reducing the transfer of heat from one region to another. Dwellings in some sections of the country can be made more livable if means are taken to keep the heat outside the year round, while dwellings in other sections can be made more livable if means are taken to keep the heat outside during the summer months and inside during the winter months.

The physical principles involved in the insulation are identical with those involved in heat transfer.

Heat is transferred by three general methods—conduction, convection, or radiation—which may operate either separately or in combination, depending upon the particular conditions. In any case the flow of heat invariably takes place from regions of higher temperature to regions of lower temperature.

The ideal insulation is still air, without radiation, which is built into a wall by the separation of the outer wall, generally by furring strips, from the inner wall. Other methods of insulation are described in the following related subjects. Study the house plans to ascertain the method, if any, of insulation. *Any* wall, or roof, of *any* kind of building material serves as an insulation and protection to the occupants of the dwelling, and that must not be lost sight of, even if more extensive methods of thermal insulation are not applied. The illustrations show how various insulations are applied.

Estimating Insulation

Obtain a piece of tracing paper, a piece of co-ordinate paper (paper with light blue lines ruled into ⅛" spaces), and a medium-weight pencil. Select a floor plan, preferably a first-floor plan, and set about rearranging the rooms. In light lines draw the existing plan, including walls, stairs, doors, windows, chimneys, etc., in exact scale. Allow ⅛" for each foot of length on the floor plan.

Decide on the change to make and readjust the lightly sketched lines accordingly. Study all points of the first-floor plan before making heavier sketched lines. After all lines have been sketched in for the first-floor plan, a study must be made of the second-floor plan to see what changes are necessitated by the rearranged rooms of the first-floor plan in order to properly design the second-floor plan.

Place a piece of tracing paper over the first-floor plan and sketch the outside walls of the second-floor plan, which will fall on the walls of the first-floor plan. Indicate, in light lines, the location of the first-floor plan partitions. In the newer arrangement of the second-floor plan, due allowance must be made for the placing of walls over the first-floor walls which must bear the weight.

After the second-floor plan has been sketched, another piece of tracing paper is placed over the first-floor plan and the sketch of the front elevation is begun. Mark off the length of the front elevation and the location of windows and doors, then remove the tracing paper and complete the vertical portion of the elevation. Do this for the side elevations and the rear elevations.

All drawing must be checked for scale, accuracy, and neatness before a final set of accurate sketches can be completed.

From the set of plans, figure the area of ceilings, walls, etc., to be insulated. From the estimate of materials, for each 1,000 square feet of net wall, ceiling, or roof area, if it too is to be insulated, figure the cost of insulating a house.

Detail the cost estimate of materials and labor for applying insulation over edges of framing members or furring strips.

The chart on page 214 shows the relative value of commercial insulating materials. The horizontal scale gives approximately the thickness in inches required to furnish insulation equivalent to one inch of the best possible practical insulation, called *ideal*, in this figure. Obtain as many samples of these various commercial materials and check the relative costs. Inspect printed sales materials of each, if possible.

WHERE TO INSULATE

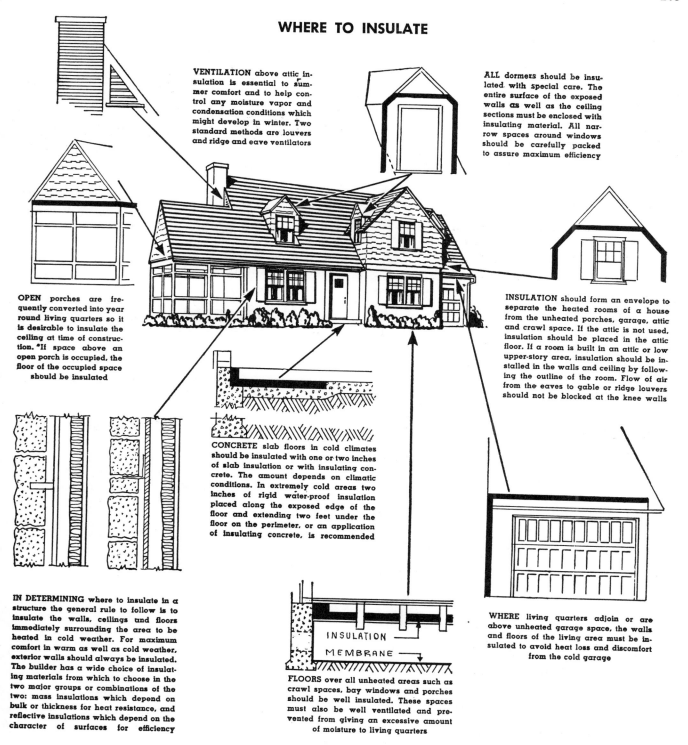

VENTILATION above attic insulation is essential to summer comfort and to help control any moisture vapor and condensation conditions which might develop in winter. Two standard methods are louvers and ridge and eave ventilators

ALL dormers should be insulated with special care. The entire surface of the exposed walls as well as the ceiling sections must be enclosed with insulating material. All narrow spaces around windows should be carefully packed to assure maximum efficiency

OPEN porches are frequently converted into year round living quarters so it is desirable to insulate the ceiling at time of construction. If space above an open porch is occupied, the floor of the occupied space should be insulated

INSULATION should form an envelope to separate the heated rooms of a house from the unheated porches, garage, attic and crawl space. If the attic is not used, insulation should be placed in the attic floor. If a room is built in an attic or low upper-story area, insulation should be installed in the walls and ceiling by following the outline of the room. Flow of air from the eaves to gable or ridge louvers should not be blocked at the knee walls.

CONCRETE slab floors in cold climates should be insulated with one or two inches of slab insulation or with insulating concrete. The amount depends on climatic conditions. In extremely cold areas two inches of rigid water-proof insulation placed along the exposed edge of the floor and extending two feet under the floor on the perimeter, or an application of insulating concrete, is recommended

IN DETERMINING where to insulate in a structure the general rule to follow is to insulate the walls, ceilings and floors immediately surrounding the area to be heated in cold weather. For maximum comfort in warm as well as cold weather, exterior walls should always be insulated. The builder has a wide choice of insulating materials from which to choose in the two major groups or combinations of the two: mass insulations which depend on bulk or thickness for heat resistance, and reflective insulations which depend on the character of surfaces for efficiency

INSULATION
MEMBRANE

FLOORS over all unheated areas such as crawl spaces, bay windows and porches should be well insulated. These spaces must also be well ventilated and prevented from giving an excessive amount of moisture to living quarters

WHERE living quarters adjoin or are above unheated garage space, the walls and floors of the living area must be insulated to avoid heat loss and discomfort from the cold garage

WHERE HEAT IS LOST OR GAINED IN A BUILDING

Heat Loss in Winter		Heat Gain in Summer	
Walls	32.9 %	Walls	33.6 %
Ceilings and roof	22.2 %	Ceilings	24.2 %
Floors	.3 %	Floors	3.7 %
Glass and doors	29.9 %	Glass and doors	26.4 %
Infiltration	14.7 %	Infiltration	12.1 %
	100 %		100.0 %

These figures were assembled from studies of typical two-story houses. The percentages would vary somewhat on one-story houses because the ceiling area would be proportionately greater and the wall area less.

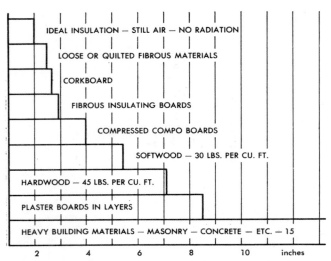

Thickness required to equal 1 inch ideal insulation. Thickness of various materials having equivalent heat-insulating values.

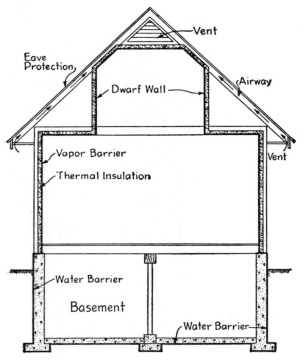

Cross section showing insulation principles.

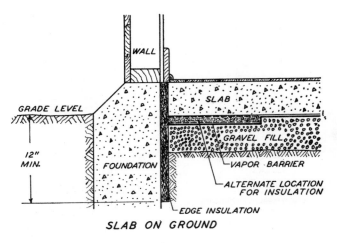

SLAB ON GROUND

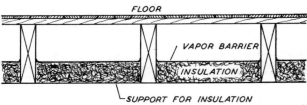

WOOD FLOOR OVER UNHEATED CRAWL SPACE

Recommended methods of insulating floors in basementless houses.

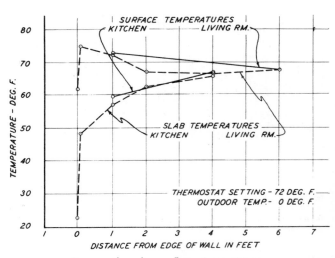

Basementless home floor temperatures.

Condensation Control

Condensation control plays an important part in the design and construction of dwellings. Paint peeling, wood decay and the trapping of excessive moisture in walls and floors is often the result of poor or no control.

The Housing and Home Finance Agency, based on studies by the Forest Products Laboratory quote the following: "A good vapor barrier should permit not more than one grain of water to pass through an area one foot square in one hour when the vapor pressure difference is calculated on the basis of one inch of mercury when tested by a dry method." The HHFA futher states that, "It should have sufficient mechanical strength to permit handling during erection without damage. It should also retain its vapor resistance qualities for the life of the building."

Vapor barriers are manufactured in a number of forms: as a type applied to the face of insulation, a rigid board type, and as a flexible film.

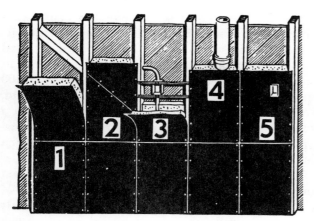

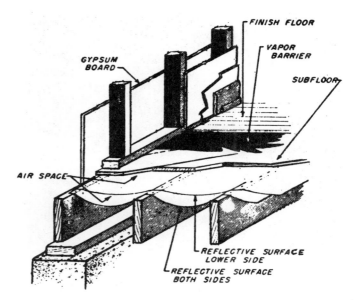

To install insulating batts start at the bottom of the stud, at the floor line, and fit each batten snugly against each successive batten and tuck into space between studding. Where there is a flange on the vapor barrier, it should be stapled to the studs. At sills, plates, and in odd-shaped places, the vapor barrier is cut a little larger than the opening, the insulation tucked back and the barrier stapled to the framing members. The sketch shows the successive steps in placing battens between studding and around service pipes.

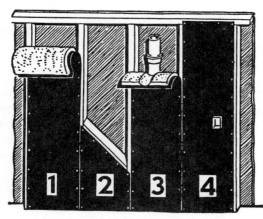

Insulating blankets are cut in continuous strips to the required length for each space between studding. In installing batts or blankets, large pipes in walls may require removal of part of the wool, but the vapor barrier is always retained. To protect water pipes from freezing, insulation should be on the cold side whenever possible and none on the warm side, but should keep the vapor barrier intact. Vapor barrier must fit snugly around outlets.

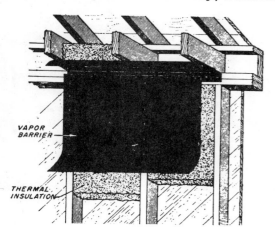

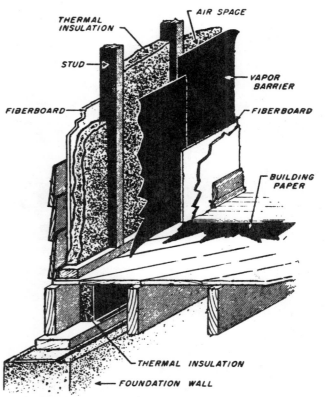

Details of outside wall and floor construction showing thermal insulation and vapor barrier placed to arrest heat transmission and condensation.

When vapor barriers are installed, whether they are an integral part of the insulation or separate units, another danger spot is the junction of attic floor, roof and side wall. The sketch at left shows how condensation control is obtained by placing a vapor barrier over the face of the studs and lower side of the attic floor joists. The lap is on the plate members of the outside wall and is securely stapled.

Spacer flange balsam wool application.

The film type made of polyethylene claims protection against cracking or deterioration with age. It is soft and tear resistant. This type can be used both summer and winter and remains flexible in below zero weather. Its weight is negligible; 30,000 square inches of .001 film weighs only a pound. This light weight makes for easy handling with a corresponding reduction in labor costs. The material can be obtained up to 16 feet in width, which can be handled with ease.

The polyethylene film is used as a vapor barrier under concrete slabs. For this purpose the .004 thickness is recommended. It is applied directly over a sub-grade that is smoothed to eliminate protrusions which would rupture the film. It is lapped not less than six inches with the top lap placed in the direction of the spreading of the concrete. The weight of the slab seals the joint.

Walls and ceilings exposed to unheated and unventilated areas should be vapor-proofed with .002 thickness to prevent the penetration of moisture—the barrier to be applied to the warm side of the construction, and joints to occur over solid backing with a minimum lap of three inches. Film is attached to studs with staples.

This material can also be used in several ways around the outside of foundation walls. After walls are finished and the forms removed the film is placed against the outside of the walls before backfilling. It can be placed on the inside of forms before pouring. In this way it is used as a form liner which permits slow curing of the concrete while allowing early removal of the forms. Care should be used to avoid puncturing the material. When the liner is used it is unnecessary to grease or shellac the forms.

Balsam wool attic application.

Sprayed fiber insulation.

Radiant heat piping is shown laid over a moisture barrier film preparatory to the pouring of concrete.

Installation of Mineral Wool Batts and Blankets

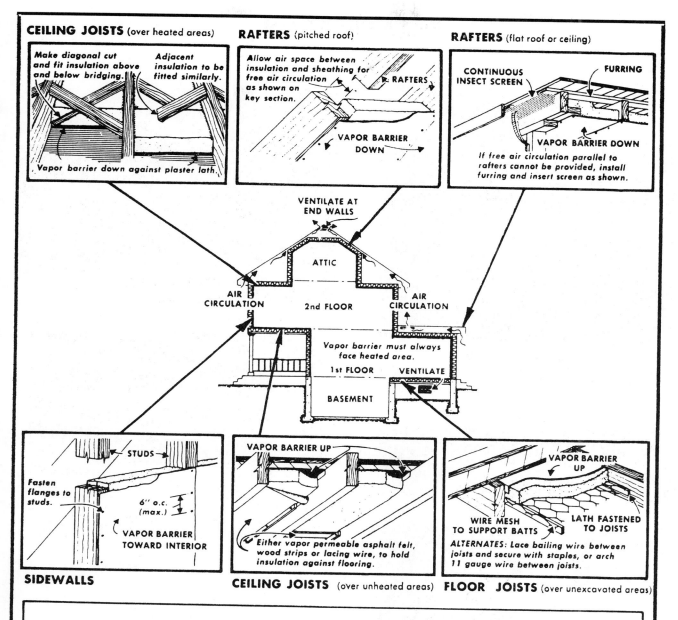

CEILING JOISTS (over heated areas)

Make diagonal cut and fit insulation above and below bridging.

Adjacent insulation to be fitted similarly.

Vapor barrier down against plaster lath.

RAFTERS (pitched roof)

Allow air space between insulation and sheathing for free air circulation as shown on key section.

RAFTERS

VAPOR BARRIER DOWN

RAFTERS (flat roof or ceiling)

CONTINUOUS INSECT SCREEN

FURRING

VAPOR BARRIER DOWN

If free air circulation parallel to rafters cannot be provided, install furring and insert screen as shown.

VENTILATE AT END WALLS

ATTIC

AIR CIRCULATION

2nd FLOOR

AIR CIRCULATION

Vapor barrier must always face heated area.

1st FLOOR

VENTILATE

BASEMENT

SIDEWALLS

STUDS

Fasten flanges to studs.

6" o.c. (max.)

VAPOR BARRIER TOWARD INTERIOR

CEILING JOISTS (over unheated areas)

VAPOR BARRIER UP

Either vapor permeable asphalt felt, wood strips or lacing wire, to hold insulation against flooring.

FLOOR JOISTS (over unexcavated areas)

VAPOR BARRIER UP

WIRE MESH TO SUPPORT BATTS

LATH FASTENED TO JOISTS

ALTERNATES: Lace bailing wire between joists and secure with staples, or arch 11 gauge wire between joists.

VAPOR BARRIERS: Vapor barriers are relatively vapor-impermeable materials used to keep inside water vapor from passing into the spaces within the walls, ceilings and floors of the structure. Their permeance should not exceed 1 perm, and they should always be installed toward the room (or heated) side of the construction. The outside (cold) wall should have a permeance of at least 5 times that of the vapor barrier, so that any vapor in the wall may escape harmlessly to the outdoors. It is important that all tears and holes that may be made in the barriers be repaired while they are installed.

METHOD OF INSTALLATION: Batts or blankets should be butted closely together in the stud or rafter space. Both should be trimmed to exactly fit the space to be insulated, with enough of the vapor barrier left over for stapling at the top and bottom. Batts and blankets with attached vapor barriers have flanges which are fastened to the framing member to hold the insulation in place and to make the vapor barrier moisture-tight. Flanges may be fastened to the framing member face, or to the inside of the member to hold the insulation in the middle of the space to be insulated. Both are acceptable practices. Staples should not be more than 6 inches apart, and should attach the flange to the framing down both sides, and across the bottom and top of sills, plates, and headers. Failure to use enough fastenings is the most common cause of poor installation. When insulating a pitched roof, the insulation should be extended up the rafters to the collar beams, and then across them. Never carry the insulation up to the peak of a pitched roof. It is extremely important to insulate behind water pipes in wall spaces.

Courtesy of National Mineral Wool Association

Appendix A

PREFABRICATION

Framing the house with precut pieces. Where site work is faster, like the trimming of the subflooring, it is not done at the lumber yard; instead is left to the building crew.

Placing the preassembled truss.

Split-ring truss is assembled at the site. All members are precut, so that the building crew does no measuring or cutting, can't make mistakes. A simple jig is all that's necessary for accurate assembly.

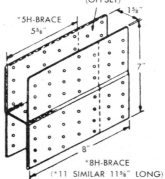

24 HOLES ONE SIDE
25 HOLES OTHER SIDE
(OFFSET)

*5H-BRACE
5⅝"

1⅝"

7"

8"

*8H-BRACE
(*11 SIMILAR 11⅝" LONG)

The H-brace gusset in the drawing is shown in the photo above used in a hip-roof truss. It provides its own nailing pattern, makes a motion-free joint, allows the trusses to be stacked.

Sheathing board is stapled on over the insulation. Any type of sheathing can be used; in this case it is a fiber-board insulating type.

A pre-hung door is set up in the partition. It is merely pushed into place, shimmed, nailed tight, and then the pre-built trim is snapped into place, as shown here.

Setting exterior wall panels in place.

The module is still basic in prefab, even though modern practice has far outstripped the early theory of on-site joining of similar-sized panels. Now larger multiples are made up on jigs in highly mechanized factories; indeed, the industry's new symbol has become a trailer that carries components as large as can be handled by two or three men. Modules guide width and placement of windows and wall elements.

Experimentation is going on all over the map. In Canada, Glenwal Ltd. of East Calgary reports use of a sandwich of gridwork containing insulation

Interior wall panels are set up. The drywall is pre-installed on one side of the panels which are four feet high, doubled up to reach ceiling.

Lu-Re-Co window panel has the window installed. Sheathing overlap is to cover the double 2 x 6 plate that runs around the house.

Interior partition components are shown in place. Studs for wall at left are precut, assembled on side. Wardrobes range in size from two feet to six feet. Ceiling height of house must be standardized for the partitons, which are non-load bearing with the truss roof.

batts, between plywood sheets enclosing an aluminum foil vapor barrier. Semico combined the principles of solid construction and plywood lamination in the trilam panel of lower grade and short lumber, interlaying felt for windproofing. Wiring—generally omitted from the package—is incorporated in panels, where local rules permit, by Precision-Built, General Industries, Ford ("with Underwriters inspection and approval"). Others, like U. S. Steel, equip panels with fish wires; or, like W. G. Best, with conduits and outlet boxes.

Typical partition arrangement is this bathroom-bedroom wall. Rear of the big wardrobe has furring strips on 16-inch centers so that drywall can be nailed to it.

Wall sections especially adapted to closets are made of hardboard. They are held together with splines, which in turn support the various storage attachments shown.

Appendix B

PRINCIPLES FOR CONSTRUCTION

Correct foundation construction begins with concrete footings placed to run continuously with the outside and lateral walls. Footings should be at least 18″ wide and 10″ deep and the top surface should be exactly level. Where basements occur, footings should project at least 6″ from the vertical line of the wall on both sides. For concrete walls, portland cement should be used at 1 to 3 of sand and 5 of stone. For masonry walls use enough portland cement in the mortar to avoid disintegration under extreme moisture. To insure a dry basement, outside walls and rough concrete floor should be waterproofed with hot tar and pitch applied over several layers of special felt. This membrane should be continuous, running entirely under the walls, over the footings and up the side walls to the grade line. The finished cement floor then is flowed on over the membrance (Fig. 1).

As the concrete foundation wall is poured (or when constructed of brick or masonry) place foundation bolts of at least ¾″ diameter at intervals of 6″ to 8″ throughout the circuit of the outside wall, but always at each corner. These should be sunk to a depth of 18″ minimum, with the threaded end protruding above the top surface high enough to extend through the thickness of the wood sills. When the concrete or cement mortar has set, place the metal termite shield in position (Figs. 1-2). Then follow with the sills, which are bored to fit over the bolts. Fasten securely, with wide-flanged gaskets and thick nuts screwed down

tightly with a wrench. By this method foundation and sills become an integral unit providing proper anchorage for the entire house structure (Fig. 2).

In framing wall studding, joists and rafters are set 16 inches on center. In two-story houses the platform or Western type of construction is recommended (Fig. 8). This provides a platform one story high, built entirely over the first floor. Second-story wall studding assemblies then are raised above the second-floor platform, resting solidly on plates spiked into position over the subfloor. Greater rigidity of framework results from this method, as compared to the balloon type in which studding runs continuously from sill to second-story ceiling joists, because, in the platform type, caps and plates incidental to the second-story construction serve as extra bracing.

Reinforce all corners by using 5 full-length studs, extending from sill to rafters. Use 6 studs in the same manner where T angles occur (Fig. 3). At all corners on the main structure and extra bracing by placing stud reinforcements at an angle of 45 degrees from the line of the sill (Fig. 4). Studs of 2 x 6 for the outside wall are preferable to 2 x 4's. They provide greater rigidity, more air space between inside and outside sheathing (an advantage when inter-wall insulation is used), greater depth, and consequently more attractive appearance to window frames and interior sills. With either width, always install one tier of blocking between studs, placed at half the height of each

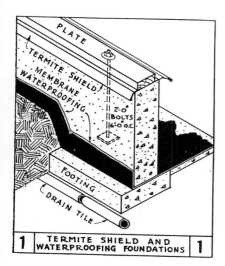

1 TERMITE SHIELD AND WATERPROOFING FOUNDATIONS 1

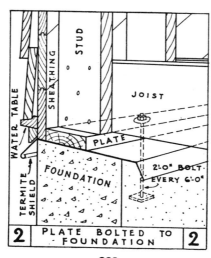

2 PLATE BOLTED TO FOUNDATION 2

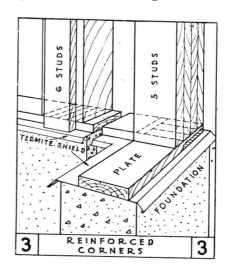

3 REINFORCED CORNERS 3

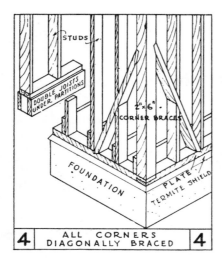

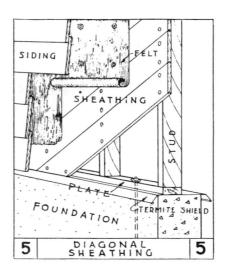

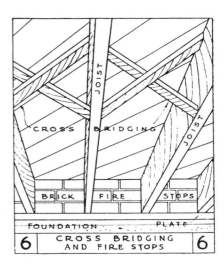

story wall. While blocking between studding prevents vibration, it should be supplemented by capping the studding with double plates at the ceiling height of each story (Fig. 9). Again, all studs which frame the outside and inside wall openings should be doubled (Fig. 11). Floor and ceiling joists should be securely spiked to the wall stud wherever they engage each other, with 4 spikes driven through both members and clinched. Floor and ceiling joists should be braced by cross bridging (Fig. 6). Run one series of such bridging for each 10 lineal feet of joist bearings.

Rafters of 2 x 6 for the roof of even the smallest house are preferred to 2 x 4's. As in the case of studs and floor joists, these rafters, where they engage the ends of the ceiling joists, should be securely spiked together and clinched (Fig. 10). Use shingle sheathing strips 1 x 4 kiln-dried material. These should be placed 3 inches apart and nailed at each joist with 2 cement-coated nails. Over these, lay edge-grain red cedar shingles, meas-

uring at least 18 inches in length and not less than 5 shingles to 2 inches of total thickness at the butt. Lay shingles not more than 4 inches to the weather, attaching them with galvanized or cut-iron nails. When shingles are dipped, be sure the stain extends at least 7 inches from the butt.

Apply outside sheathing at an angle of 45 degrees to the vertical line of the studding (Fig. 5). Sheathing material should be 1 x 6 or 1 x 8 kiln dried, surfaced four sides, and preferably center-matched and even end-matched. This pattern affords a tight, integrated wall of useful bracing strength. If center-matched stock is not available, kiln dried shiplap is preferable to square-edged boards. Over the sheathing apply a complete interliner of standard building felt, attaching it to the sheathing with short, broad-headed nails. Over this apply the clapboard, lap, or drop-siding exterior wall, using not less than 3 cement-coated nails driven through the face of each piece at each stud. At this stage, the painter should follow closely be-

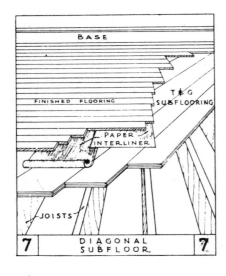

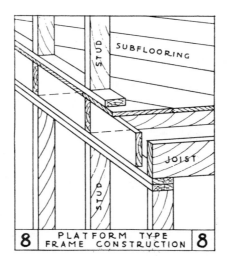

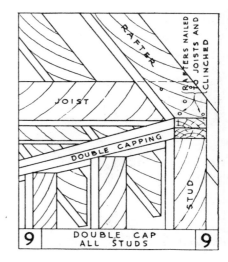

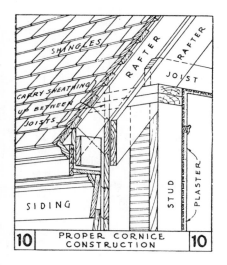

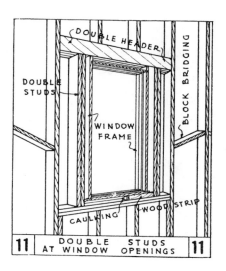

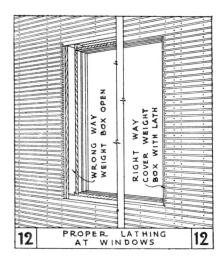

hind the carpenter, applying the priming coat of lead and oil, so that no unpainted surface of the outside finished wall may be exposed to the weather overnight.

Lay subfloors at an angle of 45 degrees to the line of the joists and nail with 2 nails at each joist (Fig. 7). While square-edged boards sometimes are specified, center-matched and end-matched kiln-dried material is preferable. The latter provides a smooth, tight floor, affording a stabilized base for the finish floor, as well as extra cross-bracing for the structure. Installation of the finish floor should be deferred until all other work inside the house has been completed.

With the plumbing roughed in, heating ducts for pipes installed, and electric wiring completed, surfacing of the interior walls follows. For plaster walls, there is no more satisfactory base than wood lath. Whether air-dried or kiln-dried lath are used, they should be soaked in water and nailed on wet. Use 2 nails at each stud and break the joints on every tenth course. Use metal lath over all areas which enclose heating or ventilating ducts. Where sash-weight boxes occur at window openings, run the lath flush to the jamb, covering the boxes (Fig. 12). Where the new type of weightless sash is used, the box is dispensed with, but lath is run to the jamb in the same way.

Installation of woodwork and paneling should await the complete drying of the plaster. Drying can be expedited by operating the heating plant for a few days, a procedure to be followed in any season, but imperative during winter building or extended periods of wet weather. Interior wall panel installations can be made over kiln-dried furring strips of 1 x 4 surfaced four sides, nailed

horizontally at right angles to the wall stud, and spaced at intervals of not more than 2 feet between the flooring and ceiling. A complete subwall of kiln-dried, center- and end-matched sheathing is preferable to these furring strips and while not essential, does provide a solid subwall of greater strength and higher insulation value.

Where partitions carry a load from the second floor or serve as an anchor for the roof bracing in one-story construction, they should be supported by double floor joists (Fig. 4) and capped by double studding (Fig. 9). Where placed over first-floor girders, double joists can be omitted. In general, extra members used to insure adequate bracing and rigidity at every point of vertical or horizontal stress more than justify the small additional cost incurred. Partitions which engage opposite outside walls at or near the center of the structure should be tied securely to both walls as a medium of extra cross-bracing.

Lay finish floors after woodwork and lighting fixtures have been installed. This provision allows the floor to be laid after all workmen, other than floorlayers, have left the premises and avoids subjecting the flooring to damage when fixtures and heating equipment are moved in. The first step is to thoroughly clean the subfloor of all plaster spots, projecting nailheads, and uneven areas, being sure that no moisture is present on the surface. Lay a complete covering of 2- or 3-ply felt of special floor interliner, lapping the seams not less than 1 inch (Fig. 7). Finish flooring is tongued and grooved, and usually end-matched. It is blind-nailed into position, 1 nail to 8 inches of linear strip. Nails should engage the joists below the subfloor as frequently as possible. Machine sand-

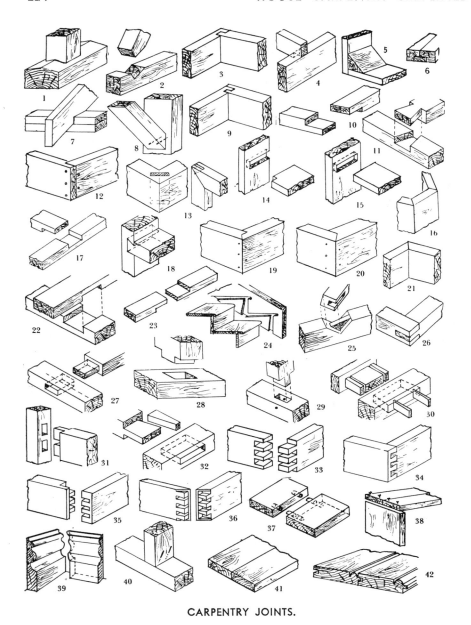

CARPENTRY JOINTS.

Carpentry joints: 1, notched; 2, thrust; 3, dado; 4, notched; 5, glued and backed; 6, fillistered; 7, bird's mouth; 8, brace; 9, dado tongue and rabbet; 10, end lap or halving; 11, dovetail lap; 12, rabbet; 13, splined miter; 14, gain; 15, housed; 16, external miter; 17, middle lap; 19, dovetail dado; 19, butt and miter; 20, stop miter; 21, internal miter; 22, cross lap; 23, end lap; 24 housed stairs; 25, straddle; 26, slip tenon; 27, through mortise; 28, stub mortise and tenon; 29, pinned mortise and tenon; 30, wedged mortise and tenon; 31, double mortise and tenon; 32, dovetail mortise and tenon; 33, through multiple dovetail; 34, lap dovetail; 35, stopped lap dovetail; 36, secret mitered dovetail; 37, doweled butt; 38, nailed butt; 39, coped; 40, square butt; 41, glued joint; 42, beaded.

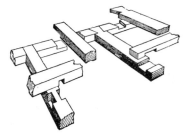

Notched joint details.

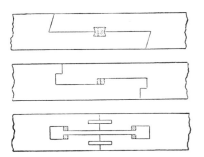

Keyed and wedged joint.

ing of the finish floor is preferable to hand-scraping, after which the final finish is applied.

There are several ways to drive a nail into a piece of stock. The most common way is called *straight nailing,* that is, the nail is always 90 degrees to the surface of the stock. Another way to drive nails is like straight nailing, except the nail is not driven all the way into the stock, allowing a small part of the nail to extend above the surface for pulling back with the claw of the hammer. This is called *draw nailing.*

Still another method of driving nails is called *toe nailing,* by which the nail is driven into the

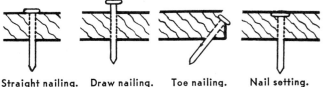

Straight nailing.   Draw nailing.   Toe nailing.   Nail setting.

stock at about 45 degrees to the surface of the stock.

Nail setting is the sinking of nails below the surface of the stock by use of a small tool called the nail set.

Obtain a piece of 1″ x 2″ x 6″ stock of wood and practice the four systems or methods of nailing as shown in the sketch.

Appendix C

SAFETY FOR THE CARPENTER

In a recent survey by the U. S. Bureau of Labor Statistics, it was indicated that powered saws, both portable and fixed, were responsible for the great majority of reported injuries occurring to carpentry workers. An analysis of the case histories involved showed that primary cause was inadequate shielding of the circular blade. Most power tools, especially saws and grinders, come equipped with protective shields mounted directly over the work surface. Many carpenters have the habit of removing the shield over the saw blade, under the mistaken impression that it "gets in the way." This simply is not so. A properly shielded blade is no more difficult to work with than an unshielded one. If for no other reason, it is easier to use because it acts as a partial trap for flying sawdust. Case histories report innumerable instances of workers stumbling into the moving blade, getting their clothes caught in it, or having fingers brought into contact with the saw blade by "kicking" of stock. Amputations occurred in over 20 per cent of the reported circular saw accidents.

All manufacturers of power equipment go to great pains to accompany their tools with complete operating instructions, including adequate safety measures. Most power tools have grounding devices, often neglected, that should always be connected to prevent shocks.

Defective tools accounted for a substantial portion of the accidents reported. Unsharpened, sprung, or improperly mounted blades cause stock to "jump," thus creating a hazard.

Hand tools, such as hammers, hatchets, knives, and chisels accounted for 7 or 8 per cent of the reported injuries. Here, typically, the major fault was in the improper use of them. With no effort here to totally describe the proper methods of using each of these tools, here are a few basic facts to remember:

Always cut or strike away from the body. It may seem more convenient at times to bend over a beam and drive a nail toward oneself or operate a chisel toward the body, but in such operation, the tools are prone to slip and the results are almost invariably disastrous.

Always use the right tool for the job. Electrical work calls for insulated tools. Fixed saws with guides should be used for cutting small, odd-shaped pieces of wood. Screwdrivers should be of the proper sizes for their respective jobs. These formulas could go on and on, but the truth is, most of them mean just a common sense attitude of the carpenter toward his tools and his work.

The workman who won't wear safety goggles while drilling into concrete is asking for trouble. Many concussions have been prevented by the use of the safety helmet. Gloves are virtually a necessity to prevent splinters and infections when handling rough or splintery stock. If one works frequently in a kneeling position, knee pads will prevent cuts and abrasions resulting from contact with rough or refuse-littered surfaces.

Of the injuries reported which were not connected with the operation of a specific tool, reports are voluminous on the subject of "poor housekeeping." By this is meant particularly failure to pick up and put in their proper places equipment, tools, and stray pieces of lumber. There is a tendency on the part of carpenters to leave lumber scraps just where they fall. These create a hazard in walking around. The old comedy situation of the man stepping on a rake lying on the ground and having it snap up and hit him in the face is presumably strictly for laughs, yet a similar situation too often exists wherever untidy carpenters work. Tools, should be returned to their proper places after use.

Many an accident has occurred because someone carelessly left a hammer or other tool on one level of a building, to be inadvertently knocked down to the next level. When a carpenter is working with other men on a building, such as masons, plumbers, or electricians, care should be taken, wherever practical, to schedule operations so they will not conflict with each other. For instance, if masons are working on one level of a house, the area below them should be clear of other men. Obviously, this is not always practical, but when it is necessary to have people on the under level of construction work, the upper level should be equipped with suitable guards to prevent material and tools from falling down to the lower work level. Even with guards, conscious precautions should be taken.

Scaffolds are always potential hazards, therefore should be inspected frequently to see that they are bolted or nailed securely, and any rope used should be checked against fraying. Ladders should always be equipped with safety feet and any imperfections in the ladder itself should be rectified immediately.

SAFE SCAFFOLDING PRACTICES

Various types of scaffolds are used in building construction, such as single pole scaffolds, independent (four pole) scaffolds, suspended scaffolds, outrigger scaffolds, and horse scaffolds. In the construction of these scaffolds the following suggestions should be carefully considered:

(a) All lumber used in scaffolds should be of good quality, reasonably straight grained and free from weakening knots and other defects.

(b) Scaffolds should be built and installed by men who thoroughly understand the principals of design and the safe loads which various members can carry.

(c) Special lumber selected for scaffold use should be painted green on the end so it can be distinguished from other miscellaneous lumber.

(d) Scaffold bracing should be installed in triangular fashion.

(e) When it is necessary to splice an upright member of a scaffold, cleats not less than 4 feet long should be nailed on two adjacent sides of the upright at the joint.

(f) Planks for flooring should be of uniform thickness. They should extend at least 6 inches and not more than 12 inches past the center of the putlog or other support.

(g) Scaffolds (with the possible exception of iron workers' or riveters' scaffolds, carpenters' bracket scaffolds, and trestle or A-ladder scaffolds), if 6 feet or more above the ground, should have substantial handrails and toe boards installed on all open sides. Handrails should be approximately 42 inches high; and toe boards not less than 5½ inches high. If the lower edge of the railing is more than 34 inches above the scaffold floor, an intermediate rail should be installed.

(h) It is advisable to install a wire screen of not more than ⅜ inch mesh between the top railing and the toeboard.

(i) If work is carried on above the men on a scaffold, the scaffold should have overhead protection or a roof of light lumber, heavy canvas or heavy wire mesh.

(j) Men should not work on an outside scaffold during a storm or in a high wind.

(k) Scaffolds should be cleaned at least daily of all rubbish. Tools, buckets, etc., should not be left on any scaffold when workers leave the job. In winter, snow and ice should be removed from the scaffold before work is started. The platform may be sprinkled with sand or ashes to prevent slipping.

(l) One or more safe means of access such as stairs or ladders should be provided to reach each scaffold platform. If a ladder is used, it should be fastened at the top and bottom so it cannot tip or slip.

(m) Scaffold members should be fenced in or otherwise protected so trucks and other vehicles cannot strike or dump material against them.

(n) Hoisting engineers should be warned not to let loads swing against scaffolds or catch on them.

(o) Outrigger scaffolds are not favored if other types of scaffolds can be used.

(p) Swinging scaffolds should be lowered to the ground or lashed to the building when men leave the job.

(q) Wire rope is recommended in preference to manila rope for suspended scaffolds.

(a) Any man who is required to go out upon a thrust-out (an overhead support to which cables are attached for suspended scaffolds) should wear a life belt. A life line should be secured to the belt and the other end made fast to some part of the building.

(s) Men should not jump on a scaffold, nor should anything be allowed to fall onto or off a scaffold.

(t) Horse scaffolds should not exceed three tiers nor a total height of 15 feet.

(u) Men should not work nor pass under scaffolds. Otherwise, their work places and passageways should be roofed over so no one will be injured by objects falling from the scaffold.

SCAFFOLD PLANKS
Safe Center Loads

Douglas Fir (Rocky Mountain Region), Sitka Spruce, White Spruce, Red Pine and Port Orford White Cedar. Extreme fiber stress of 1300 pounds per sq. in.

Span in Feet	Nominal size of plank in inches					
	2x8	2x10	2x12	3x8	3x10	3x12
6	230	290	355	610	775	935
8	170	210	260	450	570	690
10	130	165	200	355	450	540
12	105	130	160	285	365	440
14	80	105	130	235	305	365
16	70	90	105	200	255	310

SPECIFICATIONS and NOTES

For other species of woods as listed below, safe center loads may be determined by multiplying tabular load above by constant indicated for each group:

Species	Fiber stress in pounds per sq. in.	Constant
1. Balsam Fir, Eastern White Pine, Ponderosa Pine, Sugar Pine and Western White Fir..	1,050	.80
2. Redwood and Tamarack...	1,400	1.07
3. White Ash, Red Oak, White Oak and Baldcypress..............	1,500	1.15
4. Douglas Fir (Coast Region) and Southern Yellow Pine............	1,750	1.34
5. Dense Douglas Fir and Dense Southern Yellow Pine.............	2,050	1.57

Above table applies to planks surfaced 4 sides, seasoned to moisture content between 15 and 8 per cent, free from shakes, decay or other defects. Slope of grain not steeper than 1 in 15. Knots in edge not larger than ⅛ of plank thickness. Knots in center of wide face not larger than ¼ of plank width, with permissible size decreasing as they approach edge to ⅛ of plank width at edge. Sum of sizes of all knots in wide face in length equal to plank width, not to exceed ¼ of plank width. Average plank weight of 30 pounds per cu. ft. included.

Courtesy National Safety Council

GLOSSARY

A

abutment. A wall which receives a thrust. A solid pier from which an arch springs.

accelerator. Ingredient for hastening natural development of strength added to portland cement concrete as it is mixed.

acoustics. The science of sound, including its production, transmission, effects, and control.

active door. The one of a pair of doors which is opened first.

adz. A long-handled shaping and finishing hand tool, used on timber having the cutting blade at right angles to the handle.

aerated concrete. A lightweight mixture of cement, sand, and hard coal cinders, used for sound and heat absorbent subfloors.

aggregate. A coarse material, such as gravel or broken stone with which cement, sand, and water are mixed to form concrete.

air brick. A brick for ventilating which is hollow or perforated. A brick-sized box of metal with grated sides for ventilating.

air conditioning. A process in which air is washed, heated or cooled to a comfortable temperature, then circulated through a room or dwelling.

air-dried lumber. Green wood with its moisture removed in order to improve its serviceability. This process involves stacking in yards or sheds for any length of time. For the United States as a whole the minimum moisture content of thoroughly air dried lumber is 12 to 15 percent and the average is somewhat higher.

air duct. A pipe, tube or passage for conveying air.

air pocket. A cavity filled with air; used for insulating purposes as in hollow tile, concrete blocks, or hollow walls.

airway. A space between roof insulation and roof boards for the movement of air.

a. l. An abbreviation for the term *all lengths of lumber,* which is applied to several pices of lumber varying in length.

alburnum. The sapwood of a tree; the living tissue between the bark and heartwood of leaf-bearing trees.

alligatoring. A coarse checking pattern in exterior painting characterized by slipping of the new coating over the old coating to the extent that the old coating can be seen through the fissures.

anchor. A metal device used in fastening stone or brickwork in place.

anchor bolt. A coarse, threaded bolt, generally having a square head, used to fasten wood or iron to wood, stone or concrete. A bolt to secure a wooden sill to concrete or masonry floor or wall.

angle bead. A vertical bead, either wood or metal, placed on the external angle of plastered walls to protect plaster, sometimes called a staff bead.

angle brace. A support, generally of formed metal, used to stiffen a frame, placed across a corner at an angle of 90 degrees to the supported member.

angle dividers. A woodworking tool used to bisect an angle in one operation, to lay out 6-8-10 sided work, and to test corners for squareness. The tool has a curved member in which a lock screw is provided for the two adjustable arms.

angle iron. A bar of L-sectioned iron used in construction work as a support to other members.

annealed wire. A soft, tough wire used in binding form work.

annual growth ring or annular ring. The growth layer of a tree put on in a single growth year, including springwood and summerwood.

apron. The flat member of the inside trim of a window placed against the wall immediately beneath the stool.

arbor. A wooden lattice work supporting vines generally covering a path; a bower.

architectural drawings. The plans, elevations, details, etc., of any structure or building prepared by an architect or an architectural draftsman.

asbestos. A chemically resistant, non-conducting, fireproof mineral used as an insulating material in stoves, walls, roofing shingles, pipes and boilers; a fibrous variety of hornblend; an anhydrous silicate of magnesium.

ashlar. A block of hewn or squared building stone in regular courses, as distinguished from rubble work.

ash pit. A reservoir under a furnace or fireplace in which ashes are dropped; a place where ashes are deposited.

asphalt. A natural semisolid bitumen, largely obtained from Trinidad, West Indies. Most native asphalt is a residue from evaporated petroleum. It is insoluble in water but is soluble in gasoline and melts when heated. Asphalt is used widely in building

for waterproofing roof coverings of many types, exterior wall coverings, floor tile, etc.

auger bit. A twist bit used to bore large holes.

auxiliary view. A secondary drawing placed in mechanical relation to a larger view showing more detail than possible on the larger projection.

average length. The mean or most often encountered or available length of lumber in a stack or pile. Abbreviated av. or av. l.

average widths. The mean or most often encountered or available width of lumber in a stack or pile. Abbreviated av. w. Lumber furnished in all widths is so designated to distinguish from a required or specified width for specific purposes. Abbreviated a. w.

awl. A marking tool; a small hand tool for boring holes.

B

back band. A molding used on the corner of a door or window casing for ornamentation or to increase the width of the trim.

back bone. A notched timber on which a series of steps are built; also known as stair horse, string board or stringer.

back fill. The replacement of excavated earth into a pit or trench or against a structure.

backing. The two chamfered edges worked on the back, or upper edge, of a hip rafter, allowing roofing boards to lie evenly with the back of adjacent rafters.

back lining. The board, opposite the jamb, enclosing the open side of the weight pocket in a wooden sash frame.

backset. The horizontal distance from the front of a lock to the center of the cylinder, knob or keyhole.

badger. A tool for cleaning excess mortar from drain joints.

balanced shrinkage framing. A method of equalizing the shrinkage in framed members in which braces and trusses are used to counteract and balance contraction.

balk. A thick, squared timber used as a tie beam.

ball catch. A brass cylinder in which a small metal ball is supported by a spring, which, when engaged in the recess of a small plate, keeps the door on a cabinet closed until pressure is applied.

balloon framing. A method of framing

outside walls in which studs extend the full length or height of the wall.

balsam wool. An insulating material of wool-like fibers saturated with aromatic resin, used in partitions, floors, roofs and outside walls.

balusters. Small spindles or members forming part of a railing for stairway or balcony, fastened between a bottom and top rail.

balustrade. A row of balusters set on a continuous plinth, surmounted by a rail; used as a fence or guard.

b and better. A designation of stock or wood of the better variety. Abbreviated b & btr.

bar clamp. A bar, of steel or wood, to which are attached two movable jaws, one actuated by a screw and one held in place by a spring hook fitting into notches of the bar.

barge board. The finished board covering the gable rafter on a gable roof.

barge couple. The two rafters forming the gable of a roof which carry the overhang of the roofing boards.

bark pocket. An opening between annual growth rings that contains bark. Bark pockets appear as dark streaks on radial surfaces and as rounded areas on tangential surfaces.

barrel roof. A roof shaped like a half barrel, cut laterally.

base block. A small piece of trim at the bottom of a door casing.

baseboard. A board placed against the wall around a room next to the floor to finish properly between floor and plaster or wall covering. A board around the outside of a frame house next to the foundation, on which the water table trim is fastened and on which the first two rows of shingles rest.

base shoe. A quarter round molding attached to the baseboard at the floor level. Also *shoe mold*.

basswood. The American linden or whitewood.

bastard sawn. Hardwood lumber in which the annual rings make angles of 30 to 60 degrees with the surface of the piece.

bat. A broken brick. Insulating wool placed between framed members. A wooden brace. An abbreviation for batten.

batten. Narrow strips of wood or metal used to cover joints. Often spoken of as bats.

batter. The inward slope of a retainwall. A plastering mortar.

batter board. One of a pair of horizontal boards nailed to posts set at the corners of an excavation, used to indicate the desired level, also as a fastening for stretched strings to indicate outlines of foundation walls.

bay window. Any window space projecting outward from the walls of a building, either square or polygonal in plan, and supported on a foundation of its own.

baywood. A coarse-grained mahogany, native to tropical America, which is lighter and softer than true mahogany.

bead. A rounded decorative molding with a small groove, used in breaking a joint in a series of boards.

bead and butt. A flush panel with a bead on both edges which butts against the vertical stile of the framing which encloses it.

beaded joint. A joint marked by a bead on the edge of the material for ornamental purposes, as in beaded ceiling.

beam. A structural member transversely supporting a load.

beam ceiling. A ceiling having heavy timbers or box-shaped false timbers, usually exposed to view for quite a depth.

bearing blocks or plates. The plates or blocks which assist in distributing the load of any structural member on a wall; the plate or block placed underneath an I-beam in a masonry wall.

bearing wall or bearing partition. A wall that supports any vertical load in addition to its own weight.

beaver board. A pressed wood pulp product used to cover and insulate walls and ceilings.

bed. The layer of cement or mortar in which masonry rests. The horizontal surface of a stone in position.

bed molding. A molding in an angle, as between the overhanging cornice, or eaves, of a building and the side walls.

bed plate. The foundation plate or base on which an object or frame member rests; the flat member of a sill unit which rests upon the foundation wall.

beech. A tree of the oak family with smooth grey bark, used in making flooring, tool handles, and furniture.

belt course. An unmolded course of brick, stone, or wood which projects slightly from the face of a building.

belt sander. A machine, used in sandpapering woodwork, in which abrasive paper in the form of a belt operating over pulleys is pressed by a wooden block against the stock to be finished.

bench mark. A durable post, block, or other device placed in the ground by surveyors to indicate a definite point from which observations are made.

bench plane. A small hand tool for smoothing wood, such as the jack plane or the block plane.

bending, steam. The process of forming curved wooden members by steaming or boiling the wood and bending it to a form.

bent gouge. A gouge bent in its length for better access to concave parts of stock.

bevel. Any angle less than a right angle; a flat molding attached to or planed on the edge of a board; a hand tool with a blade adjustable to any angle.

beveled siding. Clapboards or weatherboards made in various widths; beveled on the face from $\frac{1}{8}$" at the top edge to $\frac{3}{8}$" at the bottom.

bevel of door. The slope of the front edge of a door, usually $\frac{1}{8}$" in 2".

bevel of lock front. The angle of the front of a mortise lock, inclined at other than a right angle to the case and conforming to the bevel of the edge of the door.

bevel square. A tool similar to a square but with a movable blade that can be set to any angle.

bind. To stick, as a door on the jamb, head, or stile of its frame.

binding joist. A beam fastened between the ceiling and bridging joists.

binding stone. A stone that passes through a stone wall to assist in making a good bond.

birch. A tree of the oak family having a white outer bark, hard and close-grained wood; used in the manufacture of doors, inside trim, and furniture.

bird peck. A small hole or patch of distorted grain resulting from birds pecking through the growing cells in the tree. In shape bird peck usually resembles a carpet tack with the point toward the bark, and it is usually accompanied by discoloration extending for a considerable distance along the grain and to a much lesser extent across the grain. The discoloration produced by bird peck causes what is commonly known as mineral streak.

bird's eye. Small localized areas in wood with fibers indented and otherwise contorted to form few to many circular or elliptical figures remotely resembling bird's eyes on the tangential surface. Common in sugar maple and used for decorative purposes, rare in other hardwood species.

bird's mouth. The seat cut at the lower end of a rafter notched out to fit the wall plate; formed by the plumb and level cuts.

bit. The cutting or working part of a bit and brace which is inserted into the jaws of the brace and made fast.

bit key. A projecting blade which engages with and actuates the bolt and tumblers of a lock.

bit stock. A carpenter's brace.

bit stop. A gauge that can be clamped to a bit to regulate the depth of the hole being bored; a bit gauge.

blank flue. A closed-off chamber built on one side of a fireplace when that space is not needed for a flue, used for economy and to balance the weight.

bleeder tile. A pipe built into the foundation walls of a building to draw off surface water from the outside tile drain to the inside drain.

blind dovetail. A joint in which the ends of the boards are mitered and the dovetail is made about ⅛″ from the front edge of the miter, so that it is hidden when the joint is put together, the joint showing as a miter. A secret dovetail.

blind mortise-and-tenon joint. A joint in which neither the mortise nor the tenon protrudes through the stile.

blind nailing. Nailing in such a way that the nailheads are not visible on the face of the work.

blind stop. A strip of wood, usually ¾″ x 1⅜″, nailed between the outside trim and outside of sashes, against which blinds, screens or storm sashes are fastened. Sometimes the stop is milled as an integral part of the outside casing.

blind tenon. A tenon which does not extend all the way through a mortise, as contrasted to a through tenon.

block and tackle. A simple device for hoisting, consisting of one or more pulleys encased in a frame over which a rope, called a tackle, is passed; identified by the number of pulleys in the block, as single, double or triple.

block plane. A small hand plane used on end wood; a butt plane.

blue print. A type of photographic reproduction of a drawing in which the lines of the drawing show white on a blue field. Also applied to any working drawing regardless of color. The unexposed yellowish paper turns blue on exposure to light and water. All process prints are made on sensitized paper by light penetrating a tracing. The common kinds of process printings are blue print, blue line print, black line print, red line print, negative Van Dyke print, positive Van Dyke print and the French blue print. Photostats are reflected copies, not penetrated.

board foot. The volume of a piece of wood one inch thick, one foot wide, and one foot long, equivalent to 144 square inches.

board measure. A method of measuring timber in which the length and breadth in feet, and thickness in inches, are multiplied together to get the number of board feet. One formula to use in figuring board feet is: $\dfrac{T'' \times W'' \times L'}{12}$, where T equals thickness in inches; W equals width in inches; L equals length in feet. The product, divided by 12, gives the number of board feet in a given piece of stock. Boards less than one inch in thickness are figured as one inch in such measurements.

board measure table. The table on the back of the blade of the steel square used to obtain the number of board feet. By reading the length of the blade and the figure corresponding to the width of the board in either direction from the figure 12 the number of board feet may be obtained. This applies only to boards not over one inch thick; for any stock over one inch thick multiply the result by the thickness in inches.

bodied linseed oil. Linseed oil that has been thickened in viscosity by suitable processing with heat or chemicals. Bodied oils are obtained in a great range in viscosity from a little greater than that of raw oil to just short of a jellied condition.

boiled linseed oil. Linseed oil in which enough lead, manganese, or cobalt salts have been incorporated to make the oil harden more rapidly when spread in thin coatings.

bolster. A short horizontal timber resting on the top of a column for the support of beams or girders.

bond. The adhesion obtained by the use of glue in holding together jointed boards. In masonry, the overlapping of bricks in a wall in alternate courses to bind the whole wall together. Various patterns are known by such names as common, Flemish, American, English, etc., bond. There are twenty-six types of bonding of bricks in a wall.

boning rod. A device shaped like a T square, used by carpenters, plumbers, masons or surveyors to check the level of a piece of work.

boom. A heavy spar on a derrick which can be raised or lowered or swung in any direction, used in hoisting heavy objects.

borrowed light. Light from any source admitted from another room through windows in the separating partitions.

Boston hip. A style of shingling, used in finishing the hip of a hip roof, in which shingles are laid in two parallel rows, lengthwise, with the edges lapped in alternate courses to make a watertight joint on the hip.

bow. The distortion in a board that deviates from flatness lengthwise but not across its faces.

box. To enclose, as a cornice in a boxed cornice design.

box column. A pillar such as one supporting a porch roof and resting upon a pier or porch floor; generally square in shape and made up of four segments of trim wood.

box cornice. A built-up portion of an outside trim housing the gutter.

box frame. A wooden window frame with long slots or boxes for sash weights.

boxed heart. The term used when the pith falls entirely within the four faces of a piece of wood anywhere in its length. Also known as boxed pith.

box sill. A sill of L-shaped cross section used in balloon frame structure, consisting of two pieces of 2″ x 8″ framing stock, one resting on the foundation with the floor joists nailed to it, and the other nailed at right angles to the one resting on the foundation, and against the ends of the floor joists.

box wood. A hard, close-grained wood of the box tree; used in inlay borders around hardwood floors.

brace. A piece of wood or metal fastened into the interior angles of a frame, between or across its members, or against it, to strengthen or support the framing.

braced framing. Supported framework of a house, especially at corners; also known as Western framing type of construction.

bracket. A wooden or metal support for shelving, cornices, gutters, etc.; the decorative shape fastened on the face of the outside string of an open-string stairway under the tread and mitered to the riser.

brad. A small nail less than one inch long, its size being described by number and length.

brad awl. A hand tool used for piercing wood for brads or screws.

brashness. A condition that causes some pieces of wood to be relatively low in shock resistance for the species, and, when broken in bending, to fail abruptly without splintering at comparatively small deflections.

breaking radius. The limiting radius of curvature to which wood or plywood can be bent without breaking.

brick veneer. A facing of brick laid against frame or tile wall construction.

bridging. Small wood or metal members that are inserted in a diagonal position between the floor joists to act both as tension and compression members for the purpose of bracing the joists and spreading the action of loads.

bridging joists. The common joists to which a floor is nailed.

bridle joint. A joint designed to resist a strong thrust, used in the construction of wooden trusses where the joint is less than a right angle, made exactly opposite to the ordinary mortise and tenon, in that the tenon is at right angles to the horizontal member and the mortise is at right angles to the inclined member.

bright. Unstained; unpainted.

broken joints. A system of staggering joints so that no two of them in successive rows are directly opposite each other.

buck. A four-legged frame, about knee high, on which to saw or otherwise work wood. Also see *doorbuck*.

builder's level. A simplified theodolite used on construction work for finding relative horizontal positions of points or objects, consisting of a tripod supporting a base on which are mounted (a) two bubble levels at right angles to each other, by which the base may be adjusted to a true horizontal position, and (b) a telescope attached to a revolving circular disk, marked in circular degrees and minutes for reading angles.

building code. The civil regulations governing the construction and repair of buildings and setting forth requirements as to dimensions of lumber, plumbing, electric wiring, methods of construction, and restrictions on the type and uses of buildings in certain zones and areas.

building felt. A lightweight paper, heavier than building paper, and lighter than roll roofing, made of wool and hair saturated with a tar product used as a deadening felt under hardwood floors and linoleum and as a protecting cover over rough siding before shingles, beveled siding, or brick veneer is applied.

building fiberboard. A broad generic term inclusive of sheet materials of widely varying densities manufactured of refined or partially refined wood (or other vegetable) fibers. Bonding agents and other materials may be added to increase strength, resistance to moisture, fire, or decay, or to improve some other property.

building inspector. An official appointed under a building code whose duty is to see that the code is observed, passing on proper construction methods and condemning those considered unsafe.

building line. A line defined by the city building code to keep the street and sidewalk lines uniform by establishing limits beyond which buildings cannot project.

building paper. A tough, tar or asphalt covered paper, used between rough and finished floors, around outside window and door casings, underneath outside walls, and roof coverings, and in similar places to reduce drafts and insulate the interior of framed dwellings.

building permit. A certificate which must be obtained from the municipal government by the property owner or contractor before a building can be erected or repaired and which must be kept posted in a conspicuous place until the job is finished and passed by the building inspector.

built-up roof. A roofing composed of three to five layers of rag felt or jute saturated with coal tar, pitch, or asphalt. The top is finished with crushed slag or gravel. Generally used on flat or low-pitched roofs.

built-up timbers. An assembly made by joining layers of lumber together with mechanical fastenings so that the grain of all laminations is essentially parallel.

bullnose. A step with a rounded corner, usually the first step in a stairway, used to obtain a decorative and finished appearance.

bungalow. A one-story house with verandas, originating in India.

butt. The end of a piece of timber; the bottom of a ladder; a kind or type of hinge. Transom, loose pin, loose joint, half surface and double-action butt hinges are the more common types of butt hinges.

butt-and-miter joint. A joint showing a butt and miter on its face, the top half being a butt, and the lower half a miter.

butterfly hinge. An ornamental hinge applied to the face of a cabinet door or stiles, in which the wings have an appearance of a butterfly.

butternut. A North American white walnut, a coarse-grained, easily worked wood used in the manufacture of cabinets, moldings, and trim.

butt gauge. A double-bar gauge for marking two parallel lines at any given distance from the edge of a board, especially a door.

butt joint. The junction where the ends of two timbers or other members meet in a square-cut joint.

butt miter. A surface beveled at an angle of 45 degrees, joined with a similar surface and not overlapping.

buttonwood. The North American sycamore.

buttress. A projection from a wall giving added strength.

C

cabinet scraper. A tool of good tool steel, rectangular in shape, with a sharp edge having a slight burr for cutting, held in the hand or in a metal frame and used to smooth wooden surfaces.

caisson. A recessed panel in a ceiling or soffit. A watertight compartment used when building a foundation under water.

calcimine. A white or tinted wash of slacked lime and water for decorating walls or ceilings.

calipers. A tool resembling a draftsman's compass, used for measuring outside or inside diameters, depending on whether the ends of the legs are bent in or out.

calking compound. A plastic filler used to fill spaces between exterior windows or door frames and the adjacent masonry to prevent the leakage of water, air, or dust into a building from the outside and to prevent the escape of warm air from the inside of a building.

camber. The amount of upward curve in an arch necessary to support its own weight or that of its load without becoming concave.

cant. To incline at an angle.

canted beam. A beam whose edges have been chamfered or beveled.

cantilever. A beam unsupported at one end, which projects outward to carry the weight of a structure above, as a balcony.

cantilever bracket. An iron bracket attached to a wall to support bathroom fixtures.

cantilever lookout. A wooden member extending outward beyond a rafter tail supported by the wall studs.

cant strip. A wedge or triangular shaped piece of lumber used at gable ends under shingles or at the junction of the house and a flat deck under the roofing to deflect rain.

cap. The upper member of a column, pilaster, door cornice, molding, newel post, either plain or molded.

cap iron. An adjustable blade attached to the face of a plane iron or cutter to regulate the thickness of the shaving taken off a board; also known as a cover iron.

capping piece. The top member or plate of a side or end wall; any horizontal timber extending over upright posts or studs to which it is framed.

carborundum. An abrasive material used in stones, wheels or paper, composed of carbon and silicon (SiC), used for grinding and sharpening tools.

carpenter's clamp. A bar of wood or iron with an adjustable stop at one end and a block actuated by a screw-threaded bar at the other; used in making glued joints and pulling framing together.

carpenter's mouse. A device composed of a short piece of lead or light chain to which a string is attached, used in inserting sash cord over pulleys when hanging sashes.

carpenter's punch. A tool commonly called a nail set for driving heads of nails below the surface of the wood.

carpenter's square. A measuring, marking, and calculating tool, consisting of a blade and a beam of steel set at right angles. The beam is also called the body and the blade the tongue. The usual "two-foot-square" is 24″ long on the beam and 16″ long on the tongue, graduated into 1/32, 1/16, 1/12, 1/10, 1/4 and 1/2 inch scales on various edges of the body and tongue. The following scales appear on most squares on various faces of the body and tongue: brace table, octagon table, Essex board measure table, 100th scale. One type, the take-down square, has a removable tongue for easier handling.

carriage. The framed member, in stair work, supporting the treads and risers.

cased. Closed in. A door or window opening after the trim has been fastened around a frame.

casement adjuster. A hinged or pivoted rod for moving and fastening the hinged sash of a casement window; a quadrant.

casement frames and sash. Frames of wood or metal enclosing part or all of the sash, which may be opened by means of hinges affixed to the vertical edges.

casement window. A window hung to open on hinges, like a door.

casing. The trim or architrave around a door or window frame. The paneling sometimes placed around columns or piers.

catch basin. A reservoir in a drainage system to hold water, regulate the drainage, or retain foreign objects not meant to go through the sewer.

cavetto. A small concave molding; a scotia.

cavity wall. Two walls built close together and joined by ties as an aid in weatherproofing. Also called *hollow wall*.

c.c. Center to center.

C clamp. A hand clamp, shaped like the letter C, through which pressure is applied by a screw, used to hold surfaces temporarily in contact.

cedar. A durable, sweet-smelling wood of the pine family; used in closets, chests and for inside trim. Incense cedar is a light weight, fairly soft wood, which shrinks little and has a low shock resistance. It is light brown in color and used mainly in the manufacture of closet linings.

sheathing, subsills, posts, and trellises.

center bit. A wood-boring tool having a cutting end consisting of a lip on one side and a spur on the other to insure a smooth, clean cut; not self-feeding as the auger bit.

center line. A line on a job from which all measurements are taken; a line on a drawing denoting the center of an object, consisting of dots and dashes.

center punch. A prick punch; a steel punch used in marking a point on metal.

center to center. The distance measured from the center of one object to the center of another. Abbreviated c.c.

center to end. The distance measured from the center of an object to its end or the end of another.

center to face. The distance measured from the center of one object to the face of another.

center up. To bring to a center or definite position.

chain mortiser. A machine used for mortising in wood, having chains of various widths, with hooked cutters. The chain revolves on two wheels, cutting and throwing out the core at the same time, making a U-shaped mortise.

chair rail. A rail molding about 4″ wide and ½″ thick, attached to the walls of a room about 3′ from the floor to protect the wall covering from damage by the backs of chairs.

chalk line. A marking or working line placed between two points. A heavy cord or string is rubbed with carpenter's chalk, held at two points, raised slightly about the center of the line and allowed to snap back into position, transferring the chalk to the work.

chalk-line spool. A heavy wooden or metal spool around which a chalk line is wound when not in use.

chalk off. To use a chalk line in marking off a job.

chamfer. A sloping or beveled edge.

chatter mark. Any of the small wavy marks formed on the surface of stock caused by a loose, chattering tool.

check. A lengthwise separation of the wood that usually extends across the rings of annual growth and commonly results from stresses set up in wood during seasoning.

checkrails. Meeting rails sufficiently thicker than a window to fill the opening between the top and bottom sash made by the parting stop in the frame. They are usually beveled.

cherry. A hardwood, reddish in color, sometimes used as inside finish.

chestnut. A hardwood tree of the beech family having a wood of reddish color sometimes used as inside finish.

chisel. A hand tool, having a long, round handle in which is secured a sharpened metal tongue or blade for cutting and shaping wood. Chisels for work in wood are known as bevel-edge, firmer, mortise, paring, socket, etc.

chisel mortiser. A machine used in cutting mortises in wood work, employing a hollow tube slotted on the sides and ground on the inside of the cutting edge. Inside the tube a twist bit revolves when the machine is operated, the tube or shell remaining rigid and under pressure, cutting the end of the mortise square while the bit bores into the wood, throwing out the core.

chord. A principal horizontal member supporting framed work. A single straight line connecting the extremities of an arc.

chuck. That part of a bit brace which holds the boring tool.

cinder block. A hollow building block made of crushed cinders and cement used in constructing walls and backing up brickwork.

circular and angular measure. A system of measuring angles by the number of degrees, or 360ths of a circle, expressed in degrees, minutes, and seconds, as follows:

60 seconds (″)	—1 minute (′)
60 minutes	—1 degree (°)
90 degrees.	—1 quadrant
4 quadrants	—1 circle or circumference

clapboard. A board of 6″ to 8″ wide used as an exterior covering on houses, tapered in thickness from ½″ on bottom to a feather edge on the top; weatherboarding.

clear. Free of unevenness such as knots, branches, suckers, etc.

clear story. The upper part of a building with windows above the roofs of nearby buildings.

cleat. A piece of wood or metal screwed or nailed across the back of a panel to brace it against buckling; a short piece of wood fastened to a wall to support the end of a shelf.

clinch. To bend over the point of a nail protruding through a board so that it is turned into the wood, forming a hook in the direction of the grain.

cloak rail. A board attached to a wall, especially in a clothes closet, as a base on which coat hooks are fastened.

close-boarded. A method of laying boards on a roof or sides of a building in which the edges of the boards are in close contact with one another, as distinguished from open boarding.

closed-string style. A staircase without an open newel.

close grain. A compact arrangement of the fibers in a piece of wood, especially hardwood, making it easy to dress and give a fine finish as contrasted to an open grain wood which is easily torn and hard to finish.

clout nail. A short, strong, barbed nail with a wide, flat head, used in fastening felt or ply roofing material in place.

coarse grain. A loose arrangement of the fibers in a piece of wood, especially softwood, which is hard to dress and finish.

coated nail. A large-headed nail coated with zinc to resist wear and weather, used chiefly to fasten outside trim, clapboards or shingles on surfaces exposed to dampness or weather.

cobblestone. A stone rounded by the action of water and friction; a field stone.

cock loft. A loft or attic directly under a roof.

code, building. See *building code*.

collar beam. A beam connecting pairs of opposite roof rafters above the attic floor.

column. A perpendicular supporting member, circular or rectangular in section, usually consisting of a base, shaft, and capital. A column is also known as a box, cased, engaged, filled, lally, porch, twisted, or wreathed supporting member.

combination doors. Combination doors have an inside removable section so that the same frame serves for both summer and winter protective devices. A screen is inserted in warm weather to make a screen door, and a glazed or a glazed and wood paneled section is inserted in winter to make a storm door. The inconvenience of handling a different door in each season is eliminated.

common brick. A brick commonly used for construction, made for building purposes rather than texture or color, including in its components overburned brick and clinker.

common joist. The timber or bridging joist in a house on which the flooring is laid.

common nails. Round, flat-headed, wire nails used in rough work. Sizes are described in multiples of a penny, originally indicating the cost in English coin of 100 such nails, as sixpenny, ten-penny, etc.

common rafter table. The table found along the front of the steel square, used in calculating rafter lengths for roofs of different slopes. This table

includes the figures or graduations on both tongue and blade. The inches and fractional parts may represent either inches or feet.

common stock. An inferior grade of lumber used in boarding, such as sheathing or subflooring stock.

compression joint. Any joint supporting a weight or force exerted in a downward direction, such as the joints in a brick wall or the ends of studs.

concrete. A mixture of cement, sand, and broken stone or gravel with water in a set ratio which gradually hardens from a plastic state to form artificial stone.

concrete blocks. Cast artificial solid or hollow building blocks made of concrete.

concrete forms. Framework panels into which concrete is poured to form the foundation, footings, walls, piers, or other parts of a structure.

condensation. Beads or drops of water, and frequently frost in extremely cold weather, that accumulates on the inside of the exterior covering of a building when warm, moisture-laden air from the interior reaches a point where the temperature no longer permits the air to sustain the moisture it holds. The use of louvers or attic ventilators will reduce moisture condensation in attics.

conductor pipe. A downspout. Heavy tin, galvanized-iron, or copper pipe used to drain water from the eave gutter to the drain at the house foundation. Generally available in circular or corrugated shapes ranging from 2″ to 6″ in diameter.

conduit. A pipe, usually metal, in which wire is installed.

continuous header. A header of 2 x 6's turned on edge going around the entire structure, which is strong enough to serve as a lintel over wall openings, thus eliminating much cutting and fitting of separate headers.

contour lines. The lines on a plot plan showing the elevation and slope of the ground.

coped joint. An interior angle formed by a length of molding cut on the end so that it fits over the face of another of the same kind, forming a close joint.

coping. The projecting finish, often with a sloping top, placed on an exterior wall.

corbel. A bracket-like support of wood or stone projecting from a wall to support a weight. A projection of courses in a wall forming a ledge.

cork board. An insulating material made of ground cork bark reduced, by grinding, to small particles from

⅜″ to ⅝″ in size, then poured into molds and subjected to pressure to bind particles to required density.

corner board. The exterior finish on the corner of a frame house extending from the baseboard to the fascia.

corner plate. An L-shaped push plate to fit the corner of a door.

corner post. The timbers forming the framed corner of a frame house, solid or built up with three pieces of 2″ x 4″ stock, or sometimes with a solid 4″ x 4″ piece.

cornice. A decorative element made up of molded members usually placed at or near the top of an exterior or interior wall.

cornice return. That portion of the cornice that continues on the gable end of a house.

cottonwood. A tree of the poplar group formerly in great demand for inside finish but now very scarce.

counterflashing. A flashing usually used on chimneys at the roof line to cover shingle flashing to prevent moisture entry.

countersink bit. A tool used to make a cone-shaped hole in wood in order to have the heads of flat-headed screws or nails flush with or below the face of the stock.

course. A row of shingles on a roof or wall.

cove molding. A three-sided molding with concave face used wherever small angles are to be covered.

cover strip. A thin strip of wood covering the joints on a wall board or wooden partition; a batten.

cramp. A device for holding or pulling joints together.

crawl space. A shallow space below the living quarters of a house. It is generally not excavated or paved and is often enclosed for appearance by a skirting or facing material.

creosote. An oily liquid distilled from wood or coal tar used in preserving wood in damp or wet places.

cricket. A small, drainage diverting roof structure of single or double slope placed at the junction of larger surfaces that meet at an angle.

cripple. Any framed member shorter than a regular member.

crossband. To place the grain of layers of wood at right angles in order to minimize shrinking and swelling; also, in plywood of five or more plies, a layer of veneer whose grain direction is at right angles to that of the face plies.

cross cut. To cut a board or log across the grain.

cross grain. Wood in which the fibers deviate from a line parallel to the sides of the piece. Cross grain may be either diagonal or spiral grain or a combination of the two.

cross-lap joint. A method of joining wooden members, at an angle, usually 90 degrees, by removing half the thickness of each member so that the members lie in the same plane.

crown. The camber given a girder to allow for settling; the highest point in an arch. To cause to round upward, to make convex.

crown molding. A molding used on cornice or wherever a large angle is to be covered.

cup. A distortion of a board in which there is a deviation flatwise from a straight line across the width of the board.

curly grain. Wood in which the fibers are distorted so that they have a curled appearance, as in birdseye wood. The areas showing curly grain may vary up to several inches in diameter.

curtain board. A box fitted over a window to which curtain rods are fastened; a box to house a valance.

curtain step. An ornamental step comprising the first step in a stairway. The outside end is usually semicircular and follows the curve of the scroll forming the end of the handrail.

cut stock. A term for softwood stock comparable to dimension stock in hardwoods.

cutting list. A prepared list of the sizes to which material must be cut for a particular job.

cylinder plate. A plain or ornamental plate placed beneath the head of a lock to produce a finished appearance.

cylinder ring. A rose, or washer, placed under the head of a standard cylinder lock to permit its use on a thin door.

cypress. A light yellow wood, native of southern United States, remarkable for durability, especially in damp places. It is used for inside and outside finishes, sashes, doors, and shingles.

D

d. An abbreviation for penny, a contraction for pennyweight. A pennyweight is one twentieth of an ounce, a Troy weight equal to 24 grains; abbreviated dwt. d is the suffix designating the size of nails, such as 6d (penny) nail, originally indicating the price as so many pence per 100 nails. The size, length and number of nails per pound are as follows: 2d, 1″, 875; 6d, 2″, 181; 8d, 2½″, 106; etc.

dado. A rectangular groove in a board or plank In interior decoration, a special type of wall treatment.

d & c m. An abbreviation for "dressed

(one or two sides) and center matched."

d & h. An abbreviation for "dressed and headed," that is, dressed one or two sides and worked to tongue and groove joints on both the edge and the ends.

d & m. An abbreviation for "dressed and matched," that is, dressed one or two sides and tongued and grooved on the other, with the match either center or standard.

d & s m. An abbreviation for "dressed (one or two sides) and standard matched."

darby. A long narrow tool with two handles, used to level plaster, as on ceilings.

datum line. In surveying, the base line from which all levels are taken; the elevation shown on a plan from which all heights are taken.

dead latch. A nigh latch in which a spring bolt is dead-locked either automatically or manually by a knob, key, or stop.

dead load. A weight that is put on by degrees and remains fixed, such as the weight of furniture and goods stored on a floor, or of a brick and stone wall on its foundation.

dead man. A block of wood or stone, buried in the earth, to which a U-shaped metal fork is attached and to which in turn guy wires are attached to support a pole or object.

deck. Any flat, floorlike platform or roof.

deck paint. An enamel with a high degree of resistance to mechanical wear, designed for use on surfaces such as porch floors.

deck roof. Any flat, horizontal roof.

delamination. Separation of plies through failure of the adhesive; often used in reference to the durability of the glue line.

dentils. Small rectangular blocks of wood uniformly spaced like teeth; use in trim.

derrick pole. A tripod leg of a portable derrick; a gin pole.

diagonal boarding. Boards nailed to the frame of a house at an angle, usually 45 degrees, for greater rigidity, since every board becomes a brace.

diagonal bracing. Braces, such as herringbone bridging in a floor or partition, usually at the corner of carrying partitions, roof trusses, etc.

diagonals. The corner braces in a frame house.

diagonal ties. Braces or ties which help stiffen a roof truss; braces attached to an angle to tie frame members together.

dimension lumber. Lumber from 2″ to but not including 5″ thick and 2″ or more wide.

dimension stock. A term largely superseded by the term hardwood dimension lumber. It is hardwood stock processed to a point where the maximum waste is left at a dimension mill, and the maximum utility is delivered to the user. It is stock of specified thickness, width and length, in multiples thereof. According to specification it may be solid or glued up; rough or surfaced; semifabricated or completely fabricated.

dog. An andiron; a holding device usually consisting of a spiked hook and metal ring; a two-pronged binding cleat or nail.

dolly. A low truck with casters used in moving heavy objects.

door buck. Rough timber built into the sides of a door opening in a masonry wall to which the door jambs are fastened.

door check. A mechanical device to insure the self closing of a door.

door jamb. The surrounding case into which and out of which a door closes and opens. It consists of two upright pieces, called jambs, and a head piece, fitted together and rabbeted.

door rails. The horizontal members or stiles of a framed door which are usually grooved to receive the panels.

door sill. The horizontal member forming the bottom of an outside door frame over which the door closes.

dooryard. The relatively small area around the rear door of a dwelling.

dormer. An internal recess, in a room, the framing of which projects from a sloping roof.

double face nailing. A method of nailing flooring in position, in which the nails are driven into the wood on both edges on the face of the board and set below the surface for stronger construction.

double header. A detail of rough framing in which two lengths of stock are inserted at the top of a window or door opening.

double joist. Two joists side by side, as under the main partition in a dwelling, or around the well holes of stairs, these double joists being called trimmers.

double trimmer. Doubled joists forming one side of the well hole of a stairway, or around a hearth or other opening.

Douglas fir. A strong, pliable wood, yellow in color with reddish markings. Grown on the Pacific Coast from Oregon north through British Columbia. Used chiefly in framing, trim, doors and veneers.

dovetail joint. A flared-shaped tenon-like joint which fits into a like shaped mortise.

dowel. A round pin of wood or metal used in the edge or end grain of boards to help hold them together and to strengthen the joint.

doweling bit. A tool used for boring holes in wood for dowel pins.

doweling jig. A device used on a bit to guide it when boring for dowels, and to regulate the depth of the hole to be bored.

downspout. A pipe, usually of metal, for carrying rainwater from roof gutters to drainage pipe or tile.

draft stop. A wooden block of framing stock placed in framed walls, between studding, to retard drafts and fire.

draw boring. The boring of holes in wood, with a pull-out force in order to clear the hole of shavings or borings.

drawknife. A cutting tool with a blade beveled on the cutting edge like a chisel, having a tang on the two ends bent at right angles to which handles are fastened. It is used for roughing down timber or framing stock. Also known as a drawshave.

dress. To plane; to shape; to work; to dress off or dress up.

dressed and matched. Boards or planks machined in such a manner that there is a groove on one edge and a corresponding tongue on the other.

drip. A member of a cornice or other horizontal exterior finish course that has a projection beyond the other parts for throwing off water. A groove in the under side of a sill to cause water to drop off on the outer edge, instead of drawing back and running down the face of the building.

drip cap. A molding placed on the exterior top side of a door or window to cause water to drip beyond the outside of the frame.

drop girt. In braced-frame house construction a girder placed below the floor joist for support.

drop siding. A finished exterior wall covering applied over outside sheathed walls consisting of a tongue on the upper edge and a groove on the lower edge, milled with a variety of patterns on the exposed or exterior face.

dry rot. A term loosely applied to any dry, crumbly rot but especially to that which, when in an advanced stage, permits the wood to be crushed easily to a dry powder. The term is actually a misnomer for any decay, since all fungi require considerable moisture for growth.

dry wall. Generally referring to plasterboard or plywood construction.

dry wedging. Temporary wedging of framing without the use of glue or paint.

dub. To dress a timber smoothly.

ducts. In a house, usually round or rectangular metal pipes for distributing warm air from the heating plant to rooms, or air from a conditioning device. Ducts are also made of asbestos and composition materials.

dumpy level. A builder's or architect's level or instrument with fixed telescope and spirit level for establishing horizontal lines or altitudes on a building site; similar to the wye level but smaller and less expensive.

duplex-headed nail. A wood fastener for use in temporary structures, designed for easy removal without damaging the wood.

Dutch door quadrant. A device for fastening together the halves of a Dutch door.

dutchman. A piece of material inserted to fill an opening, or a poor joint, or a worn part.

dwarf partition. A low, capped partition, which does not reach the ceiling, usually used in offices.

dwt. An abbreviation for pennyweight; also abbreviated d, which see.

E

easement. A legal right or permission acquired to use another person's property, generally for ingress or egress.

eaves. The margin or lower part of a roof projecting over the face of the main wall, in most instances housing the gutter.

eave trough. A metal gutter, usually stamped from galvanized iron, attached to roofing boards at the eave to catch water and convey it to a downspout. Eave troughs are also made of stamped copper and of wood.

ebony. A tough, hard, heavy wood, black to dark green in color, used chiefly in cabinet work.

economy brick. Modular bricks, 3½″ x 3½″ x 7½″, related to every 4-inch module in height, thickness, and length. The other basic sizes designed for use in modular dimension walls are *oversize brick, standard brick,* and *twin-brick.*

edge and center. A method of finishing lumber. The following abbreviations are used in the lumber industry referring to milled ceiling, flooring, or other finish stocks. E&CB1S—edge and center bead one side (surfaced on two sides and with a longitudinal edge and center bead on a surfaced face); E&CB2S—edge and center bead two sides (all four surfaced and with a longitudinal edge and center V-shaped groove on each of the two faces); E&CV1S—edge and center V one side (surfaced one or two sides with a longitudinal edge and center V-shaped groove on each of the two faces); E&CV2S—edge and centered V two sides (all four surfaces and with a longitudinal edge and center V-shaped groove on each of the two faces); ECM—ends center matched.

edge-grained lumber. Lumber that has been sawed so that the wide surfaces extend approximately at right angles to the annual growth rings. Lumber is considered edge-grained when the rings form an angle of 45 degrees to 90 degrees with the wide surface of the piece.

edge nailing. Blind or secret nailing; a method used in laying and nailing hardwood flooring.

efflorescence. A white crust or powder formed on stone or brick surfaces after exposure to air has brought about evaporation of water.

eight-point. A method of designating the number of saw teeth per inch, for example, eight-point means eight teeth per inch of length at the cutting side.

elbow catch. A latch used to fasten cupboard doors, usually attached to the inside of the stile of the left-hand door.

elevation. The vertical view of the front, back or ends of a building.

ell. An extension built on the side of a house giving it the form of a letter L.

elm. A tough, brown wood used in heavy construction, at times, but most generally in the manufacture of furniture.

emboss. To ornament surfaces with raised work.

emery cloth. An abrasive made by cementing powdered emery to cloth, used in polishing metals and rubbing down painted work.

emery grinder. A wheel-shaped abrasive tool made from compressed emery powder, used for grinding an edge on tools, an emery wheel.

encina. The live-oak tree, especially of California, having fine wearing qualities due to its density; used as interior trim and flooring and in furniture making.

enclosure. The fence erected around or in front of a building under construction; the land enclosed.

end check. A crack occurring on the end of a piece of lumber.

end cut. The square or splayed cut of a board.

end grain. The grain of wood as seen on the end of a board or block.

end joint. The place where two pieces of wood are jointed together end to end, commonly by scarfing and gluing.

end to center. A measurement in which the distance is measured from the end of one object to the center of another.

end-to-end joint. A butt joint.

end to face. A measurement in which the distance is measured from the end of one object to the face of another.

end tread. The tread at the bottom or top of a stairway.

equilibrium moisture content. The moisture content at which wood neither gains nor loses moisture when surrounded by air at a given relative humidity and temperature.

escutcheon. A plate containing a key-hole, one of the parts of a lock set, usually held in place by small brass nails known as escutcheon pins.

excavation. A cavity or hole in the earth made by scooping or digging away the soft earth and stone structure for the placement of foundation footings and foundation walls of a building. A trench dug out for drainage tile or conduit.

excavation lines. Cords stretched taut from batter board to batter board to indicate the extreme bounds of the excavation.

expansion joint. A bituminous fiber strip used to separate blocks or units of concrete to prevent cracking due to expansion as a result of temperature changes.

expansion shield. A jacket of malleable iron, split and hinged for expanding when inserted in brick, concrete, marble, or slate as a lag screw is turned into the shield.

exposed to weather. In siding or shingle work, that portion of a member not covered by the adjacent overlapping portion; the distance between bottom edges of such members.

exposure. The relation to the points of the compass; a dwelling facing south is said to have a southern exposure.

exposure to weather. The distance from the butt of one shingle to another, or the distance from the bottom of one clapboard to the bottom of the one above or below it.

extension plank. A lightweight form of staging plank, consisting of 1″ x 3″ boards, on edge, sliding beside each other, being held together by iron bands, which can be adjusted to different lengths.

F

fabricated house. A house for which the material is cut to exact measurements, each part being numbered so that the whole structure can be shipped to any given place and erected without much cutting and fitting. See prefabricated house.

facade. The front or principal face of a building.

face measure. Measurements taken on the surface, as in finding the number of square feet on the surface or face of a wall or ceiling, or the number of squares of shingles required for a roof; square measure.

face nailing. A method of driving nails through a board at a right angle to the face, as compared with secret nailing, in which nails are driven through the edge of the board, as in secret nailing.

facia. The same as fascia, which see.

facing. Any trim used to cover the edges of an exterior finish.

factory and shop lumber. Lumber intended to be cut up for use in further manufacture. It is graded on the basis of the percentage of the area that will produce a limited number of cuttings of a special minimum size and quality.

faience. Blocks made of glazed terra cotta used as facing for buildings or fireplaces.

fall. The rope forming part of a block and tackle; the slope given a drainage pipe or eave trough to permit water to run off quickly; any slope of a member in place.

false beam. A form of ornamental framework having the appearance of being a solid beam and usually made from three planks, the sides being grooved on the inside to receive the bottom member, which is tongued on both edges.

false work. Temporary timbering or scaffolding used to brace or protect work during construction.

fan light. A semicircular window with muntins radiating from the center like an open fan, especially one over an outside door; a sash over the transom of a door.

fascia. A flat board, band or facing, used sometimes by itself but usually in combination with moldings, often located at the outer face of the cornice.

feather. A loose tongue of wood placed in facing grooves of two boards to strengthen the joint and prevent dust from filtering through. A slip tongue.

feather-edge board. A board having a thin edge, such as a clapboard.

feather-edged coping. A coping on a building or wall beveled in one direction only in order to throw off water.

felt. A pressed and rolled cloth usually made of wool and hair or wool alone. It is used as an insulator between studding and floor joists or between a rough floor and finished floor, and as packing in joints. See also *building felt*.

felt paper. A building paper of strong, tough paper base saturated with hot asphalt and rolled smooth; used under roofing and siding materials as a protection against moisture and heat.

fenestration. The distribution or arrangement of windows in a wall.

ferrule. A wide ring of metal placed on the handle of tools at the point where the blade is inserted into the handle. The metal reinforcement prevents the splitting of the wooden handle.

fiber board. See *building fiber board*.

fiber plaster. A strong, light panel made from plaster of Paris with a burlap or canvas backing.

field stone. A cobble stone or any natural surface stone, smooth or irregular, of a size suitable for rubble masonry.

field tile. Short lengths of round, vitreous pipe laid in the ground to drain off surface water.

file. A hard steel tool with the surface cut diagonally into sharp-edged grooves or ridges in parallel rows in different shapes and sizes, such as mill, taper, round, cant, flat, half round, pillar, rat-tail, etc. Files for wood are usually called rasps.

fill. Loose earth thrown back into the open trench between a foundation wall and the solid earth.

filled ground. Earth or ground, generally at grade level, formed from dumped earth or debris.

filler. A heavily pigmented preparation used for filling and leveling off the pores in open-pored woods.

fillet. A small, flat or concave molding used to separate the more important elements of a cornice or other molded surface.

fillister. A rabbet plane which can be adjusted; a joint formed by such a plane.

fine grain. Wood with narrow, inconspicuous annual rings. Close grained wood. The term is sometimes used to designate wood having small and closely spaced pores, but in this sense the term, "fine textured" is more often used.

finish boards. Smoothly surfaced boards, sanded four sides, used for interior trim, furnished in sizes generally varying from 1″ x 4″ x 14″ in size and varying thicknesses.

finish hardware. Hardware used on the inside of a house, such as locks, hinges, bolts, catches, sash fasteners, and lock sets.

finished string. The outside string of an open-string stair, cut to fit under treads and mitered to the risers, and on which the return nosing and brackets are fastened after the balusters are in place.

fir. A tough, springy, pale wood, used for timbers and framing, obtained from an evergreen tree native to northern North America.

firebrick. Brick made of a siliceous material such as fire clay, which can withstand high heat without fusing.

fire cut. A diagonal cut on the end of a floor joist built into a brick wall. The long point of the cut is on the bottom of the joist and is seated on the wall. If a fire occurs the joist can be pulled from the wall so that the burning floor will fall into the center of the building and will not endanger the lives of firemen.

fire partition. A wall constructed of noncombustible material which will retard or stop a fire.

fireproofing. Making wood resistant to fire. Wood cannot be treated chemically so that it will not char or decompose at temperatures of about 280 degrees F, and higher. What effective fireproofing does is to make wood difficult to ignite, keep it from supporting its own combustion, and delay the spread of flame over the wood surface.

fire-resistive. In the absence of a specific ruling by the authority having jurisdiction, applies to materials for construction not combustible in the temperatures of ordinary fires and that will withstand such fires without serious impairment of their usefulness for at least one hour.

fire-retardant chemical. A chemical or preparation of chemicals used to reduce flammability or to retard spread of fire.

firestop. A solid, tight closure of a concealed space, placed to prevent the spread of fire and smoke through such a space.

fire wall. A fireproof partition of concrete or brick extending to the roof of a building in order to retard the spread of a fire.

fish joint. A butt joint made by bolting either wood or iron plates to the sides or top and bottom of two beams placed end to end.

fish plate. One of a pair of wooden or iron plates bolted to the sides or top and bottom of two timbers to form a beam.

flagstone. Flat stones, from 1″ to 4″ thick, used for rustic walks, steps, floors, and the like. Also known as flagging or flags.

flashed joint. A joint covered with sheet metal shaped to turn water, as

a roof valley, the intersection of a dormer with a roof; or the junction of a vent stack or chimney with a roof.

flashing. Sheet metal or other material used in a roof and wall construction to protect a building from seepage of water.

flat-grained lumber. Lumber that has been sawed in a plane approximately perpendicular to a radius of the log. Lumber is considered flat-grained when the annual growth rings make an angle of less than 45 degrees with the surface of the piece.

flat paint. An interior paint that contains a high proportion of pigment, and dries to a flat or lusterless finish.

fliers. The treads in a straight flight of stairs.

flitch. A portion of a log sawed on two or more sides and intended for re-manufacture into lumber or sliced or sawed veneer. The term is also applied to the resulting sheets of veneer laid together in sequence of cutting.

flitch beam. A beam composed of two or more pieces of lumber bolted together, with an iron or steel plate between.

flitch plate. The steel or iron plate fastened between the timbers composing a flitch beam.

floating foundation. A foundation used in swampy or unstable soil, made of a raft like concrete slab reinforced with steel rods or mesh.

floating partition. A partition resting on a floor between two floor joists and parallel to them.

floor joist. One of the main framing timbers placed between the walls and girders in a building to support the flooring.

floor load. The maximum load a floor is built to support, including its own weight.

floor plan. A detailed drawing showing a horizontal section through a building with the arrangement or layout of each room.

floor sander. An electrical machine containing a rotary cylinder faced with sandpaper, by which flooring may be cleaned and smoothed.

flue. The space or passage in a chimney through which smoke, gases, or fumes ascend to the outside. Each passage is called a flue, which, together with any others and the surrounding masonry, make up the chimney.

flue gathering. A method of changing the direction of a flue by corbelling over the bricks.

flue lining. Fire clay or terra-cotta pipe, round or square, usually made in all of the ordinary flue sizes and

in 2-foot lengths, used for the inner lining of chimneys with the brick or masonry work around the outside. Flue lining should run from the concrete footing to the top of the chimney cap.

flush. Even; on a level with an adjacent surface.

flush joint. A joint even or level with the surrounding surface.

flush ring. A metal device used on doors, especially double doors, recessed into the wood to present a smooth surface. The ring is raised by the finger for operating the latch or bolt.

flying shore. A beam placed between two structures which provides a support for both; the shore is, in turn, supported by braces from each wall in order to distribute the strain and prevent the timber from buckling.

footing. The spreading course or courses at the base or bottom of a foundation wall, pier, or column.

footing drain. A drain having field tile placed in loose stones at the foundation footings to catch and allow drainage water to run off from the structure and into the sewage system.

footing forms. Panels of wood or steel placed in trenches to form foundation footings of poured concrete.

foot of rafter. The cut on the bottom of a rafter at the wall plate; the seat cut.

forms. Panels of wood or steel built up to received poured concrete to form foundation walls, steps, etc.

foundation. The bearing structure of a dwelling, usually of stone or concrete, resting on the ground, on which a building is erected. The foundation is made up of the footings and foundation walls.

foundation plan. The plan or top view showing the shape of the bearing structure, in horizontal section. The plan includes the length, width, height and thickness of walls, location of basement windows, doors, drains, thickness of basement floor, width and height of footings, position of chimneys, etc.

foxtail wedging. A method of holding framing together by inserting wedges into the end of a tenon when the mortise is cut through; the bottom of the mortise forces the wedge into the tenon and spreads it thus forming a tight joint.

frame. The rough timbers of a house, cut and assembled according to plan, including joists, girders, sills, corner posts, studs, plates, and rafters. To fit and adjust, to join together.

frame building. A building with exterior walls constructed of wood; a building sheathed with boards and partially or entirely veneered on the outside with a single thickness of brickwork or other masonry, or with metal or asbestos sheathing.

framed roof. The uppermost part of a building on which the roofing material is placed, made by framing or joining rafters at designated angles.

framing. Lumber used for the structural members of a building, such as studs and joists, etc. Balloon framing is a system of framing a building in which all vertical structural elements of the bearing walls and partitions consist of single pieces extending from the top of the soleplate to the roof plate and to which all floor joists of each story rest on the top plates of the story below or on the foundation sill for the first story, and the bearing walls and partitions rest on the subfloor of each story.

framing plan. A plan, and portion of a set of house plans, showing the framing of wood or metal building parts with required details and dimensions.

framing square. A steel square having a blade 24″ long and a tongue 18″ long, on which are various tables for the use of builders in the construction of a dwelling.

French window. A double door to a porch or terrace, hinged at the sides and opening in the middle, made of panes of glass like a window.

frieze. Any sculptured or ornamental band in a structure. The horizontal member of a cornice set vertically against the wall.

frieze panel. The top panel in a door which has five or more panels.

frontage. The property line which borders on the street; the front face of a building; the main face.

front elevation. A view, in a set of house plans, of the face of a building, showing the main entrance and style or architecture.

frostline. The depth of frost penetration in soil. This depth varies in different parts of the country and footings must be placed below this depth to prevent movement of the structure.

furring. Strips of wood or metal applied to a wall or other surface to even it, to form an air space, or to give the wall an appearance of greater thickness.

furring channel. A steel member used to separate metal lath from the surface over which it is fastened; also, the smallest horizontal member of a suspended ceiling, and the largest horizontal member of an attached ceiling.

G

gable. That portion of a wall contained between the slopes of a double sloped roof or that portion contained between the slope of a single sloped roof and a line projected horizontally through the lowest elevation of the roof construction.

gable end. An end wall having a gable.

gain. A notch or groove made across the grain of timber into which another piece is fitted.

gambrel roof. A rigid roof with a broken slope; the upper section next to the ridge has but little pitch, but the lower section has a steep pitch down to the eaves. Also spelled gambriel.

gate pier. A brick, stone, or concrete post to which a gate or gates are hung. A gate post.

gimlet. A small boring tool having a spiral cutting edge and a pointed screw tip, turned by hand with a small bar handle.

gingerbread work. Overdone ornamental finish or trim.

gin pole. A secured and braced pole projecting over the parapet of a building used for hoisting material.

girder. A large or principal beam used to support concentrated loads at points along its length. The main beam supporting floor joists.

girt. A timber, usually 4″ x 6″ in cross section, framed into the corner posts of a framed and braced building, supported by the framing studs on the first floor.

glazed. Fitted with panes of glass.

glazing points. Small, triangular pieces of metal driven into the rabbet of a sash to hold the glass in place before puttying.

glue pot. A double vessel in which glue is softened either by gas or electric heat.

grade. The designation of the quality of a manufactured piece of wood or of logs. The slope of the ground around a building.

grade line. A line on a drawing of a set of blueprints showing the required slope of ground surrounding a building.

grain. The direction, size, arrangement, or quality of the fibers in wood. See *close-grained wood, coarse-grained wood, cross-grained wood, curly-grained wood, edge-grained lumber, fine-grained wood,* and *flat-grained lumber.* An interlocked grain is one in which the fibers are inclined in one direction in a number of rings of annual growth, then gradually reverse and are inclined in an opposite direction in succeeding growth rings, then reverse again. Open-grained

wood has large pores, such as oak, ash, chestnut, and walnut. Open-grained wood is also known as coarse-textured wood.

In spiral-grained wood the fibers take a spiral course about the trunk of the tree instead of the normal vertical course. Spiral grain is a form of cross grain.

In straight-grained wood the fibers run parallel to the axis of a given piece of stock.

green. Freshly sawed lumber, or lumber that has received no intentional drying; unseasoned. The term does not apply to lumber that may have become completely wet through waterlogging.

grille. An ornamental, open-work metal guard or grating to protect windows and other openings.

grounds. Strips of wood, of same thickness as lath and plaster, that are attached to walls before the plastering is done. Used around windows, doors, and other openings as a plaster stop and in other places for attaching baseboards or other trim.

ground joist. A joist resting on dwarfed walls, or on supports laid on the ground.

ground plan. The plan of the ground floor of a building, or of the plot surrounding it. The first floor plan.

ground sill. The lowest horizontal timber into which other timbers of a wooden framework are inserted.

ground water. Water near the surface of the ground or grade, which may seep into cellars.

grout. Mortar made of such consistency by the addition of water that it will just flow into the joints and cavities of the masonry work and fill them solid.

gumwood. The wood of the eucalyptus tree or of the sweetgum trees of southern United States; used as inside trim and the making of doors.

gusset. A metal plate riveted or bolted at joints to stiffen corners or joints.

gutter. A shallow channel or conduit of metal or wood set below and along the eaves of a house to catch and carry off rainwater from the roof.

gutter hangers. Iron straps or wires attached to the overhang of the rafters to support the eave trough.

gypsum. Hydrous calcium sulphate, used as a building material, or, after begin heated, as plaster of Paris.

gypsum plaster. Gypsum formulated to be used with the addition of sand and water for base coat plaster.

H

hack saw. A fine, hardened steel saw used for cutting metal.

hackmatack. The juniper, the American larch tree.

haft. The handle of a tool.

hagging. Marking or notching wood for cutting.

halflap joint. A joint used in splicing timbers in which half the thickness of each timber is removed, permitting the members to fit closely and to be firmly joined.

half-round. A molding, bar or file, semicircular in shape or cross section.

half section. An interior view, extending to a center line, or center cutting plane, having the exterior view as the remaining half.

half timbering. A method of constructing an inside or outside wall, with exposed timber framework forming panels filled with plaster, brick, or stucco.

halving. A method of joining two timbers by cutting away half the thickness of each on opposite sides and then lapping.

hand breath. A linear measure about 4″ in length.

hand drill. A geared tool used in turning small bits to bore holes in wood or metal.

hand of a door. If the hinges of a door are on the left, facing the door from the outside, it is a *left-hand door;* if the hinges are on the right, it is a *right-hand door.* If the door swings out, the terms are *left-hand reverse* and *right-hand reverse.*

hand saw. Any saw used with one hand in cutting wood either with or across the grain, such as a crosscut saw, rip saw, panel saw, back saw, etc.

hard pine. North Carolina pine; in Canada, pitch pine.

hardware. Builder's hardware includes such items as locks, double acting hinges, window latches and pulls, sash cord, sash hangers, hinges, drawer pulls, etc., and are designated as finish hardware. Rough or structural hardware includes such items as nails, screws, cleats, etc.

hardwood. Generally of the botanical group of trees that have broad leaves in contrast to the conifers or softwoods. The term has no reference to the actual hardness of the wood. The beech, birch, maple, ash, hickory, and oak are known as hardwoods. Some hardwoods are actually soft in texture.

hasp. A hinged clasp passing over a staple to which it may be secured by a padlock or a metal pin.

hatch. An entrance to a roof or basement from outside the building.

hatchway. An opening in a floor, leading to a basement, usually protected by a hinged covering flush with the floor.

haunching. The act of reducing the width of a tenon to the length of the mortise in order that the tenon will not show across the end of the stile.

header. A beam placed perpendicular to joists and to which joists are nailed in framing for chimney, stairway, or other opening. A wooden lintel. The upper member of a rough, window or door frame opening, usually two timbers laid on edge.

header joint. A joint formed by placing the ends of two pieces of material together, as in a butt joint in flooring.

header joist. The beam into which the common joists are fitted around openings for chimneys, stairs, or other openings in a floor or roof.

heartwood. The wood extending from the pitch to the sapwood, the cells of which no longer participate in the life process of the tree. Heartwood may be infiltrated with gums, resins, and other materials that usually make it darker and more decay-resistant than sapwood.

heel of rafter. The seat cut of a rafter, that part which rests on the wall plate.

heel strap. A rectangular iron strap passing over the heel of the principal rafter in a wooden truss; its ends are bolted through the tie beam to anchor the rafter firmly in its seat.

helve. The handle of a hand tool such as a hatchet or adz.

hemlock. A large evergreen tree of the pine family which yields short grained, brittle wood, used in some localities for rough boarding and subfloors, the wood being too brittle to use for staging.

hickory. A tree of the walnut family, yielding hard, straight-grained flexible wood, used for spokes and tool handles.

hinge. A metal joint on which doors, covers, blinds, etc., swing, fold, open or close. Some of the more common hinges are the surface hinge, strap hinge, parliament hinge, loose-pin hinge, floor hinge, butterfly hinge, and the butt hinge.

hinge bound. When one leaf of a hinge of a series of hinges on a door is fitted into the door jamb or stile somewhat deeper than the opposite leaf, the door binds on closing.

hinge gauge. A hand tool used in fitting hinges, consisting of a metal block containing two gages, independently adjustable for the thickness and width of each hinge to be set in place.

hip. The external angle formed by the meeting of two sloping sides of a roof.

hip roof. A roof that rises by inclined planes from all four sides of a building.

hollow back. The grooved portion of a door or window trim or casing hollowed out to insure a good fit against any irregularities in a plastered wall.

hollow-core construction. A panel construction with faces of plywood, hardboard, or similiar material bonded to a framed core assembly of wood lattice, paperboard rings, or the like, which support the facing at spaced intervals.

holly. A wood used extensively as inlay in cabinetmaking and to some extent as interior trim.

honeycomb. A construction of thin sheet material, such as resin impregnated paper or fabric, which has been corrugated and bonded, each sheet in opposite phase to the phases of adjacent sheets, to form a core material whose cross section is a series of mutually continuous cells similar to natural honeycomb.

hook strip. A board fastened to a wall or in a closet to which hooks are attached for hanging clothing; a standard wood molding, used as a casing or door trim in low-cost construction.

horse. A strong trestle with four legs used as a support for stock and materials in working.

housed joint. A joint in which the end of a timber fits into a groove across the grain of another timber.

housed string. A stair stringer with gained or housed grooves to receive the treads and risers.

I

I-beam. A steel beam with a cross section resembling the letter "I". It supports floor joists, carrying the dead weight of the building from foundation wall to foundation wall and is usually supported about every ten feet by a steel column.

Idaho white pine. A soft, uniform-textured, straight-grained, lightweight, easily worked wood. The color ranges from white to pink. Used in the making of moldings, paneling, etc.

indented joint. A scarf joint, in which the housings of one piece forming the joint are fitted into the projections of the other.

ingle nook. A fireplace, especially with a seat or bench; a corner with a fireside; an ingleside.

inside stop. The strip of inside trim fastened to the inside of a sash frame to hold the lower sash in place.

insulating board or fiberboard. A low-density board made of wood, sugar-cane, cornstalks, or similar materials, usually formed by a felting process, dried and usually pressed to thicknesses of 1/2″ to 25/32″. Building insulation is any material high in resistance to heat transmission, that, when placed in the walls, ceilings, or floors, of a structure, will reduce the rate of heat flow. Thermal insulation is any material that retards the transfer of heat when placed between two heat conducting materials.

interior finish. Trim of all descriptions, wall coverings or paints, plastering, etc., used to complete the inside of a building, floor, walls, and ceilings more artistically and comfortably.

interior opening. An opening in a partition inside a building.

invisible lines. A line of short dashes in a drawing indicating hidden edges behind some part of a structure.

iron lintel. A horizontal structural member spanning a window or door opening, carrying the weight above. The lintel is used in brickwork and is made of steel.

irons. Cutters used in hand planes or power-driven machines.

J

jack. A portable device for lifting or raising a heavy body a short distance. Screw type jacks are used for lifting exceptionally heavy objects.

jack rafter. A rafter that spans the distance from a wall plate to a hip, or from a valley to a ridge.

jack rafter cheek. The beveled plumb cut at the top of a hip jack rafter or the seat cut of a valley jack rafter; both are nailed to the hip or valley rafter.

jack screw. A mechanical device used singly or in groups to lift heavy loads, such as a building.

jack stud. A block or short stud nailed to rough door or window studding to add strength and provide a solid bearing and nailing member for the finished door jamb or window frame.

jamb. One of the upright sides of a doorway, window opening, or fireplace. The side post or lining of a doorway, window, or other opening.

jamb blocks. Wooden blocks built into a rough brick jamb of a door opening to which the door jambs are fastened.

jamb joint. A weathertight joint on the abutting edges of casement sashes, in which the edge of one is convex and the other concave to a radius equal to one half of the thickness of the sash.

jamb linings. The head and sides of a door or window frame into which the doors and windows are fitted.

jambs. The sides of a finished opening for a door or window; the sides of a mantel.

Janus-faced lock. A rim lock with both sides alike, so that either may be applied to a door, making the lock either right-or left-handed.

jig. A guiding tool or template used in producing numerous shapes of the same kind.

jig saw. A vertical power saw used in cutting scrolls or other curved work.

joinery. Skilled work in wood, such as inside finish in a building or cabinet work.

jointer or surfaces. A powered planing machine used in evening the surfaces of timber.

joist. One of a series of parallel beams used to support floor and ceiling loads, and supported in turn by larger beams, girders, or bearing walls.

joist bridging. Short diagonal braces placed between floor joists as stiffeners.

joist cleat. A wooden strip nailed to the face of a flush girder to assist in supporting floor joists.

joist hanger. An iron forging, shaped like a stirrup, bent so it can be hung on the main beam to provide support for the end of a joist.

juniper. Any of the various evergreen shrubs or trees of the pine family.

K

kalsomine. A white or colored wash used in coating plastered walls, furnished in powdered form to be used with water solvent. Some types of kalsomine are washable when dry; also spelled calcimine.

kerf. A cut or groove made by a saw.

key. That part of the first coat of plaster which is forced between the laths in a lath and plaster partition.

keystone. The vital wedge-shaped stone at the top of an arch, which locks all the stones together.

king post. The upright member in the center of a simple truss, extending from the apex to the middle of the beam.

knocked down. The condition of a prefabricated object whose parts are delivered unassembled, but usually numbered or accompanied by a blueprint so it can readily be put together.

knotty pine. Pine boards containing numerous knots, used extensively in paneling for decorative purposes. The stock is selected for an even and liberal sprinkling of sound knots, burls, and other defects which en-

hance its beauty but do not impair the surface. Generally furnished in ¾″ thicknesses, 6″, 8″, 10″ and 12″ widths, and 8′ to 16′ lengths.

knuckle. That part of a hinge containing the pin on which the door swings.

knurl. The roughened part of a thumbscrew or nailset which is grasped by the fingers to prevent slipping.

L

label. A projecting molding, band, or fillet over a door or window to check the flow of water.

ladder brackets. Iron brackets that can be attached to a ladder to support a light scaffold.

ladder hook. A large iron hook attached to a ladder which may be hooked over the ridge of a roof to keep the ladder in place.

lag screw. A heavy screw for wood with a square head and coarse thread used chiefly where a bolt would not be suitable, as in fastening timbers to a brick or stone wall.

laminate. A product made by bonding together two or more layers (laminations) of material or materials. A multilayered panel made by compressing sheets of resin impregnated paper together into a coherent solid mass is called a paper-base laminate.

landing. A platform between flights of stairs or at the termination of a flight of stairs.

landing board. The first board on a landing immediately over the last riser. Its edge is usually rounded to conform with the nosing on the stair treads and is given the same projection over the riser as the stair treads.

landmark. A peg, stake, or fixed object marking the boundaries of a tract of land. A bench mark.

lap. The distance over which one piece of material covers another. The exposure given shingles and clapboards.

lap dovetail. A joint used in drawer fronts, in which the dovetail is not exposed on the front of the drawer.

lapped joint. A half-lap joint. A joint made by cutting away half the thickness from the face of one piece and half the thickness from the back of another, thus making the surfaces flush when joined. Lapped joints are generally made with the members at right angles but may be made at any angle. A half lap is generally considered to be at right angles and a miter lap at an angle of other than 90 degrees.

larch. A cone bearing tree of the pine family yielding tough, durable wood.

lath. A building material of wood, metal, gypsum, or insulating board that is fastened to the frame of a building to act as a plaster base.

lathe. A machine or device in which wood or metal stock is held, turned, and shaped by a variety of tools pressed against the stock.

lath nails. Short, flat-headed nails, often galvanized, used to attach laths to studs and joists.

lattice. An assemblage of wood or metal strips, rods, or bars made by crossing them to form a network.

laying out. Marking off cutting or dimension lines on stock in preparation for work.

leader. A downspout; a pipe to convey water from an eave trough to a drain.

lead screw anchor. A lead plug used in brick, stone, or concrete walls into which a screw can be driven for fastening material in place.

ledger board. A horizontal board supporting the planks on a light staging.

ledger strip. A strip of lumber nailed along the bottom of the side of a girder on which joists rest.

let in. To sink or gain one member into another in joining.

leveling board. A straight edge on which a level is placed when leveling an object.

leveling pegs. Pegs driven into the ground and leveled to a fixed height, to which an earth fill or foundation is gauged.

leveling rod. A device made of wood on which are graduations of the foot in tenths used in measuring vertical distances between points on the earth or given points and the line of sight of a leveling instrument.

light. Space in a window sash for a single pane of glass. A pane of glass.

lignum vitae. A very hard, heavy, brownish green wood used in making mallets and bushings, obtained from a tropical tree.

linoleum. A floor covering made of solidified linseed oil, compounded with gums, cork dust, wood flour, pigments, and a burlap or canvas backing.

linseed oil. A pale yellow oil extracted from flaxseed, one of the chief ingredients of paint.

lintel. A horizontal structural member that supports the load over an opening such as a door or window.

lip. A cutting edge, especially the cutting edge on an auger bit.

lock keeper. The metal receptacle fastened to or in the door jab into which the lock bolts project.

lock rail. The rail in a door to which the lock is fastened, generally about three feet from the floor.

lock set. A complete lock combined

with its knobs, escutcheon plates, and screws.

lock strike. The metal plate into which the lock bolt and latch are extended when the door is closed.

locust. A medium-sized tree having fragrant flowers and yielding hard, durable wood.

long-leaf pine. A superior grade of pine, white in color, having a fairly close grain, and in a great demand for fine work and heavy construction because it is remarkably free from knots.

lookout. A short wooden bracket or cantilever to support an overhanging portion of a roof or the like, usually concealed from view.

lot. A parcel of land for building purposes or a plot of land on which a house is to be erected.

louver. An opening with a series of horizontal slats so arranged as to permit ventilation but to exclude rain, sunlight, or vision. See attic ventilator.

lug. The projection on the stiles of a sash extending beyond the meeting or check rail.

M

magnolia. A moderately light hardwood, brownish yellow in color; used chiefly in the manufacture of millwork and fixtures.

mahogany. A reddish brown, hard, close-grained wood of a tree grown in the tropics. It takes a good polish, showing ribbon stripes when quartered. It is used chiefly in the manufacture of panel stock, veneers, cabinets, furniture, and fixtures.

mansard roof. A roof with a double pitch on all sides, the lower slope being almost vertical, the upper slope similar to a hip roof pitch.

mantel. The shelf above a fireplace. Originally referred to the beam or lintel supporting the arch above the fireplace opening. The term also refers to the entire finish around a fireplace, covering the chimney breast in front and sometimes on the sides.

maple. A hard, close-grained wood of which there are different varieties, such as bird's-eye, rock, etc. Maple is used chiefly for finish flooring and in the making of furniture.

marginal light. A long, narrow sash fixed in a door frame on either side of the door.

marking gauge. A hand tool for marking working lines on stock. The tool has four parts: a beam or bar, sliding head, set-screw, and pin. The pin is inserted in one end of the beam and the set-screw is housed in the movable head.

masonry. Stone, brick, concrete, hollow tile, concrete block, gypsum block, or other similar building units or materials or a combination of the same, bonded together with mortar to form a wall, pier, buttress, or similar mass.

mastic. A compound made of organic elastomer, fillers, plasticizers, etc., in a solvent, having the consistency of putty. It is used in bonding wall- and floor-covering materials. Mastic can be used wherever a flexible bond is required.

maul or mall. A heavy mallet or hammer.

m. b. m. An abbreviation for one thousand feet of board measure.

meeting rail. The top horizontal member of a bottom sash and the bottom horizontal member of the top sash in a set of double-hung sash.

mending plate. A large steel plate, about 3″ x 12″ in size, placed on garage doors or other large doors at the junction of cross rails to add strength to the joint.

metal lath. Sheets of metal that are slit and drawn out to form openings on which plaster is spread.

mill. A factory manufacturing millwork such as sashes, doors, inside and outside trim, cabinet work, etc.

millwork. Generally all building materials made of finished wood and manufactured in millwork plants and planing mills are included under the term millwork. It includes items such as inside and outside doors, window and door frames, blinds, porchwork, mantels, panelwork, stairways, moldings, and interior trim. It does not include flooring, ceiling, or siding.

mineral wool. Wool-like refuse from a slag furnace, used in deadening sound and for insulation in frame houses, furnished in bulk, bat, and blanket form.

miter. The joining of two pieces at an angle that bisects the angle of junction.

miter clamp. A clamp in which a mitered joint is held while being glued and nailed.

miter plane. A small hand tool, less than 6″ in length, used in woodworking for smoothing miters and planing end grain.

miter square. A metal square having a miter of 45 degrees on the stock member and an attached blade, making a fixed miter.

m. l. An abbreviation for "mixed lengths," designating lumber lengths of various extents.

module. The size of one part taken as a measure for regulating the proportions of other parts.

moisture content of wood. Weight of the water contained in the wood, usually expressed as a percentage of the weight of the oven dried wood.

moisture gradient. A condition of graduated moisture content between successive thickness zones of wood that may be losing or absorbing moisture. During seasoning the graduations are between relatively dry surface zones and wet zones at the center of the piece.

molding. Material, usually patterned strips, used to provide ornamental variation of outline or contour, whether projections or cavities, such as cornices, bases, window and door jambs, heads, etc. There are some 80 moldings made for the dwelling construction industry, a few being the annular molding, apron molding, back molding, band molding, bed molding, cable molding, casement molding, cornice molding, crown molding, dentil molding, fluted molding, half round molding, neck molding, quarter round molding, raised molding, scotia molding, shoe molding, etc.

molly expansion anchor. A metal fastener for use in plaster or masonry walls, which stays secure. It is a bolt encased in a shell which expands within the wall to a size larger than the hole drilled to receive it.

monolithic. A term pertaining to a concrete structure cast in one piece or made of a continuous mass of material.

mortar. A mixture of cement, lime, and sand, known as cement mortar, or a mixture of lime and sand, known as lime mortar, used in laying bricks, stones, etc.

mortise. A slot cut into a board, plank, or timber, usually edgewise, to receive the tenon of another board, plank, or timber to form a joint. Also spelled mortice.

mortise and tenon. A joint used in framing, formed by placing a tenon in a mortise in order to hold the framing solidly together.

mortise rim and lock set. A lock set consisting of a rim latch or lock and a mortise latch with a pair of knobs and one rose, also a large escutcheon for the outside of the door.

mouse. A metal weight attached to a cord used to drop through inaccessible openings, also know as a carpenter's mouse. It is used chiefly in sash hanging.

mullion. A slender bar or pier forming a division between panels or units of windows, screens, or similar frames.

mullion frame. A window frame having one or more mullions.

muntin. The members dividing the glass openings of sash, doors, and the like.

N

nail set. A small, punch type tool, used in sinking the head of a nail below the wood's surface. The set is held in one hand over the nail and a blow is given the head of the set by a hammer held in the other hand.

nailer type steel joist. A steel joist having a groove running down the top of the flange into which nails can be driven, the nail being held in place by compression.

nailing blind. A method of fastening flooring or other tongued-and-grooved stock in which the nail is driven into the edge of the board just above the tongue and at an angle to conceal the head by the edge of the next board; secret nailing.

nailing concrete. A comparatively soft type of concrete made by mixing sand, lime, and some cement, into which nails can be easily driven.

nailing strips. Strips of wood, usually 1" x 2" in size, fastened to brick or concrete walls to provide grounds for nailing on laths, sheathing, moldings, draft stops, etc.

natural finish. A transparent finish, usually of drying oil, sealer, or varnish, applied on wood for the purpose of protection against soiling or weathering. Such a finish may not seriously alter the original color of the wood or obscure its grain pattern.

needling. The act of supporting a wall or building on beams resting on posts or piers during alterations or repairs to the foundation.

newel. A post to which the end of a stair railing or balustrade is fastened. Any post to which a railing or balustrade is fastened.

night latch. A spring catch on a door opened from the outside by a key, and from the inside by a knob.

nogging. Timbers built into masonry walls to receive nails. Brickwork used to fill the spaces between studding in a frame house, sometimes called firestopping.

nonbearing wall. A wall supporting no load other than its own weight.

nonload-bearing clay. A clay that, due to its moist, plastic nature, cannot support a heavy structure.

North Carolina pine. A straight grained, yellow, semi-hardwood used extensively in framing, flooring, doors and trim.

northern white cedar. A soft lightweight wood. It is used extensively in the manufacture of shingles as it splits and works easily.

northern white pine. A soft, lightweight wood, easily worked, straightgrained, used chiefly in framing and for millwork.

Norway pine. A medium to heavy hardwood, fairly strong, pale red in color; used chiefly in general construction work and millwork.

nosing. The projecting edge of a molding or drip. The term is usually applied to the projecting molding on the edge of a stair tread.

nosing strip. A bull-nosed shaped piece of stock or trim placed on edges of boards, treads, etc.

O

oak. A hard, close-grained wood, white, red, or brown in color. It is used extensively for flooring, inside trim, doors, and in some framing where durability and strength are required.

o. c. An abbreviation for the term, on center, the measurement of spacing for studding, rafters, joists, etc., from the center of one member to the center of the next member.

ogee. A molding with a profile in the form of a letter S; having the outline of a reversed curve. Often abbreviated o. g.

ogee gutter. A wooden or metal channel at the eaves for carrying away water; more especially referring to a wooden gutter most generally milled from solid fir stock.

oilstone. A smooth stone, either natural or manufactured, moistened with lubricating oil when sharpening edged tools.

open boarding. A method of laying roofing boards in which the boards are placed at least 2" apart.

open grain. The loose grain in a softwood board, such as soft pine, which is easily torn or lifted when planing.

open-truss steel joist. A light, strong, continuous-web metal joist used chiefly to carry a lightweight floor of concrete or a heavy floor of wood.

open valley. A gutter formed by the intersection of two roofs.

Oregon fir or pine. A species of pine growth in northwestern United States from which wide boards for inside trim are made. The Douglas fir. It is remarkably free from knots.

orthographic projection. A graphic method of representing all faces of an object by projecting lines perpendicular to the plane of projection. Top, front, and end views are most generally used, but all six views may be shown with auxiliary views if necessary.

out of true. Not straight or plumb; warped, or in twist.

outside base. The baseboard around the outside of a frame building.

outside string. The string of a staircase farthest from the wall, opposite the wall string.

oven-dried wood. Wood dried to constant weight in an oven or above the temperature of boiling water (usually 101 to 105 degrees C., or 214 or 221 degrees F.).

oversize brick. Modular brick, 2½″ x 3½″ x 7½″, related to the 4-inch module, every 12 inches in height.

P

package trim. Mill-finished window and door trim, packed in cartons, sanded, and ready to install.

panel. A large, thin board or sheet of lumber, plywood, or other material. A thin board with all its edges inserted in a groove of a surrounding frame of thicker material. A portion of a flat surface recessed or sunk below the surrounding area, distinctly set off by a molding or some other decorative device. Also, a section of floor, wall, ceiling, or roof, usually prefabricated and of large size, handled as a single unit in the operations of assembly and erection.

paneled framing. Framework such as doors consisting of stiles, rails, and muntins held together by mortise and tenons, with openings filled by panels.

parapet. A low wall or railing protecting the edge of a roof, bridge, terrace, balcony, etc.

parting stop. A small wooden piece used in the side and head jambs of double-hung windows to separate upper and lower sash.

partition. A wall that subdivides spaces within any story of a building.

party wall. An architectural term pertaining to a wall built on the property line of adjoining buildings, the rights and responsibilities of which are shared by the two owners.

peck. Pockets or areas of disintegrated wood caused by advanced stages of localized decay in the living tree. It is usually associated with cypress and incense cedar. There is no further peck once the lumber is seasoned.

pediment. The ornametal triangular space shaped like a low gable over the front of a building or portico or over a door or window opening.

peg. A wooden pin or dowel used as a fastening. A small stake used for leveling. To mark out a foundation by driving stakes or pegs in the ground.

penny. A measure of nail length, abbreviated by the letter "d". It originally indicated the price per hundred nails.

perimeter. The distance around the sides or circumference of a plane or solid figure.

perspective. A visible scene, especially a scene giving a distinct impression of distance. A perspective sketch or drawing representing objects as they appear to the eye, those further away being relatively smaller.

pictorial view. In standardized methods of shape representation a pictorial view or pictorial projection is classified as isometric, oblique or cabinet projection. See *orthographic projection*. In pictorial projection the various views or faces are related to and are component parts of the axis. Pictorial projection combines the advantages of perspective drawing in that a third dimension is used, which is not the case in orthographic projection.

pier. A column of masonry, usually rectangular in horizontal cross section, used to support other structural members.

pier glass. A long mirror in a door, taking the place of a panel; a large mirror on a wall between windows.

pigment. A powdered solid in suitable degree of subdivision for use in paint or enamel.

pilaster. A projecting square column forming part of a wall, as a supplement to a pier; the flat molded decorative columns on either side of a doorway, having a cap, a base and a molding, as in a column.

pile. A heavy, pointed timber or concrete column driven into the ground to support the foundation of a building in sandy or swampy soil.

pillar. Any column supporting a structure.

pin. The pin passing through the knuckles of a loose-pin butt hinge. A short, headless, pointed nail driven through the mortises and tenons in sashes and doors for greater security.

pinch bar. A steel bar, from 48″ to 60″ in length and 1″ to 1½″ in diameter, used as a lever to move or roll heavy objects.

pine. Any of several evergreen, cone-bearing trees, with needle-like leaves. The wood is used largely in building for inside and outside finish, doors, sashes, and framing lumber.

pitch. The incline or rise of a roof. Pitch is expressed in inches or rise per foot of run, or by the ratio of the rise to the span. An accumulation of resin in wood cells.

pitch board. A triangular template used

in setting out rafters or stairs; the sides of a triangle representing the run, rise, and pitch of a stairway or rafter.

pitch pocket. An opening extending parallel to the annual rings of growth that usually contains, or has contained, either solid or liquid pitch.

plancher. The under side of the corona or cornice; also spelled plancier, planch, or planche.

plane. A hand tool used in preparing the surface of wood. Various hand planes are the block plane, fore plane, jack plane, jointer plane, rabbet plane, router plane, scrub plane, etc. See Chapter 1—Tools.

plans. A set of working drawings used in constructing a building, such as the plot plan, foundation plan, basement floor plan, first, second or attic floor plans, roofing plan, and framing plans. Elevations and sectional drawings are included in a set of house plans.

plaster. A mixture of sand, lime, and water used in covering walls and partitions. Hair is sometimes mixed with this material to assist in binding.

plaster board. A wall covering composed of prepared material in sheets of various sizes, taking the place of the first two coats of plaster.

plaster grounds. Wooden strips of furring generally placed around the perimeter of a wall, to which wooden lath or expanded metal lathing may be attached.

plasticizing wood. Softening wood by hot water, steam or chemical treatment to increase its moldability.

plastic wood. A mixture of wood and adhesive plastics in putty form which is used for patching blemishes in wooden articles, floors, trim, etc. When hard, plastic wood can be worked like wood, will hold nails or screws, and take finishes.

plate. A horizontal structural member placed on a wall or supported on posts, studs, or corbels to carry the trusses of a roof or to carry the rafters directly. A shoe, or base member, as of a partition or other frame. A small, relatively flat member placed on or in a wall to support girders, rafters, etc.

plate rail. An ornamental molding placed on the walls of a room, the top side of which is grooved to receive plates or pictures.

plenum chamber. A chamber, especially in an attic, in which the air pressure is greater than the atmospheric pressure.

pliers. A bending or cutting tool, similar to a pincers, in different forms such as wire-cutting, long-nose, and side-cutting pliers. There are some 50 different pliers for many uses.

plinth block. A square or beveled block at the base of a door casing against which the skirting or baseboard butts.

plot plan. One sheet of a set of house plans on which are detailed the location of the house, outbuildings, driveways, drainage system, etc., in relation one to another and the street line.

plug. A piece of wood or lead driven into a hole cut in brick, stone, or concrete wall for attaching grounds; a piece of wood placed in the face of a board to hide the head of a screw or to replace small, loose knots.

plum. A big undressed stone used with other similar stones in wall footings, making a smaller amount of concrete necessary.

plumb. Exactly perpendicular, vertical.

plumb bob. A shaped brass or lead weight which keeps the line taut on a plumb line or rule.

plumb cut. Any vertical cut; the top cut of a rafter, the vertical cut on the seat cut of a rafter.

plumb level. A tool to determine the true vertical or horizontal position of work.

ply. A term to denote the number of thicknesses or layers of roofing felt, veneer in plywood, or layers in built-up materials, in any finished piece of such material.

plywood. A crossbanded assembly made of layers of veneer or of veneer in combination with a lumber core or plies joined with an adhesive. Two types of plywood are recognized, namely, (1) veneer plywood and (2) lumber core plywood. The grain of adjoining plies is usually laid at right angles, and almost always an odd number of plies are used to obtain balanced construction. Molded plywood is glued to the desired shape either between curved forms or more commonly by fluid pressure applied with flexible bags or blankets (bag molding) or other means. Post formed plywood is formed by reshaping, by means of steaming or other plasticizing agent, flat plywood into a curved shape.

ponderosa pine. A soft, medium lightweight wood, easily worked. It finishes smoothly, seldom splits, shrinks very little, and is creamy white to pale yellow in color. It is used in the manufacture of sashes, doors, moldings and inside trim.

poplar. The tulip tree; the light, softwood of this quick-growing tree.

portland cement. Commercial cement made from limestone and clay mixed, burned, and afterward ground into a fine powder. Used extensively in making concrete and in cement work. The derivation is from the Isle of Portland, England.

Port Orford cedar. A medium, softwood, fairly hard, strong and durable, with a fine texture. It is easily worked. It has a spicy fragrance and is used in the manufacture of sashes, doors, and interior trim.

post and beam construction. A method of construction in which post and beam framing units of wood, structural steel or concrete are the basic load-bearing members. Drawbacks of this method are the need for extra insulation and the problem of concealing wires and ducts.

precast stone. Imitation stone made of cast concrete or cement.

prefabricated house. A house or dwelling having walls, partitions, floors, ceilings, and a roof made up of sections or panels varying in size which have been fabricated in a factory prior to erection on the building foundation. This is in contrast to the conventionally built house which is constructed piece by piece on the building site. A precut house has the parts cut in a factory and assembled at the building site.

prefabricated joist. A form of light, reinforced concrete or rolled-steel I-beam joist.

preservative. Any substance that, for a reasonable length of time, will prevent the action of wood-destroying fungi, borers of various kinds, and similar destructive life when the wood has been properly coated or impregnated with it.

pressed wood. A hard, composite material, composed of sawdust, glue, cane fiber, etc., made under great pressure into panels or moldings, and used in building construction.

primer. The first coat of paint in a paint job that consists of two or more coats; also the paint used for a first coat.

projection. A figure represented by lines, points, and surfaces of a solid object, as in isometric, or orthographic projection. The distance rafters extend over the plate.

property line. A surveyor's line marking the limits or boundaries to a certain plot of land.

punch. A small hand tool shaped like a nail punch but having a sharp end and a flat head, used in making marks or punching holes when struck.

purchase. Any mechanical advantage or hold secured in raising or moving an object by a lever.

purlin. A timber laid horizontally across the principal rafters in a roof to support the common rafters.

push plate. A large plate of glass or metal attached on a swinging door, about shoulder high, for the protection of the finish as the hand is used in pushing the door.

putty. A type of cement usually made of whiting and boiled linseed oil, beaten or kneaded to the consistency of dough; used in sealing glass in sash, filling small holes and crevices in wood, and for similar purposes.

pwt. An abbreviation for "pennyweight." Also abbreviated "d" or "dwt." See *penny*.

Q

quadrille ruled. A cross-section paper used in the drafting room, ruled in blue on both sides with lines of equal thickness to various fractional divisions of an inch. Rulings run from 4 x 4 to the inch to 10 x 10 to the inch.

quarter round. A molding that presents a profile of a quarter circle. Abbreviated, qr. rd.

quarter-sawed. See edge-grain lumber.

queen bolt. A bolt used as a queen post instead of a framed member.

queen post. A vertical post in a queen post truss or other framed truss having a vertical post.

quirk. A longitudinal groove separating plane surfaces from those that are curved or molded.

quirk bead. A small bead molding separated from the surface on one side by a groove or quirk.

R

rabbet. A rectangular longitudinal groove cut in the corner of a board or other piece of material.

rabbet joint. A joint in which a rectangular groove cut lengthwise to the required depth and thickness in the edge of a board receive the edge or tongue of another board, as in flooring and some types of siding. A rabbeted joint is one formed by two boards, rabbeted on opposite sides.

radial. Coincident with a radius from the axis of the tree or log to the circumference. A radial section is a lengthwise section in a plan that passes through the center line of the tree trunk.

radial bar. A device for marking large curves, consisting of a marker (such as a pencil point) attached to a wooden bar.

radiant heating. A method of heating, usually consisting of cells or pipes placed in the floor, wall, or ceiling.

rafter. One of a series of structural members of a roof designed to support roof loads. The rafters of a flat roof are sometimes called roof joints.

For descriptions of the various types of rafters see Chapter 13.

rafter plate. A wall or top plate at the uppermost portion of the side wall framing.

rafter plumb cut. The top cut of a rafter; the cut at right angles to the seat cut of a rafter.

rafter seat cut. The bottom cut of a rafter resting on the wall plate; a bird's-mouth cut.

rafter tail. That part of a rafter extending beyond the wall plate; the overhang.

rail. A horizontal bar or timber of wood or metal extending from one post or support to another as a guard or barrier in a fence, balustrade, staircase, door, blind, or any paneled assembly.

raised grain. A roughened condition of the surface of dressed lumber in which the hard summerwood is raised above the softer springwood but not torn loose from it.

rake. The trim members that run parallel to the roof slope and from the finish between wall and roof.

raking joint. Any joint deviating from a plumb-cut joint.

random lengths. Pieces of lumber varying in length.

random widths. Pieces of lumber varying in width.

ratchet brace. A hand tool for boring holes, having a pawl and ratchet, permitting it to be worked back and forth in narrow spaces where a full circular sweep is impossible.

rear elevation. A view of the rear of a structure, as shown on the elevation drawing or blueprint of a structure.

rebate. The same as *rabbet,* which see; also pronounced, rab' et.

red cedar. A large tree of the pine family having a reddish wood of fragrant odor.

red fir. A coniferous tree found from British Columbia to Texas, valued for its durable timber.

red gum. The wood of the eucalyptus, used in making doors and inside trim.

red maple. A moderately heavy, stiff, strong hardwood, used chiefly in the manufacture of flooring, millwork, etc.

red oak. A hardwood, close-grained and red in color, used in flooring, doors and trim, and in heavy construction where durability and strength are essential.

redwood. A sequoia grown in California; its dark red wood, used as inside and outside finish, has an open grain and is easily worked.

reeding. A small, half-round molding, the reverse of fluting.

reflective insulation. Sheet material with one or both surfaces of comparatively low heat emissivity that, when used in building construction so that the surfaces face air spaces, reduces the radiation across the air space.

reinforcing. Steel rods or metal fabric placed in concrete slabs, beams, or columns to increase their strength.

relief. The projection of a figure beyond the ground on which it is formed; the effect of elevation and depth produced by the application of colors or shading in a painted design.

resin. A solid or gummy secretion from various plants, or synthetic preparations of similar character, such as rosin.

resinoid. A synthetic resin used in the manufacture of plastics.

resinous wood. Various trees yielding a resin or rosin, such as the pine, fir and balsam trees.

return. Continuation of a cornice or molding generally at right angles to its original direction, as the return nosing on an open-string stair, or the return of a cornice on the end of a house.

return nosing. Any mitered nosing of a stair tread extending beyond the balustrade.

reveal. The sides of a window or door opening into which the frame is fitted; the jamb. When cut at an angle other than a right angle a reveal is known as a splay reveal.

reverse bevel. A bevel or miter on a piece of molding cut for a cope joint. A lock in which the bevel of the latch bolt is reversed from that of the ordinary lock.

rib. The curved framework forming the center of an arch; any projecting band on a ceiling, vault wall, etc.

ribbon. A narrow board let into the studding to add support to joists.

ridge. The horizontal line at the junction of the top edges of two sloping roof surfaces. The rafters at both slopes are nailed at the ridge.

ridge board. The board placed on edge at the ridge of the roof to support the upper ends of the rafters.

right-hand door. A door having hinges on the right-hand side as the door is opened toward the person facing it.

right-side elevation. The right-hand side of the dwelling, in a set of house plans, as one faces the front elevation.

ripper. A tool used to cut nails in removing damaged pieces of slate from a roof. It has a bent handle and a long, thin steel blade, hooked on the end.

ripping. Sawing or splitting wood with

the grain or, along the length of the stock.

rise. The height of a roof rising in horizontal distance (run) from the outside face of a wall supporting the rafters or trusses to the ridge of the roof. In stair construction, the perpendicular height of a step or flight of steps.

rise per foot of run. The vertical distance, in inches, a rafter is elevated for each 12″ of horizontal distance or run.

riser. Each of the vertical boards closing the spaces between the treads of stairways.

roll roofing. Roofing material, composed of fiber and saturated with asphalt, that is supplied in rolls containing 108 square feet in 36″ widths. It is generally furnished in weights of 55 to 90 pounds per roll.

roof boards. The covering of wood placed on the roof rafters upon which the finished roofing material is laid. Sheathing.

roofers. Inferior tongued-and-grooved boards used as a roof covering over rafters as a base for roofing material.

roof plate. A wall or top plate capping the studding.

roof purlin. A horizontal timber connecting the trusses in a truss roof.

roof saddle. Two wide boards placed with edges overlapping at the ridge and on top of the uppermost row of shingles to form a finished, watertight joint.

roof sheathing. The boards or sheet material fastened to the roof rafters on which the shingle or other roof covering is laid. See roofers.

roof tie or beam. One of the several timbers connecting the bottom of the roof rafters and wall or top plates to prevent rafters from forcing out the side walls. Roof ties may also form the ceiling joists for the room under the rafters.

rose. A circular, oblong or square plate through which the spindle of a door knob is inserted into the lock.

rose bit. A countersink bit used in a brace when countersinking holes in wood for screws.

rose nail. A decorative nail with a rose shaped head used to ornament solid exterior doors.

rosin. A derivative of *resin,* which see.

rough framing. The concealed framing in a dwelling such as joists, studding, rafters, etc.

rough in. To lay out the general scheme of a design. To build up a substructure to house or hold finished material.

rough opening. An opening left in a wall or frame work to receive door or window frames, stairs, chimneys, etc.

rout. To plow out wood with a router plane; to gouge out wood with a chisel.

router. A chisel having a slightly curved end to clean out a mortise or groove.

rule of thumb. A principle handed down from one generation to another until it becomes an established method of operation based on custom.

run. In reference to roofs, the horizontal distance from the face of a wall to the ridge of the roof. Referring to stairways, the net width of a step; also the horizontal distance covered by a flight of steps.

run of rafter. The horizontal distance over which a rafter extends. The run of a common rafter is half the distance of the span of the roof.

run of stair. The horizontal distance from the face of the first riser to a point directly below the face of the top or final riser of a stairway.

S

saddle. Finished trim placed between the jambs of an inside door frame, which is fastened to the flooring. A threshold.

sander. A powered machine used in sanding floors, doors, etc., in a mill or at the building site. A mill sander is not unlike a large planer, while a portable sander has one or two revolving discs or drums.

sander belt. An endless belt of sandpaper revolving horizontally over two pulleys. A table is placed under the upper portion of the belt to support the material to be sanded. The table is worked back and forth at right angles to the belt.

sandpaper. A tough paper on one side of which a coating of sand is glued; used in cleaning and smoothing wood.

sandpaper block. A piece of cork or wood to which a piece of sandpaper is fastened or clamped to obtain a firm, even surface with which to work when sanding.

sapwood. The outer zone of wood, next to the bark. In the living tree it contains some living cells (the heartwood contains none), as well as dead and dying cells. In most species, it is lacking in decay resistance.

sash. A single frame containing one or more lights of glass. The sash fits into the window frame and may be either sliding, fixed, pivoted or hinged.

sash balance. A device, usually operated with a spring, designed to counterbalance window sash. Use of sash balances eliminates the need for sash weights, pulleys, and sash cord.

sash center. A bearing for a transom or other sash, turning on a horizontal axis, consisting of a pair of plates, one with a pin and the other with a socket. The socket plate is attached to the jamb or frame, and the plate with a pin to the sash.

sash cord. A plaited cord or rope used to connect a vertical sliding sash with its counterweight.

sash fastener. A device applied to the top side of both meeting rails in a double-hung sash, which draws the sashes together and prevents either being opened until the fastener is released.

sash frame. A milled frame housing sashes which may be hung on hinges, suspended on balanced weights or fixed in place. A typical frame is made up of a sill, jambs, outside casings and drip cap. Frames vary for the walls in which they are housed.

satinwood. A yellowish brown wood of the mahogany family from the East Indies. An orange colored wood of Florida and the West Indies. This wood is used in paneling and tool handles.

saw. A tool for cutting wood, metal or stone, consisting of a thin disk, blade or band of steel with toothed or serrated edges. The saw may be worked by hand or mechanically. Typical hand or powered saws used in dwelling construction are: bead saw, combination saw, cross cut saw, grooving saw, hand powered saw, key hole saw, panel saw, rip saw, stair builder's saw, swing saw and tenon saw.

saw file. A tapered double-cut file having three flat sides with edges rounded to shape the gullet of the saw tooth. Variations are known as regular taper, slim taper, extra slim taper, and double end taper.

saw filing clamp. A wooden or iron clamp in which a saw is held for filing by hand.

saw jointer. A metal device for holding a flat file, used in leveling the teeth of a hand saw before filing.

saw kerf. That portion of a log, timber, or other piece of wood removed by the saw in parting the material into two pieces. Grooves or notches made in cutting with a saw.

saw set. A device for setting or bending slightly to the right or left, alternately, the points of the teeth of a hand saw to provide clearance for the blade. A group of saw blades, generally three in number, with a slot to slip into an ordinary saw handle.

scaffold. A temporary structure composed of steel tubing or wooden poles, ledger boards, braces, plank, or wooden horses, which support

workmen and materials during construction or repair work.

scale. The relative proportion of a diagram to the object represented, as in a drawing to a scale such as $\frac{1}{4}''$ equals $1'$, in which $\frac{1}{4}''$ on the drawing represents $1'$ on the object drawn.

scant. A bit less than full measurement.

scarf joint. An end joint formed by joining with glue the ends of two pieces that have been tapered or beveled to form sloping plane surfaces, usually to a feather edge, and with the same slope of the plane with respect to the length of both pieces. In some cases, a step or hook may be machined into the scarf to facilitate alinement of the two ends, in which case the plane is discontinuous and the joint is known as a stepped or hooked scarf joint.

SCR brick (Structural Clay Research). Actual dimensions are $2\frac{1}{6}''$ x $5\frac{1}{2}''$ x $11\frac{1}{2}''$; when the $\frac{1}{2}''$ allowance for joints is added, the brick has, for construction purposes, a nominal size of $2\frac{2}{3}''$ x $6''$ x $12''$; its weight is usually about 8 pounds; it has 10 round vertical holes that constitute about 25% of its total volume; in the end of each brick a $\frac{3}{4}''$ x $\frac{3}{4}''$ jamb slot is provided to facilitate construction around openings.

scratch awl. A small hand tool having a ball-shaped handle of wood in which is inserted a sharp steel point with which working lines on stock are marked.

scratch coat. The first coat of plaster, which is scratched to form a bond for the second coat.

screed. A straight wooden, plaster, or metal strip used as a guide for even thickness and levelness of plaster or concrete. Nailing strips for flooring.

screw driver bit. An interchangeable tool used in a bit brace for driving screws.

screw nail. A nail having a spiral groove on its outside surface which turns when being driven, used to hold wooden members together or metal members to wood.

scribe. To mark with a compass or dividers, as in marking a board to fit irregular surfaces; the fitting of one molding to the face of another in an interior angle.

scribing. Fitting woodwork to an irregular surface.

scutcheon. An *escutcheon*, which see.

scuttle. A small opening, with a hinged or fitted lid, providing access to a roof.

sealer. A finishing material, either clear or pigment, that is usually applied directly over undercoated wood for the purpose of sealing the surface.

seasoned timber. Timber that has been dried by natural means in the open air or artifically in kilns, so it will be less likely to warp or shrink when worked up.

seat cut. The cut on the end of a rafter which rests on and is fastened to the wall plate of a building.

secret nailing. A method of nailing flooring in which the nail is driven into the edge of the plank, and is concealed by the next flooring board.

section. A drawing representing a building or other object as if cut by an imaginary intersecting plane.

section drawing. A drawing or print showing dimensions of an object which cannot be shown on plan or elevation drawings.

select lumber. Lumber having a very limited number of defects, finished with a smooth surface and suitable for finished work.

semidetached house. One of two houses built together having a common wall.

semigloss paint or enamel. A paint or enamel made with a slight insufficiency of nonvolatile vehicle so that its coating, when dry, has some luster but is not very glossy.

septic tank. A concrete, wooden, or steel tank in which sewage is retained until it disintegrates and flows directly through an outlet into the ground. The solid matter or sludge is cleaned out at intervals.

sequoia. A stately tree of the pine family which is a native of California, including the redwood and other big trees.

set. A permanent deformation, either in compression or tension, of wood fibers that are kept from shrinking or swelling, with loss or gain of moisture, by adjoining fibers that are at a different moisture content.

setback. A method of constructing a building in which successive stories or groups of stories are built with smaller areas than those below.

set of drawings. The drawings made of a building or project by an architect or draftsman, which include plans, elevations, sections, details, etc. A set of blueprints.

sewer trap. A fixture placed in a sewer line to prevent sewer gas from entering into the house connections yet permitting a free flow of sewage.

s four sides. One of a series of symbols or abbreviations used to designate the method of finishing mill stock. For example, s four sides or s 4 s means, surface four sides of the stock. A few other symbols are: s & e, surface one side and edge; s l e, surface one edge; s l s 2 e, surface one side and two edges; s 2 & s m, surfaced on two sides and center or standard matched.

shake. A hand-split shingle, usually edge-grain. A separation along the grain, the greater part of which occurs between the rings of annual growth.

shape description. Delineation of any object according to recognized methods of projection, such as orthograph, oblique, isometric, by a draftsman.

shaper. A machine with a vertical spindle which rotates at a very high rate of speed and to which cutters of various shapes and sizes are fastened, used in rabbeting and molding wood to various shapes.

sheathing. The structural covering, usually wooden boards, plywood, or wallboards, placed over exterior studding or rafters of a structure.

shellac. A transparent coating made by dissolving lac, a resinous secretion of the lac bug (a scale insect that thrives in tropical countries, especially India), in alcohol.

shims. Thin wedges of material used in leveling, such as slate, flat stone, wood or metal.

shingles. Roof covering of asphalt, asbestos, wood, tile, slate or other material cut to stock lengths, widths and thicknesses. Various kinds of shingles, some especially designed, that can be used as the exterior side wall covering for a structure are known as siding shingles.

shingle strip. A composition shingle made in strips of two, three or four shingles wide which are fastened to roofing boards with broad headed, galvanized or copper nails.

shiplap. Boards that have their edges rabbeted so that when laid edge to edge a half-lap joint is formed.

shoe. See *sole plate.*

shore. A beam placed vertically, horizontally, or at an angle, to support part of a building during alteration or repair.

short-leaf southern pine. A soft-textured, easily worked, moderately heavy wood, free from hard streaks and pitch, having a pale yellowish heartwood. It is used in trim and structural work.

short length. Lumber less than 8 feet long.

side cut. The term used when the pith is not present in a piece. The top cut on a jack rafter where it is fastened to the side of the hip; also the cut on either side of a hip valley rafter.

side light. One of the glass panels on either side of an entrance door.

siding. The finish covering of the out-side wall of a frame building, whether made of weatherboards, vertical boards with battens, shingles, or other material. Beveled or lap siding is used as the finish siding on the exterior of a house or other structure. It is usually manufactured by resawing dry square surfaced boards diagonally to produce two wedge-shaped pieces. These pieces commonly run from $3/16''$ thick on the thin edge to $1/2''$ to $3/4''$ thick on the other edge, depending on the width of the siding. Drop siding is usually $3/4''$ thick and $6''$ wide, machined into various patterns. Drop siding has tongued-and-grooved joints, is heavier, has more structural strength, and is frequently used on buildings that require no sheathing, such as garages and barns.

sill. The lowest member of the frame of a structure, resting on the foundation and supporting the uprights of the frame. The member forming the lower side of an opening, as a door sill, window sill, etc.

single-strength glass. Window glass which is a scant $1/8''$ thick.

Sitka spruce. A fine, clear variety of spruce used where elasticity and strength are first considerations.

six-eight-ten method of squaring up. The square of the hypotenuse of a right triangle is equal to the sum of the squares of the other two sides. See Chapter 4 for illustration.

skeleton framing. The framed members of wood or steel forming the walls and roof upon which the outside and inside finishes and trim of a building are attached and supported.

sketching pad. Sheets of paper. in tablet form, having either isometric lines, cross sectioned lines or a plain surface for rough or accurate penciled sketches.

skirting board. A baseboard, mop board, wainscoat, or kick board.

slag wool. An insulating material similar to asbestos made by blowing steam through fluid slag.

slashed grain. A method of cutting timber to bring out its wearing qualities. It is also known as vertical, rift, or edge-grain.

slash pine. A pine found in the swampy regions of southeastern United States, particularly Florida.

slat. A narrow, thin piece of stock used in making trellises.

slate. A natural rock which splits easily into thin, flat sheets. Used chiefly as a finished roofing material.

sleeper. A heavy, horizontal timber, usually resting directly on the ground, as a support for other framing members.

slip feather. A thin strip of wood or metal housed in a groove as a loose tongue in joining stock.

sleeper wall. A low or dwarf wall which supports floor joists.

slip tongue. A long strip of wood or metal acting as a loose tongue in the groove in joining boards. A feather.

slot mortiser. A powered wood-boring machine, having a hollow chisel bit which cuts a square-shouldered hole in wood.

snow board. A board placed on the roof, just above the eaves, to break the force of sliding snow.

soffit. The under side of the members of a building, such as a staircase, cornice, beam, and arch, relatively minor in area as compared with ceilings.

soil cover. A light roll roofing used on the ground of crawl spaces to minimize moisture permeation of the area.

soil stack. A general term for the vertical main of a system of soil, waste, or vent piping.

sole plate. A member, usually a 2 by 4, on which wall and partition studs rest. A shoe.

solid wood partition. A partition of wood composed of studding sheathed on both sides.

soot pocket. An extension in a chimney flue opening 8 to 10 inches below the smoke pipe entrance, use to keep soot from collecting in it.

southern pine. Pine wood native of the southern states, generally yellow in color; used in heavy construction as well as in millwork and farm buildings.

span. The distance between structural supports such as walls, columns, piers, beams, girders, and trusses. The horizontal distance between the seat cuts of two opposite common rafters. The run of a common rafter is half the span of a roof.

specifications. A detailed listing of the quantity and quality of stock, material or items to be used in the construction of a dwelling.

spike. A large, steel or wire nail, usually over 4″ in length.

spiral sash balance. A tubular fixture operating a tension coil spring used in hanging sashes.

spirit level. A hand tool having a glass tube containing spirits set with the rounded face of the tube uppermost, causing the bubble formed by the spirits to come to the center when the level is in a true horizontal position. The tool is placed against work to test for true horizontal position.

splayed jamb. A door jamb that is not placed at right angles to the face of the wall.

spliced joint. A lapped joint.

spline. A *feather,* which see.

spokeshave. A small hand tool with handles at either ends of a frame which houses a cutting blade in the center. It is used for shaping curved or circular work.

spruce. A tree of the genus of evergreen trees of the pine family, bearing swinging cones and needle-shaped leaves.

square. A unit of measure, 100 square feet, usually applied to roofing material. Side-wall coverings are often packed to cover 100 square feet and are sold on that basis.

square, steel. See *carpenter's square.*

squaring by 6, 8, 10, method. A manner of squaring a corner in which a distance of 6′ is measured along the wall or sill of a building from a corner, and a distance of 8′ along the wall or sill at right angles. If the corner is square the length of the hypotenuse connecting the ends of the measured lines will be 10′.

staging. A scaffold or temporary platform, on which mechanics work, during construction.

stair well. A framed opening in the floor or floors of a dwelling in which the stairway is constructed.

staking out. Measuring and marking off an area by driving stakes into the ground to locate the excavation boundaries.

standard brick. Common brick, approximately 2¼″ x 3¾″ x 8″.

sticker. A woodworking machine having swiftly revolving heads which shape finished trim stock.

stickers. Strips or boards used to separate the layers of lumber in a pile and thus permit air to circulate between the layers.

stile. The vertical trim or member of a door or window.

stirrup. Strap metal, generally made of iron or steel, shaped with a hook and U-shaped base, hooked over a main beam and into which floor joists are set.

stool. The flat, narrow shelf forming the top member of the interior trim at the bottom of a window.

stoop. A platform in front of the door of a house, especially one not covered by a roof.

stop. A strip of trim fastened to the jambs and door head against which the door closes.

story rod. A pole used to measure the height of a stairway from one floor level to the other. Also termed story pole.

striking a line. Marking the position of partitions on rough floors or a row of shingles by snapping a chalked line held taut over the position desired.

string. A timber or other support for cross members. In stair work, the support on which the stair treads rest; also known as stringer or stringboard.

structural sandwich construction. A layered construction comprising a combination of relatively high-strength facing materials intimately bonded to and acting integrally with a low density core material.

structural timbers. Pieces of wood of relatively large size, the strength of which is the controlling element in their selection and use. Examples are: trestle timbers (stringers, caps, posts, sills, bracing, bridge ties, guard rails); car timbers (car framing, including upper framing, car sills); framing for buildings (posts, sills, girders, framing joints); ship timbers (timbers, decking); and crossarms for poles.

stucco. Most commonly refers to an outside plaster made with portland cement as its base.

stud. One of a series of slender wood or metal structural members placed as supporting elements in walls and partitions.

subfloor. Boards or sheet material laid on joists over which a finish floor is to be laid.

sugar pine. A very large cone-bearing member of the pine family used extensively in building. The wood is even in texture, shrinks but a trifle, and has a satiny finish.

sump. A drainage reservoir.

sweet gum. A North American hardwood oftimes used to imitate mahogany wood.

sycamore. A hard, fairly heavy, cross-grained wood. It is used in the manufacture of furniture and millwork. The heartwood is light brown in color.

T

tackle. A mechanical device with pulleys and ropes to form a lifting appliance to hoist or lower heavy objects in construction work.

tail beam. A relatively short beam or joist supported in a wall on one end and by a header on the other end.

tail cut. The final cut of a rafter at the end opposite the plumb cut. The tail cut is parallel to the plumb cut or ridge cut.

take-down square. A carpenter's framing square having a joint in the body of the square into which the tongue slips and is locked by a set screw. This tool is not as accurate as the one-piece square but may be dismantled for easy storage and moving.

taking off quantities. Making lists, from a set of house plans, of all items of stock, finish material, hardware, etc., needed to construct a particular dwelling.

tamarack. A medium heavy, strong, hard, and durable wood of the American larch family of trees. It is light brown in color, and is used in rough construction work and for millwork.

tang. The pointed end of a hand tool, opposite the cutting edge, which is inserted into the handle.

tangential. Strictly, coincident with a tangent at the circumference of a tree or log, or parallel to such a tangent. In practice, however, it often means roughly coincident with a growth ring. A tangential section is a longitudinal section through a tree or limb perpendicular to a radius. Flat-grained lumber is sawed tangentially.

template. A pattern of metal or wood used as a guide when superimposed over stock which is to be worked.

tenon. A tongued projection remaining after cutting away a small portion of the main stock, this tongue being inserted into the mortise member of a mortise-and-tenon joint.

termite. An insect destructive to wooden structures. See Chapter 6 for description.

termite shield. A shield, usually of non-corrodible metal, placed in or on a foundation wall or other mass of masonry or around pipes to prevent passage of termites.

terrace. A portion of the lawn, especially near the house proper, raised above the established grade.

texture. A term often used interchangeably with grain. Sometimes used to combine the concepts of density and degree of contrast between springwood and summerwood. Texture generally refers to the finer structure of the wood rather than the annual rings.

thermoplastic glues and resins. Glues and resins that are cured by cooling from the heated condition but soften when subsequently subjected to high temperatures.

thermosetting glues and resins. Glues and resins that are cured with heat but do not soften when subsequently subjected to high temperatures.

three-four-five method. See *six-eight-ten method.*

threshold. A strip of wood or metal beveled on each edge and used above the finished floor under outside doors.

tile-setting adhesives. Waterproof mastics used for setting tile.

tilt-up construction. A form of prefabricated construction for walls which are poured (if concrete) or put together (if wood) in flat panels and then moved to the building site.

timber connectors. Metal devices used in connecting heavy framing members. Toothed-ring, split-ring, and shear-plate connectors all require heavy bolts and nuts to hold them in place at the joints.

toed. Turned obliquely, as a diagonally driven nail.

toenailing. To drive a nail at a slant with the initial surface in order to permit the nail to penetrate into a second member.

tongue. A raised portion or rib on the edge of a board which is housed in a groove of another membering piece of stock.

tongued-and-grooved joint. A method of joining stock with one piece having a rib or tongue which fits into a groove in the joining piece. Most roof and wall sheathing stock is tongued and grooved.

top plate. A wall plate, the structrual member on which rafters rest.

top view. A plan view; a view looking down on an object; a floor plan.

tracing. Placing a sheet of transparent linen or paper on an original drawing in order to make a copy for reproducing by process printing. The lines are produced on the transparent linen or paper in pencil or ink and may be used any number of times for as many copies as desired.

tread. The horizontal board in a stairway on which the foot is placed.

tree nail. A wooden dowel used in fastening timbers in framing such as attaching a girt to a corner post.

trestle. A large horse, consisting of a horizontal beam and spreading legs, used to support planks for a staging from which workmen can reach higher places.

trim. The finish materials in a building, such as moldings, applied around openings (window trim, door trim) or at the floor and ceiling of rooms (basboard, cornice, picture molding).

trimmer. A beam or joist to which a header is nailed in framing for a chimney, stairway, or other opening.

trim set. A group of trim, made up of side and head casings, back band, jambs, etc., for doors, and of casings, stool, apron, stop, etc., for windows; furnished in packaged sets for standard door or window openings.

trunnel. A *tree nail,* which see.

truss. An assembly of members, such as beams, bars, rods, and the like, so combined as to form a rigid framework that cannot be deformed by the application of exterior force without deformation of one or more members.

two-by-four. A scantling, used mostly for studding in frame houses. The size of a two by four is 1⅝″ in thickness by 1⅜″ in widths.

U

undercoat. A coating applied prior to the finishing or top coats of a paint job. It may be the first of two or the second of three coats. In some usage of the word it may become synonymous with the priming coat.

undercut. A cut slightly less than 90 degrees in order to have a tight fit against any beveled surface.

underpinning. Shores or posts supporting any part of a building during repairs.

V

valley. The internal angle formed by the junction of two sloping sides of a roof.

valley flashing. Tin, zinc, lead, or copper sheets placed at the intersections of roofs. An open valley flashing exposes the metal while a closed valley flashing has the metal covered with the final roof covering.

vapor barrier. Material used to retard the flow of vapor or moisture into walls and thus to prevent condensation within them. There are two types of vapor barriers, the membrane that comes in rolls and is applied as a unit in the wall or ceiling construction, and the paint type, which is applied with a brush. The vapor barrier must be a part of the warm side of the house.

vee joint. A joint formed by boards having beveled edges.

veneer. A thin layer or sheet of wood cut on a veneer machine. Rotary-cut veneer is cut in a lathe which rotates a log or bolt, chucked in the center, against a knife. Sawed veneer is produced by sawing. Sliced veneer is sliced off a log, bolt, or flitch with a knife.

vent. A pipe installed to provide a flow of air to or from a drainage system or to provide a circulation of air within such system to protect trap seals from siphonage and back pressure.

verge. The edge of shingles, slates, or tiles projecting over the gable end of a roof.

verge board. Outside trim attached to the gable end of a dwelling having the same slope as the roof and placed directly under the roof covering.

vermiculite. A mineral closely related to mica, with the faculty of expanding on heating to form lightweight material with insulation qualities. Used as a bulk insulation and also as aggregate in insulating concrete floors.

vertical section. A sectional view of a dwelling, from basement to roof, showing exact construction details.

vitrified tile. Smooth glazed waterproof tile.

W

wainscot. Paneling attached to the walls of a room extending, generally, from the floor to the level of the window sills.

wallboard. Wood pulp, gypsum, or other materials made into large, rigid sheets that may be fastened to the frame of a building to provide a surface finish.

wall bracket. A support attached to an exterior wall to hold scaffolding for workmen.

wall plate. The horizontal timber fastened to the top of studding in wall framing. Wall plates are also used in brick or stone wall construction to anchor roof rafters.

wall string. The inside trim or baseboard attached to a wall in stair construction.

wane. Bark, or lack of wood or bark from any cause, on edge of corner of a piece of timber.

ward. A projection in the lock case or keyhole obstructing the entrance or rotation of an unmatched key, also the notch made in the key to correspond with the ward in the lock.

wash. The upper surface of a member or material when given a slope to shed water.

water bar. A stripping inserted in a window sill joint to keep out rain.

waterproof paper. The same as *building paper*, which see.

waterproofing. The coating of exterior walls of a foundation with tar or asphaltum to render impervious to water.

water repellent. A liquid designed to penetrate into wood and to impart water repellency to the wood.

water table. A ledge or offset on or above a foundation wall, for the purpose of shedding water.

weatherboard. Exterior finish on framed houses, tapered across its width from a thin edge at the top to about ½″ on the bottom.

weathering. The mechanical or chemical disintegration and discoloration of the surface of wood that is caused by exposure to light, the action of dust and sand carried by winds, and the alternate shrinking and swelling of the surface fibers with the continual variation in moisture content brought by changes in weather. Weathering does not include decay.

weather strip. Narrow strips made of metal, or other material, so designed that when installed at doors or windows they will retard the passage of air, water, moisture, or dust around the window or door sash.

wedged and glued. A through mortise-and-tenon joint having glued wedges driven in on either side of the exposed end of the tenon.

weep hole. An opening placed in a retaining wall formed by omitting a small stone or inserting a small drain tile for draining off surface water.

weight pocket. The space in a window frame through which the sash weight and cord move up and down.

well hole. The open shaft around which a staircase turns.

west coast hemlock. A medium lightweight wood, yellowish brown in color, fairly soft, strong and stiff. It retains nails firmly, being used chiefly in building construction and milled products.

western framing. Braced framing used in dwellings having studding carried to the header at the next floor level and the studding of that floor rest on the sole plate, as distinguished from balloon or through stud framing, platform framing, or repeat story framing.

western red cedar. A red wood having a pleasing odor, fairly knotty, used in lining clothes closets, wardrobes, and chests.

white ash. A heavy, hard, strong, tough, elastic, and close-grained wood. The color of the heartwood is brown while the sapwood is pale. Used chiefly in the manufacture of tool handles, millwork, and furniture.

white cedar. A tree growing in swampy places in the North Atlantic States and Canada, producing a durable and valuable commercial timber.

white fir. A lightweight softwood, odorless and grayish brown in color. This wood is used in the manufacture of flooring, sheathing, and framing stock.

white oak. A hard, durable wood, used for inside finish and flooring and heavy construction.

white pine. A long-leaf pine, a most important wood in building construction. Used for trim, sashes, doors, etc.

windshake. A cup-shaped split in wood where the annual rings have separated, probably from force of wind, as the tree was growing.

window sash. The sliding, hinged, or fixed frame into which the window-pane is inserted. See *sash*.

window seat. A seat, a trifle lower than the height of the window stool, built around a bay-window recess.

wire glass. Window glass into which wire mesh is embedded, as a prevention against shattering and a protection against intruders.

withe. A partition wall separating flues in a common chimney stack. Also two separate walls of a cavity wall.

working drawings. The drawings or set of prints made to scale from which tradesmen take measurements and details to construct a dwelling.

wreath. The curved section of a stair headrail joined to the newel post.

Y

yellow pine. Short-leaf pine used in house framing, less strong than long-leaf yellow pine. North Carolina pine.

yellow poplar. A lightweight, soft, straight-grained wood. It shrinks very little and is easily worked. The color of the heartwood is greenish to yellow brown. It is used in the manufacture of millwork, fixtures, and furniture.

Z

zonolite concrete. An insulating concrete used in prefabricated floor slabs for dwellings without basements.

INDEX